Johnny

MATHEMATICAL
RECREATIONS AND ESSAYS

MATHEMATICAL
RECREATIONS & ESSAYS

BY

W. W. ROUSE BALL

LATE FELLOW OF TRINITY COLLEGE, CAMBRIDGE

REVISED BY

H. S. M. COXETER

PAST FELLOW OF TRINITY COLLEGE, CAMBRIDGE

MACMILLAN AND CO., LIMITED
ST. MARTIN'S STREET, LONDON
1944

COPYRIGHT

First Edition,	1892.
Second Edition,	1892.
Third Edition,	1896.
Fourth Edition,	1905.
Fifth Edition,	1911.
Sixth Edition,	1914.
Seventh Edition,	1917.
Eighth Edition,	1919.
Ninth Edition,	1920.
Tenth Edition,	1922.
Reprinted,	1926.
,,	1928.
,,	1981.
,,	1937.
Eleventh Edition,	1939.
Reprinted,	1940.
,,	1942.
,,	1944.

AUTHOR'S PREFACE

THIS book contains descriptions of various problems of the kind usually termed Mathematical Recreations, and a few Essays on some analogous questions. I have excluded all matter which involves advanced mathematics. I hasten to add that the conclusions are of no practical use, and that most of the results are not new. If therefore the reader proceeds further he is at least forewarned. At the same time I think I may say that many of the questions discussed are interesting, not a few are associated with the names of distinguished mathematicians, while hitherto several of the memoirs quoted have not been easily accessible to English readers. A great deal of new matter has been added since the work was first issued in 1892.

As now presented, the book contains fourteen chapters, of which the subjects are shown in the Table of Contents. Several of the questions mentioned in the first four chapters are of a somewhat trivial character, and had they been treated in any standard English work to which I could have referred the reader, I should have left them out : in the absence of such a work, I thought it better to insert them and trust to the judicious reader to omit them altogether or to skim them as he feels inclined. I may add that in discussing problems where the complete solutions are long or intricate I have been generally content to indicate memoirs or books in which the methods are set out at length, and to give a few illustrative examples. In some cases I have also stated problems which still await solution.

I have inserted detailed references, as far as I know them, to the sources of the various questions and solutions given; also, wherever I have given only the result of a theorem, I have tried to indicate authorities where a proof may be found. In general, unless it is stated otherwise, I have taken the references direct from the original works; but, in spite of considerable time spent in verifying them, I dare not suppose that they are free from all errors or misprints.

W. W. ROUSE BALL.

EDITOR'S PREFACE

IN revising Rouse Ball's delightful book, it has been my aim to preserve its spirit, adding the kind of material that he himself would have enjoyed. After consultation with several mathematicians, I have felt it desirable to strike out the fifth, eighth, and fifteenth chapters of the tenth edition. (For String Figures, the reader is referred to any previous edition, or to Rouse Ball's little book on that subject.) The twelfth chapter has been broken up and distributed among the first, third, fourth and eleventh chapters.

The present fifth chapter is new; so is most of the second and eighth chapters, and a good deal of the third and seventh. Moreover, the fourteenth, on Cryptographs and Ciphers, has been completely rewritten by Abraham Sinkov, a Cryptanalyst in the U.S. War Department. To him and many other helpers I would express my sincere thanks, especially to D. H. Lehmer, who constructively criticized the second chapter in manuscript; to J. M. Andreas, who provided a number of diagrams for the fifth chapter; and to P. S. Donchian for the photographs of his models (facing pages 130 and 134).

I shall be grateful for notices of additions or corrections which may occur to any of my readers.

H. S. M. COXETER.

University of Toronto,
   Jan., 1938.

TABLE OF CONTENTS

CHAPTER I. ARITHMETICAL RECREATIONS.

CHAPTER II. ARITHMETICAL RECREATIONS (*continued*).

CHAPTER XIII. CALCULATING PRODIGIES.

" Les hommes ne sont jamais plus ingénieux que dans l'invention des jeux ; l'esprit s'y trouve à son aise. . . . Après les jeux qui dépendent uniquement des nombres viennent les jeux où entre la situation. . . . Après les jeux où n'entrent que le nombre et la situation viendraient les jeux où entre le mouvement. . . . Enfin il serait à souhaiter qu'on eût un cours entier des jeux, traités mathématiquement." (Leibniz : letter to De Montmort, July 29, 1715.)

CHAPTER I

ARITHMETICAL RECREATIONS

I COMMENCE by describing some arithmetical recreations. The interest excited by statements of the relations between numbers of certain forms has been often remarked, and the majority of works on mathematical recreations include several such problems, which, though obvious to anyone acquainted with the elements of algebra, have to many who are ignorant of that subject the same kind of charm that mathematicians find in the more recondite propositions of higher arithmetic. I devote the bulk of this chapter to these elementary problems.

Before entering on the subject, I may add that a large proportion of the elementary questions mentioned here are taken from one of two sources. The first of these is the classical *Problèmes plaisans et délectables*, by Claude Gaspar Bachet, sieur de Méziriac, of which the first edition was published in 1612 and the second in 1624 : it is to the edition of 1624 that the references hereafter given apply. Several of Bachet's problems are taken from the writings of Alcuin, Pacioli di Burgo, Tartaglia, and Cardan, and possibly some of them are of oriental origin, but I have made no attempt to add such references. The other source to which I alluded above is Ozanam's *Récréations mathématiques et physiques*. The greater portion of the original edition, published in two volumes at Paris in 1694, was a compilation from the works of Bachet, Mydorge, and Leurechon : this part is excellent, but the same cannot be said of the additions due to Ozanam. In the *Biographie Universelle* allusion is made to subsequent editions issued in 1720, 1735, 1741, 1778, and 1790 ; doubtless these references are correct, but the following editions, all of which I have seen, are the only ones of which I have any knowledge.

In 1696 an edition was issued at Amsterdam. In 1723—six
years after the death of Ozanam—one was issued in three
volumes, with a supplementary fourth volume, containing,
among other things, an appendix on puzzles. Fresh editions
were issued in 1741, 1750 (the second volume of which bears
the date 1749), 1770, and 1790. The edition of 1750 is said to
have been corrected by Montucla on condition that his name
should not be associated with it; but the edition of 1790 is
the earliest one in which reference is made to these corrections,
though the editor is referred to only as Monsieur M***.
Montucla expunged most of what was actually incorrect in the
older editions, and added several historical notes, but unfortunately his scruples prevented him from striking out the
accounts of numerous trivial experiments and truisms which
overload the work. An English translation of the original
edition appeared in 1708, and I believe ran through four
editions, the last of them being published in Dublin in 1790.
Montucla's revision of 1790 was translated by C. Hutton, and
editions of this were issued in 1803, in 1814, and (in one
volume) in 1840 : my references are to the editions of 1803
and 1840.

I proceed to enumerate some of the typical elementary
questions connected with numbers which for nearly three
centuries have formed a large part of most compilations of
mathematical amusements. They are given here largely for
their historical—not for their arithmetical—interest; and
perhaps a mathematician may well omit this chapter.

Many of these questions are of the nature of tricks or puzzles,
and I follow the usual course and present them in that form.
I may note, however, that most of them are not worth pro-
posing, even as tricks, unless either the method employed is
disguised or the result arrived at is different from that expected ;
but, as I am not writing on conjuring, I refrain from alluding
to the means of disguising the operations indicated, and give
merely a bare enumeration of the steps essential to the success

of the method used. To the non-mathematician even to-day some of those results seem astonishing, but the secret is at once revealed as soon as the question is translated by symbols into mathematical language.

To Find a Number Selected by Someone

There are innumerable ways of finding a number chosen by someone, provided the result of certain operations on it is known. I confine myself to methods typical of those commonly used. Anyone acquainted with algebra will find no difficulty in framing new rules of an analogous nature.

First Method.* (i) Ask the person who has chosen the number to treble it. (ii) Enquire if the product is even or odd : if it is even, request him to take half of it; if it is odd, request him to add unity to it and then to take half of it. (iii) Tell him to multiply the result of the second step by 3. (iv) Ask how many integral times 9 divides into the latter product : suppose the answer to be n. (v) Then the number thought of was $2n$ or $2n + 1$, according as the result of step (i) was even or odd.

The demonstration is obvious. Every even number is of the form $2n$, and the successive operations applied to this give (i) $6n$, which is even; (ii) $\frac{1}{2}6n = 3n$; (iii) $3 \times 3n = 9n$; (iv) $\frac{1}{9}9n = n$; (v) $2n$. Every odd number is of the form $2n + 1$, and the successive operations applied to this give (i) $6n + 3$ which is odd; (ii) $\frac{1}{2}(6n + 3 + 1) = 3n + 2$; (iii) $3(3n + 2) = 9n + 6$; (iv) $\frac{1}{9}(9n + 6) = n +$ a remainder; (v) $2n + 1$. These results lead to the rule given above.

Second Method.† Ask the person who has chosen the number to perform in succession the following operations. (i) To multiply the number by 5. (ii) To add 6 to the product. (iii) To multiply the sum by 4. (iv) To add 9 to the product. (v) To multiply the sum by 5. Ask to be told the result of the last operation : if from this product 165 is subtracted, and

---

* Bachet, *Problèmes*, Lyons, 1624, problem I, p. 53.

† A similar rule was given by Bachet, problem IV, p. 74.

then the remainder is divided by 100, the quotient will be the number thought of originally.

For let n be the number selected. Then the successive operations applied to it give: (i) $5n$; (ii) $5n + 6$; (iii) $20n + 24$; (iv) $20n + 33$; (v) $100n + 165$. Hence the rule.

Third Method.* Request the person who has thought of the number to perform the following operations. (i) To multiply it by any number you like, say a. (ii) To divide the product by any number, say b. (iii) To multiply the quotient by c. (iv) To divide this result by d. (v) To divide the final result by the number selected originally. (vi) To add to the result of operation (v) the number thought of at first. Ask for the sum so found : then, if ac/bd is subtracted from this sum, the remainder will be the number chosen originally.

For, if n was the number selected, the result of the first four operations is to form nac/bd; operation (v) gives ac/bd; and (vi) gives $n + (ac/bd)$, which number is mentioned. But ac/bd is known; hence, subtracting it from the number mentioned, n is found. Of course a, b, c, d may have any numerical values it is liked to assign to them. For example, if $a = 12$, $b = 4$, $c = 7$, $d = 3$, it is sufficient to subtract 7 from the final result in order to obtain the number originally selected.

Fourth Method.† Ask someone to select a number less than 90. Request him to perform the following operations. (i) To multiply it by 10, and to add any number he pleases, a, which is less than 10. (ii) To divide the result of step (i) by 3, and to mention the remainder, say b. (iii) To multiply the quotient obtained in step (ii) by 10, and to add any number he pleases, c, which is less than 10. (iv) To divide the result of step (iii) by 3, and to mention the remainder, say d, and the third digit (from the right) of the quotient; suppose this digit is e. Then, if the numbers a, b, c, d, e are known,

* Bachet, problem v, p. 80.

† *Educational Times*, London, May 1, 1895, vol. XLVIII, p. 234. This example is said to have been made up by J. Clerk Maxwell in his boyhood : it is interesting to note how widely it differs from the simple Bachet problems previously mentioned.

the original number can be at once determined. In fact, if the number is $9x + y$, where $x \leqslant 9$ and $y \leqslant 8$, and if r is the remainder when $a - b + 3(c - d)$ is divided by 9, we have $x = e, y = 9 - r$.

The demonstration is not difficult. Suppose the selected number is $9x + y$. Step (i) gives $90x + 10y + a$. Let $y + a = 3n + b$, then the quotient obtained in step (ii) is $30x + 3y + n$. Step (iii) gives $300x + 30y + 10n + c$. Let $n + c = 3m + d$, then the quotient obtained in step (iv) is $100x + 10y + 3n + m$, which I will denote by Q. Now the third digit in Q must be x, because, since $y \leqslant 8$ and $a \leqslant 9$, we have $n \leqslant 5$; and since $n \leqslant 5$ and $c \leqslant 9$, we have $m \leqslant 4$; therefore $10y + 3n + m \leqslant 99$. Hence the third or hundreds digit in Q is x.

Again, from the relations $y + a = 3n + b$ and $n + c = 3m + d$, we have $9m - y = a - b + 3(c - d)$: hence, if r is the remainder when $a - b + 3(c - d)$ is divided by 9, we have $y = 9 - r$. [This is always true, if we make r positive; but if $a - b + 3(c - d)$ is negative, it is simpler to take y as equal to its numerical value; or we may prevent the occurrence of this case by assigning proper values to a and c.] Thus x and y are both known, and therefore the number selected, namely $9x + y$, is known.

Fifth Method.* Ask anyone to select a number less than 60. Request him to perform the following operations. (i) To divide it by 3 and mention the remainder; suppose it to be a. (ii) To divide it by 4, and mention the remainder; suppose it to be b. (iii) To divide it by 5, and mention the remainder; suppose it to be c. Then the number selected is the remainder obtained by dividing $40a + 45b + 36c$ by 60.

This method can be generalized and then will apply to any number chosen. Let a', b', c', ... be a series of numbers prime to one another, and let p be their product. Let n be any number less than p, and let $a, b, c, \ldots$ be the remainders

---

* Bachet, problem VI, p. 84: Bachet added, on p. 87, a note on the previous history of the problem.

when n is divided by a', b', c', ... respectively. Find a
number A which is a multiple of the product $b'c'd'$... and which
exceeds by unity a multiple of a'. Find a number B which is
a multiple of $a'c'd'$... and which exceeds by unity a multiple
of b', and similarly find analogous numbers C, D, ... Rules
for the calculation of A, B, C, ... are given in the theory of
numbers, but in general, if the numbers a', b', c', ... are small,
the corresponding numbers A, B, C, ... can be found by inspection. I proceed to show that n is equal to the remainder
when $Aa + Bb + Cc + ...$ is divided by p.

Let $N = Aa + Bb + Cc + ...$, and let $M(x)$ stand for a
multiple of x. Now $A = M(a') + 1$, therefore $Aa =
M(a') + a$. Hence, if the first term in N—that is, Aa—is
divided by a', the remainder is a. Again, B is a multiple of
$a'c'd'$.... Therefore Bb is exactly divisible by a'. Similarly
Cc, Dd, ... are each exactly divisible by a'. Thus every term
in N, except the first, is exactly divisible by a'. Hence,
if N is divided by a', the remainder is a. Also if n is divided
by a', the remainder is a.

Therefore $\qquad\qquad N - n = M(a')$.
Similarly $\qquad\qquad N - n = M(b')$,
$\qquad\qquad\qquad\quad N - n = M(c')$,

$\qquad\qquad\qquad$. . . . .

But a', b', c', ... are prime to one another. Therefore

$$N - n = M(a'b'c'...) = M(p),$$
that is, $\qquad\qquad N = M(p) + n.$

Now n is less than p, hence if N is divided by p, the remainder
is n.

The rule given by Bachet corresponds to the case of $a' = 3$,
$b' = 4$, $c' = 5$, $p = 60$, $A = 40$, $B = 45$, $C = 36$. If the
number chosen is less than 420, we may take $a' = 3$, $b' = 4$,
$c' = 5$, $d' = 7$, $p = 420$, $A = 280$, $B = 105$, $C = 336$,
$D = 120.$

To Find the Result of a Series of Operations Performed on Any Number (*unknown to the operator*) Without Asking any Questions

All rules for solving such problems ultimately depend on so arranging the operations that the number disappears from the final result. Four examples will suffice.

First Example.* Request someone to think of a number. Suppose it to be n. Ask him (i) to multiply it by any number you please, say a; (ii) then to add, say, b; (iii) then to divide the sum by, say, c. (iv) Next, tell him to take a/c of the number originally chosen; and (v) to subtract this from the result of the third operation. The result of the first three operations is $(na + b)/c$, and the result of operation (iv) is na/c: the difference between these is b/c and therefore is known to you. For example, if $a = 6$, $b = 12$, $c = 4$, then $a/c = 1\frac{1}{2}$, and the final result is 3.

Second Example.† Ask A to take any number of counters that he pleases: suppose that he takes n counters. (i) Ask someone else, say B, to take p times as many, where p is any number you like to choose. (ii) Request A to give q of his counters to B, where q is any number you like to select. (iii) Next, ask B to transfer to A a number of counters equal to p times as many counters as A has in his possession. Then there will remain in B's hands $q(p + 1)$ counters: this number is known to you; and the trick can be finished either by mentioning it or in any other way you like.

The reason is as follows. The result of operation (ii) is that B has $pn + q$ counters, and A has $n - q$ counters. The result of (iii) is that B transfers $p(n - q)$ counters to A: hence he has left in his possession $(pn + q) - p(n - q)$ counters—that is, he has $q(p + 1)$.

For example, if originally A took any number of counters, then (if you chose p equal to 2), first you would ask B to take

---

* Bachet, problem viii, p. 102.

† Bachet, problem xiii, p. 123: Bachet presented the above trick in a form somewhat more general but less effective in practice.

twice as many counters as A had done; next (if you chose q equal to 3) you would ask A to give 3 counters to B; and then you would ask B to give to A a number of counters equal to twice the number then in A's possession; after this was done you would know that B had $3(2 + 1)$—that is, 9 left.

This trick (as also some of the following problems) may be performed equally well with one person, in which case A may stand for his right hand and B for his left hand.

Third Example. Ask someone to perform in succession the following operations. (i) Take any number of three digits, in which the difference between the first and last digits exceeds unity. (ii) Form a new number by reversing the order of the digits. (iii) Find the difference of these two numbers. (iv) Form another number by reversing the order of the digits in this difference. (v) Add together the results of (iii) and (iv). Then the sum obtained as the result of this last operation will be 1089.

An illustration and the explanation of the rule are given below.

(i)	237	$100a + 10b + c$
(ii)	732	$100c + 10b + a$
(iii)	495	$100(a - c - 1) + 90 + (10 + c - a)$
(iv)	594	$100(10 + c - a) + 90 + (a - c - 1)$
(v)	1089	$900 + 180 + 9$

The result depends only on the radix of the scale of notation in which the number is expressed. If this radix is r, the result is $(r - 1)(r + 1)^2$; thus if $r = 10$, the result is 9×11^2—that is, 1089. Similar problems can be made with numbers exceeding 999.

Fourth Example.* The following trick depends on the same principle. Ask someone to perform in succession the following operations. (i) To write down any sum of money less than £12, in which the difference between the number of pounds and the number of pence exceeds unity. (ii) To *reverse* this sum—that is, to write down a sum of money obtained from it by interchanging the numbers of pounds and pence. (iii) To find the difference between the results of (i) and (ii). (iv) To reverse this difference. (v) To add together the results of (iii) and (iv). Then this sum will be £12 18s. 11d.

For instance, take the sum £10 17s. 5d.; we have

			£	s.	d.
(i)	.	.	10	17	5
(ii)	.	.	5	17	10
(iii)	.	.	4	19	7
(iv)	.	.	7	19	4
(v)	.	.	12	18	11

The following analysis explains the rule, and shows that the final result is independent of the sum written down initially.

				£	s.	d.
(i)	.	.	.	a	b	c
(ii)	.	.	.	c	b	a
(iii)	.	.	.	$a - c - 1$	19	$c - a + 12$
(iv)	.	.	.	$c - a + 12$	19	$a - c - 1$
(v)	.	.	.	11	38	11

Mr. J. H. Schooling has used this result as the foundation of a slight but excellent conjuring trick. The rule can be generalized to cover any system of monetary units.

PROBLEMS INVOLVING TWO NUMBERS

I proceed next to give a couple of examples of a class of problems which involve two numbers.

First Example. * Suppose that there are two numbers, one even and the other odd, and that a person A is asked to select one of them, and that another person B takes the other. It is desired to know whether A selected the even or the odd number. Ask A to multiply his number by 2, or any even number, and B to multiply his by 3, or any odd number. Request them to add the two products together and tell you the sum. If it is even, then originally A selected the odd number, but if it is odd, then originally A selected the even number. The reason is obvious.

Second Example. † The above rule was extended by Bachet to any two numbers, provided they are prime to one another and one of them is not itself a prime. Let the numbers be m and n, and suppose that n is exactly divisible by p. Ask A to select one of these numbers, and B to take the other. Choose a number prime to p, say q. Ask A to multiply his number by q, and B to multiply his number by p. Request them to add the products together and state the sum. Then A originally selected m or n, according as this result is not or is divisible by p. The numbers, $m = 7$, $n = 15$, $p = 3$, $q = 2$, will illustrate the rest.

PROBLEMS DEPENDING ON THE SCALE OF NOTATION

Many of the rules for finding two or more numbers depend on the fact that in arithmetic an integral number is denoted by a succession of digits, where each digit represents the product of that digit and a power of ten, and the number is equal to the sum of these products. For example, 2017 signifies $(2 \times 10^3) + (0 \times 10^2) + (1 \times 10) + 7$—that is, the 2 represents 2 thousands, *i.e.* the product of 2 and 10^3, the 0 represents 0 hundreds, *i.e.* the product of 0 and 10^2; the 1 represents 1 ten, *i.e.* the product of 1 and 10, and the 7 represents 7 units. Thus every digit has a local value. The application to tricks connected with numbers will be understood readily from three illustrative examples.

* Bachet, problem IX, p. 107. † Bachet, problem XI, p. 113.

First Example.* A common conjuring trick is to ask a boy among the audience to throw two dice, or to select at random from a box a domino on each half of which is a number. The boy is then told to recollect the two numbers thus obtained, to choose either of them, to multiply it by 5, to add 7 to the result, to double this result, and lastly to add to this the other number. From the number thus obtained, the conjurer subtracts 14, and obtains a number of two digits which are the two numbers chosen originally.

For suppose that the boy selected the numbers a and b. Each of these is less than ten—dice or dominoes ensuring this. The successive operations give: (i) $5a$; (ii) $5a + 7$; (iii) $10a + 14$; (iv) $10a + 14 + b$. Hence, if 14 is subtracted from the final result, there will be left a number of two digits, and these digits are the numbers selected originally. An analogous trick might be performed in other scales of notation if it was thought necessary to disguise the process further.

Second Example.† Similarly, if three numbers, say a, b, c, are chosen, then, if each of them is less than ten, they can be found by the following rule. (i) Take one of the numbers, say a, and multiply it by 2. (ii) Add 3 to the product. (iii) Multiply this by 5, and add 7 to the product. (iv) To this sum add the second number, b. (v) Multiply the result by 2. (vi) Add 3 to the product. (vii) Multiply by 5, and, to the product, add the third number, c. The result is $100a + 10b + c + 235$. Hence, if the final result is known, it is sufficient to subtract 235 from it, and the remainder will be a number of three digits. These digits are the numbers chosen originally.

Third Example.‡ The following rule for finding a person's

---

* Some similar questions were given by Bachet in problem XII, p. 117; by Oughtred or Leake in the *Mathematicall Recreations*, commonly attributed to the former, London, 1653, problem XXXIV; and by Ozanam, part I, chapter X. Probably the *Mathematicall Recreations* were compiled by Leake, but as the work is usually catalogued under the name of W. Oughtred, I shall so describe it: it is founded on the similar work by J. Leurechon, otherwise known as H. van Etten, published in 1626.

† Bachet gave some similar questions in problem XII, p. 117.

‡ Due to Royal V. Heath.

age is of the same kind. Tell him to think of a number (preferably not exceeding 10); (i) square it; (ii) subtract 1; (iii) multiply the result by the original number; (iv) multiply this by 3; (v) add his age; (vi) give the sum of the digits of the result. You then have to guess his age within nine years, knowing that it has this same digit-sum.

The algebraic proof of the rule is obvious. Let a be the age, and b the number thought of. The successive operations give (i) b^2; (ii) $b^2 - 1$; (iii) $b(b^2 - 1)$; (iv) $3b(b^2 - 1)$; (v) $a + 3b(b^2-1)$; (vi) the digit-sum of a, because $3b(b^2 - 1)$ is always a multiple of 9.

Other Examples.* Another such problem, but of more difficulty, is the determination of all numbers which are integral multiples of their reversals. For instance, among numbers of four digits, $8712 = 4 \times 2178$ and $9801 = 9 \times 1089$ possess this property.

Again, we might ask for two numbers whose product is the reversal of the product of their reversals; for example,

$$312 \times 221 = 68952, \quad 213 \times 122 = 25986.$$

The number 698896 is remarkable as being a perfect square, equal to its own reversal.

Just four numbers have the property of being equal to the sum of the cubes of their digits :† $153 = 1^3 + 5^3 + 3^3$, $370 = 3^3 + 7^3 + 0^3$, $371 = 3^3 + 7^3 + 1^3$, $407 = 4^3 + 0^3 + 7^3$.

The properties of the recurring decimal for $\frac{1}{7}$ are notorious. Troitsky has shown ‡ that 142857 and 285714 are the only numbers less than a million which become multiplied when we remove the first digit and put it after the last.

OTHER PROBLEMS WITH NUMBERS IN THE DENARY SCALE

I may mention here two or three other problems which seem to be unknown to most compilers of books of puzzles.

---

* *L'Intermédiaire des Mathématiciens*, Paris, vol. xv, 1908, pp. 228, 278; vol. xvi, 1909, p. 34; vol. xix, 1912, p. 128. M. Kraïtchik, *La Mathématique des Jeux*, Brussels, 1930, pp. 55, 59.

† *Sphinx*, 1937, pp. 72, 87.   ‡ *L'Echiquier*, 1930, p. 663.

First Problem. The first of them is as follows. Take any number of three digits, the first and third digits being different : reverse the order of the digits : subtract the number so formed from the original number : then, if the last digit of the difference is mentioned, all the digits in the difference are known.

For suppose the number is $100a + 10b + c$, then the number obtained by reversing the digits is $100c + 10b + a$. The difference of these numbers is equal to $(100a + c) - (100c + a)$ —that is, to $99(a - c)$. But $a - c$ is not greater than 9, and therefore the remainder can only be 99, 198, 297, 396, 495, 594, 693, 792, or 891 ; in each case the middle digit being 9 and the digit before it (if any) being equal to the difference between 9 and the last digit. Hence, if the last digit is known, so is the whole of the remainder.

Second Problem. The second problem is somewhat similar, and is as follows. (i) Take any number ; (ii) reverse the digits ; (iii) find the difference between the number formed in (ii) and the given number ; (iv) multiply this difference by any number you like to name ; (v) cross out any digit except a nought ; (vi) read the remainder. Then the sum of the digits in the remainder subtracted from the next highest multiple of nine will give the figure struck out. This is clear since the result of operation (iv) is a multiple of nine, and the sum of the digits of every multiple of nine is itself a multiple of nine. This and the previous problem are typical of numerous analogous questions.

Third Problem. If n digits are required in the pagination of a book, how many pages are contained therein—for instance, $n = 3001$?

The analysis is obvious. The first 999 pages require the use of $(9 + 180 + 2700)$ digits. But 112 additional digits are employed, and these suffice to identify 28 more pages. Therefore the total number of pages is $999 + 28$, that is, 1027.

Fourth Problem. The numbers from 1 upwards are written consecutively. What is the nth digit—for instance, $n = 500000$?

The numbers from 1 to 99999 inclusive require 488889 digits. Hence we want the 11111th digit in the series of six-digit numbers starting with 100000. We have $11111 = 6 \times 1851 + 5$. Hence we want the 5th digit in 101851, and this is 5.

Empirical Problems. There are also numerous empirical problems, such as the following. With the ten digits, 9, 8, 7, 6, 5, 4, 3, 2, 1, 0, express numbers whose sum is unity : each digit being used only once, and the use of the usual notations for fractions being allowed. With the same ten digits express numbers whose sum is 100. With the nine digits, 9, 8, 7, 6, 5, 4, 3, 2, 1, express numbers whose sum is 100. To the making of such questions there is no limit, but their solution involves little or no mathematical skill.

Four Digits Problem. I suggest the following problem as being more interesting. With the digits 1, 2, 3, 4, express the consecutive numbers from 1 upwards as far as possible : each of the four digits being used once, and only once, in the expression of each number. Allowing the notation of the denary scale (including decimals), as also algebraic sums, products, and positive integral powers, we can get to 88. If the use of the symbols for square roots and factorials (repeated if desired a finite number of times) is also permitted, we can get to 264 ; if negative integral indices are also permitted, to 276 ; and if fractional indices are permitted, to 312. Many similar questions may be proposed, such as using four out of the digits 1, 2, 3, 4, 5. With the five digits 1, 2, 3, 4, 5, each being used once and only once, I have got to 3832 and 4282, according as negative and fractional indices are excluded or allowed.

Four Fours Problem. Another traditional recreation is, with the ordinary arithmetic and algebraic notation, to express the consecutive numbers from 1 upwards as far as possible in terms of four " 4's." Everything turns on what we mean by ordinary notation. If (a) this is taken to admit only the use of the denary scale (*e.g.* numbers like 44), decimals, brackets, and the symbols for addition, subtraction, multiplication, and division, we can thus express every number up to 22 inclusive.* If (β) also we grant the use of the symbol for square root (repeated if desired a finite number of times), we can get to 30; but note that though by its use a number like 2 can be expressed by one " 4," we cannot for that reason say that ·2 is so expressible. If (γ), further, we permit the use of symbols for factorials, we can express every number to 112.† Finally, if (δ) we sanction the employment of integral indices expressible by a " 4 " or " 4's " and allow the symbol for a square root to be used an infinite number of times, we can get to 156; but if (ϵ) we concede the employment of integral indices and the use of sub-factorials,‡ we can get to 877. These interesting problems are typical of a class of similar questions. Thus, under conditions γ and using no indices, with four " 1's " we can get to 34, with four " 2's " to 36, with four " 3's " to 46, with four " 5's " to 36, with four " 6's " to 30, with four " 7's " to 25, with four " 8's " to 36, and with four " 9's " to 66.

PROBLEMS WITH A SERIES OF THINGS WHICH ARE NUMBERED

Any collection of things numbered consecutively lend themselves to easy illustrations of questions depending on elementary properties of numbers. As examples I proceed to enumerate a few familiar tricks. The first two of these are commonly shown by the use of a watch, the last four may be exemplified by the use of a pack of playing cards.

First Example.§ The first of these examples is connected with the hours marked on the face of a watch. In this puzzle some-

---

* *E.g.*, $22 = (4 + 4)/(\cdot\dot{4}) + 4$.

† *E.g.*, $99 = 4 \times 4! + \sqrt{4/(\cdot\dot{4})}$.

‡ Sub-factorial n is equal to $n! (1 - 1/1! + 1/2! - 1/3! + \ldots \pm 1/n!)$. On the use of this for the four " 4's " problem, see the *Mathematical Gazette*, May 1912.

§ Bachet, problem xx, p. 155; Oughtred or Leake, *Mathematicall Recreations*, London, 1653, p. 28.

one is asked to think of some hour, say m, and then to touch a number that marks another hour, say n. Then if, beginning with the number touched, he taps each successive hour marked on the face of the watch, going in the opposite direction to that in which the hands of the watch move, and reckoning to himself the taps as m, $(m + 1)$, etc., the $(n + 12)$th tap will be on the hour he thought of. For example, if he thinks of v and touches IX, then, if he taps successively IX, VIII, VII, VI, ..., going backwards and reckoning them respectively as 5, 6, 7, 8, ..., the tap which he reckons as 21 will be on the v.

The reason of the rule is obvious, for he arrives finally at the $(n + 12 - m)$th hour from which he started. Now, since he goes in the opposite direction to that in which the hands of the watch move, he has to go over $(n - m)$ hours to reach the hour m : also it will make no difference if, in addition, he goes over 12 hours, since the only effect of this is to take him once completely round the circle. Now $(n + 12 - m)$ is always positive, since n is positive and m is not greater than 12, and therefore if we make him pass over $(n + 12 - m)$ hours we can give the rule in a form which is equally valid whether m is greater or less than n.

Second Example. The following is another well-known watch-dial problem. If the hours on the face are tapped successively, beginning at VII and proceeding backwards round the dial to VI, V, etc., and if the person who selected the number counts the taps, beginning to count from the number of the hour selected (thus, if he selected X, he would reckon the first tap as the 11th), then the 20th tap as reckoned by him will be on the hour chosen.

For suppose he selected the nth hour. Then the 8th tap is on XII and is reckoned by him as the $(n + 8)$th ; and the tap which he reckons as $(n + p)$th is on the hour $(20 - p)$. Hence, putting $p = 20 - n$, the tap which he reckons as 20th is on the hour n. Of course, the hours indicated by the first seven taps are immaterial : obviously also we can modify the presentation by beginning on the hour VIII and making 21 consecutive taps,

C

or on the hour IX and making 22 consecutive taps, and so on.

Third Example. The following is another simple example. Suppose that a pack of n cards is given to someone who is asked to select one out of the first m cards and to remember (but not to mention) what is its number from the top of the pack; suppose it is actually the xth card in the pack. Then take the pack, reverse the order of the top m cards (which can be easily effected by shuffling), and transfer y cards, where $y < n - m$, from the bottom to the top of the pack. The effect of this is that the card originally chosen is now the $(y + m - x + 1)$th from the top. Return to the spectator the pack so rearranged, and ask that the top card be counted as the $(x + 1)$th, the next as the $(x + 2)$th, and so on, in which case the card originally chosen will be the $(y + m + 1)$th. Now y and m can be chosen as we please, and may be varied every time the trick is performed; thus anyone unskilled in arithmetic will not readily detect the method used.

Fourth Example.* Place a card on the table, and on it place as many other cards from the pack as with the number of pips on the card will make a total of twelve. For example, if the card placed first on the table is the five of clubs, then seven additional cards must be placed on it. The court cards may have any values assigned to them, but usually they are reckoned as tens. This is done again with another card, and thus another pile is formed. The operation may be repeated either only three or four times or as often as the pack will permit of such piles being formed. If finally there are p such piles, and if the number of cards left over is r, then the sum of the number of pips on the bottom cards of all the piles will be $13(p - 4) + r$.

For, if x is the number of pips on the bottom card of a pile, the number of cards in that pile will be $13 - x$. A similar argument holds for each pile. Also there are 52 cards in the

* A particular case of this problem was given by Bachet, problem XVII, p. 138.

pack; and this must be equal to the sum of the cards in the p piles and the r cards left over. Thus we have

$$(13 - x_1) + (13 - x_2) + \ldots + (13 - x_p) + r = 52,$$
$$13p - (x_1 + x_2 + \ldots + x_p) + r = 52,$$
$$x_1 + x_2 + \ldots + x_p = 13p - 52 + r$$
$$= 13(p - 4) + r.$$

More generally, if a pack of n cards is taken, and if in each pile the sum of the pips on the bottom card and the number of cards put on it is equal to m, then the sum of the pips on the bottom cards of the piles will be $(m + 1)p + r - n$. In an écarté pack $n = 32$, and it is convenient to take $m = 15$.

Fifth Example. It may be noticed that cutting a pack of cards never alters the relative position of the cards provided that, if necessary, we regard the top card as following immediately after the bottom card in the pack. This is used in the following trick.* Take a pack, and deal the cards face upwards on the table, calling them one, two, three, etc., as you put them down, and noting in your own mind the card first dealt. Ask someone to select a card and recollect its number. Turn the pack over, and let it be cut (not shuffled) as often as you like. Enquire what was the number of the card chosen. Then, if you deal, and as soon as you come to the original first card, begin (silently) to count, reckoning this as one, the selected card will appear at the number mentioned. Of course, if all the cards are dealt before reaching this number, you must turn the cards over and go on counting continuously.

Sixth Example. Here is another simple question of this class. Remove the court cards from a pack. Arrange the remaining 40 cards, faces upwards, in suits, in four lines thus. In the first line, the 1, 2, . . . 10, of suit A; in the second line, the 10, 1, 2, . . . 9, of suit B; in the third line, the 9, 10, 1, . . . 8, of suit C; in the last line, the 8, 9, 10, 1, . . . 7, of suit

* Bachet, problem xix, p. 152.

D. Next take up, face upwards, the first card of line 1, put below it the first card of line 2, below that the first card of line 3, and below that the first card of line 4. Turn this pile face downwards. Next take up the four cards in the second column in the same way, turn them face downwards, and put them below the first pile. Continue this process until all the cards are taken up. Ask someone to mention any card. Suppose the number of pips on it is n. Then if the suit is A, it will be the $4n$th card in the pack; if the suit is B, it will be the $(4n + 3)$th card; if the suit is C, it will be the $(4n + 6)$th card; and if the suit is D, it will be the $(4n + 9)$th card. Hence by counting the cards, cyclically if necessary, the card desired can be picked out. It is easy to alter the form of presentation, and a full pack can be used if desired. The explanation is obvious.

ARITHMETICAL RESTORATIONS

I take next a class of problems dealing with the reconstruction of arithmetical sums from which various digits have been erased. Some of these questions are easy, some difficult. This kind of exercise has attracted a good deal of attention in recent years. I give examples of three kinds of restoration.

Class A. The solutions of one group of these restoration questions depend on the well-known propositions that every number

$$a + 10b + 10^2c + 10^3d + \cdots$$

is equal to any of certain expressions such as

$$M(9) \ + a + b + c + d + \cdots$$
$$M(11) + a - b + c - d + \cdots$$
$$M(33) \ + (a + 10b) + (c + 10d) + (e + 10f) + \cdots$$
$$M(101) + (a + 10b) - (c + 10d) + (e + 10f) - \cdots$$
$$M(m) \ + (a + 10b + 10^2c) + (d + 10e + 10^2f) + \cdots$$
$$M(n) \ + (a + 10b + 10^2c) - (d + 10e + 10^2f) + \cdots$$

where, in the penultimate line, $m = 27$, or 37, or 111, and in the last line, $n = 7$, or 13, or 77, or 91, or 143.

Examples, depending on such propositions, are not uncommon. Here are four easy instances of this class of questions.

(i) The product of 417 and . 1 . . . is 9 . . . 057. Find the missing digits, each of which is represented by a dot. If the undetermined digits in the multiplier are denoted in order by a, b, c, d, and we take the steps of the multiplication in their reverse order, we obtain successively $d = 1$, $c = 2$, $b = 9$. Also the product has 7 digits, therefore $a = 2$. Hence the product is 9,141,057.

(ii) The seven-digit number 70 . . 34 . is exactly divisible by 792. Find the missing digits, each of which is represented by a dot. Since 792 is $8 \times 9 \times 11$, we can easily show that the number is 7,054,344.

(iii) The five-digit number 4 . 18 . is divisible by 101. Find the missing digits.*

Denote the two missing digits, from right to left, by x and y. Applying the theorem for 101, noting that each of the unknowns cannot exceed 9, and for convenience putting $y = 10 - z$, this equation gives $z = 1$, $x = 7$, $y = 9$. Hence the number is 49,187.

(iv) The four-digit number . 8 . . is divisible by 1287. Find the missing digits.†

Denote these digits, from right to left, by x, y, z. We have $1287 = 9 \times 11 \times 13$. Applying the suitable propositions, and noting that each of the unknowns cannot exceed 9, we get $x = 1$, $y = 6$, $z = 3$. Hence the number is 3861.

(v) As a slightly harder example of this type, suppose we know that 6 . 80 . 8 . . 51 is exactly divisible by 73 and 137. Find the missing digits.‡ The data suffice to determine the number, which is 6,780,187,951.

* P. Delens, *Problèmes d'Arithmétique Amusante*, Paris, 1914, p. 55.
† *Ibid.*, p. 57.
‡ *Ibid.*, p. 60.

Class B. Another and more difficult class of restoration problems is illustrated by the following examples. Their solutions involve analytical skill which cannot be reduced to rules.

(i) I begin with an easy instance, said to be of Hindoo origin, in which the problem is to restore the missing digits in the annexed division sum where a certain six-digit number when divided by a three-digit number gives a three-digit result.*

$$
\begin{array}{r}
\ldots)\ldots\ldots(\ldots \\
.\,0\,.\,. \\
\overline{} \\
.\,.\,.\,. \\
.\,5\,0\,. \\
\overline{} \\
.\,.\,. \\
.\,4\,. \\
\overline{}
\end{array}
$$

The solution involves no difficulty. The answer is that the divisor is 215, and the quotient 573; the solution is unique.

(ii) As a more difficult specimen I give the following problem, proposed in 1921 by Prof. Schuh of Delft. A certain seven-digit integer when divided by a certain six-digit integer gives a result whose integral part is a two-digit number and whose fractional part is a ten-digit expression of which the last nine digits form a repeating decimal, as indicated in the following work, where a bar has been put above the repeating digits. It is required to restore the working.† This problem is remarkable from the fact that not a single digit is given explicitly.

* *American Mathematical Monthly*, 1921, vol. xxviii, p. 37.
† *Ibid.*, p. 278.

. . . . . .) . . . . (. . . . .
          . . . . . .
          ‾‾‾‾‾‾
          . . . . . .
          . . . . . .
          ‾‾‾‾‾‾‾
           . . . . . .
           . . . . . .
           ‾‾‾‾‾‾‾
            . . . . . .
            . . . . . .
            ‾‾‾‾‾‾‾
             . . . . . .
             . . . . . .
             ‾‾‾‾‾‾‾
              . . . . . .
              . . . . . .
              ‾‾‾‾‾‾‾
               . . . . . .
               . . . . . .
               ‾‾‾‾‾‾‾
                . . . . . .
                . . . . . .
                ‾‾‾‾‾‾
                . . . . . .

The answer is that the divisor is 667334 and the dividend is 7752341.

Here are three additional examples of arithmetical restorations.* The solutions are lengthy and involve much empirical work.

(iii) The first of these Berwick questions is as follows. In the following division sum all the digits, except the seven

* All are due to W. E. H. Berwick. The " 7 " problem appeared in the *School World*, July and October 1906, vol. VIII, pp. 280, 320; the " 4 " problem appeared in the *Mathematical Gazette*, 1920, vol. x, pp. 43, 359—360; the " 5 " problem in the same paper, vol. x, p. 361, vol. XI, p. 8.

" 7's " shown, have been erased : each missing digit may be
1, 2, 3, 4, 5, 6, 7, 8, 9, or (except in the first digit of a line) 0.
Observe that every step in the working consists of two lines
each of which contains an equal number of digits. The problem
is to restore the whole working of the sum. The solution is
unique and gives a divisor of 125473 and a quotient of 58781.

```
. . . . 7 . ) . . 7 . . . . . . . . ( . . 7 . .
              . . . . . .
              ‾‾‾‾‾‾‾‾‾‾‾
              . . . . . 7 .
              . . . . . . .
                . 7 . . . .
                . 7 . . . .
                ‾‾‾‾‾‾‾‾‾‾‾
                . . . . . . .
                . . . . 7 . .
                ‾‾‾‾‾‾‾‾‾‾‾
                  . . . . . .
                  . . . . . .
                  ‾‾‾‾‾‾‾‾‾
```

(iv) The second problem is similar and requires the restoration of the digits in the following division sum, where the
position of four " 4's " is given,

```
. . . ) . . . . . . 4 ( . 4 . .
       . . .
       ‾‾‾‾
       . . 4 .
       . . . .
       ‾‾‾‾‾
         . . . .
         . 4 .
         ‾‾‾‾
           . . . .
           . . . .
           ‾‾‾‾
```

To this problem there are four solutions, the divisors being 846, 848, 943, 949; and the respective quotients 1419, 1418, 1418, 1416.

If we propound the problem (using five " 4's ") thus :

```
. . . ) . . . . . . . 4 ( . 4 . . .
        . . .
        ─────
        . . 4 .
        . . . , 4
        ───────
        . . . .
        . . 4 .
        ─────
        . . . .
        . . . .
        ─────
```

there is only one solution, and some will think this is a better form in which to enunciate it.

(v) In the last of these Berwick examples, it is required to restore the working of the following division sum where all the digits, except five " 5's," have been erased.

```
. . . ) . 5 5 . . 5 . ( . 5 .
        . . 5 . .
        ─────────
        . . . . .
        . . . . .
        ─────────
        . . . .
        . . . .
        ───────
```

To this problem there is only one solution, the divisor being 3926 and the quotient 652.

Class C. A third class of digit problems depends on finding the values of certain symbols which represent specified numbers. Two examples will suffice.

(i) Here is a very simple illustrative specimen. The result

of multiplying bc by bc is abc, where the letters stand for certain numbers. What are the numbers ? A brief examination shows that bc stands for 25, and therefore a stands for 6.

(ii) Here is another example. The object is to find the digits represented by letters in the following sum : *

$$a\,b\,)\,c\,d\,e\,e\,b\,(\,b\,f\,b$$
$$c\,e\,b$$
$$\overline{}$$
$$g\,g\,e$$
$$g\,c\,h$$
$$\overline{}$$
$$c\,e\,b$$
$$c\,e\,b$$
$$\overline{}$$

A solution may be obtained thus : Since the product of b by b is a number which ends in b, b must be 1, 5, or 6. Since the product of ab by b is a number of three digits, b cannot be 1. The result of the subtraction of h from e is e, hence $h = 0$, and therefore if $b = 5$ we have f even, and if $b = 6$ we have $f = 5$. Also the result of the subtraction of c from g is c, hence $g = 2c$, and therefore c cannot be greater than 4 : from which it follows that b cannot be 6. A few trials now show that the question arose from the division of 19,775 by 35.

It is possible to frame digit restoration examples of a mixed character involving the difficulties of all the examples given above, and to increase the difficulty by expressing them in a non-denary scale of notation. But such elaborations do not add to the interest of the questions.

Calendar Problems

The formulae given by Gauss and Zeller, which I quoted in former editions of this work, serve to solve all questions likely to occur about dates, days of the week, Easter, etc. Here are two easy but elegant questions on the Gregorian Calendar of a somewhat different nature.

* *Strand Magazine,* September–October, 1921

The first is as follows : it is due, I believe, to E. Fourrey. In the century and a half between 1725 and 1875 the French fought and won a certain battle on 22 April of one year, and 4382 days later, also on 22 April, they gained another victory. The sum of the digits of the years is 40. Find the dates of the battles.

To solve it we notice that $4382 = 12 \times 365 + 2$. Hence the date of the second battle was 12 years after that of the first battle; but only two leap years had intervened, and therefore the year 1800 must be within the limiting dates. Thus 1788 and 1800, 1789 and 1801, . . ., 1800 and 1812, are the only possible years. Of the years thus suggested, 1796 and 1808 alone give 40 as the sum of their digits. Hence the battles were fought on the 22 April, 1796 (Mondovi under Napoleon), and 22 April, 1808 (Eckmuhl under Davoust).

The other of these questions is to show that the first or last day of every alternate century must be a Monday. This follows from knowing any one assigned date, and the fact that the Gregorian cycle is completed in 400 years ($= 20871$ weeks). The same principle is involved in B. H. Brown's assertion * that the thirteenth day of the month is more likely to be a Friday than to be any other day of the week.

MEDIEVAL PROBLEMS IN ARITHMETIC

Before leaving the subject of these elementary questions, I may mention a few problems which for centuries have appeared in nearly every collection of mathematical recreations, and may therefore claim what is almost a prescriptive right to a place here.

First Example. The following is a sample of one class of these puzzles. A man goes to a tub of water with two jars, of which one holds exactly 3 pints and the other 5 pints. How can he bring back exactly 4 pints of water ? The solution presents no difficulty.

* *American Mathematical Monthly*, 1933, vol. XL, p. 607.

Second Example.* Here is another problem of the same kind. Three men robbed a gentleman of a vase, containing 24 ounces of balsam. Whilst running away they met a glass-seller, of whom they purchased three vessels. On reaching a place of safety they wished to divide the booty, but found that their vessels contained 5, 11, and 13 ounces respectively. How could they divide the balsam into equal portions? Problems like this can be worked out only by trial.

Third Example.† The next of these is a not uncommon game, played by two people, say A and B. A begins by mentioning some number not greater than (say) six, B may add to that any number not greater than six, A may add to that again any number not greater than six, and so on. He wins who is the first to reach (say) 50. Obviously, if A calls 43, then whatever B adds to that, A can win next time. Similarly, if A calls 36, B cannot prevent A's calling 43 the next time. In this way it is clear that the key numbers are those forming the arithmetical progression 43, 36, 29, 22, 15, 8, 1; and whoever plays first ought to win.

Similarly, if no number greater than m may be added at any one time, and n is the number to be called by the victor, then the key numbers will be those forming the arithmetical progression whose common difference is $m + 1$ and whose smallest term is the remainder obtained by dividing n by $m + 1$.

The same game may be played in another form by placing p coins, matches, or other objects on a table, and directing each player in turn to take away not more than m of them. Whoever takes away the last coin wins. Obviously the key numbers are multiples of $m + 1$, and the first player who is able to leave an exact multiple of $(m + 1)$ coins can win.

---

* Some similar problems were given by Bachet, Appendix, problem III, p. 206; problem IX, p. 233: by Oughtred or Leake in the *Mathematicall Recreations*, p. 22 : and by Ozanam, 1803 edition, vol. I, p. 174; 1840 edition, p. 79. Earlier instances occur in Tartaglia's writings. See also Kraïtchik, p. 11.

† Bachet, problem XXII, p. 170.

Perhaps a better form of the game is to make that player lose who takes away the last coin, in which case each of the key numbers exceeds by unity a multiple of $m + 1$.

Another variety * consists in placing p counters in the form of a circle, and allowing each player in succession to take away not more than m of them which are in unbroken sequence : m being less than p and greater than unity. In this case the second of the two players can always win.

These games are simple, but if we impose on the original problem the restriction that each player may not add the same number more than (say) three times, the analysis becomes by no means easy. I have never seen this extension described in print, and I will enunciate it at length. Suppose that each player is given eighteen cards, three of them marked 6, three marked 5, three marked 4, three marked 3, three marked 2, and three marked 1. They play alternately ; A begins by playing one of his cards ; then B plays one of his, and so on. He wins who first plays a card which makes the sum of the points or numbers on all the cards played exactly equal to 50, but he loses if he plays a card which makes this sum exceed 50. The game can be played by noting the numbers on a piece of paper, and it is not necessary to use cards.

Thus suppose they play as follows. A takes a 4, and scores 4 ; B takes a 3, and scores 7 ; A takes a 1, and scores 8 ; B takes a 6, and scores 14 ; A takes a 3, and scores 17 ; B takes a 4, and scores 21 ; A takes a 4, and scores 25 ; B takes a 5, and scores 30 ; A takes a 4, and scores 34 ; B takes a 4, and scores 38 ; A takes a 5, and scores 43. B can now win, for he may safely play 3, since A has not another 4 wherewith to follow it ; and if A plays less than 4, B will win the next time. Again, suppose they play thus. A, 6 ; B, 3 ; A, 1 ; B, 6 ; A, 3 ; B, 4 ; A, 2 ; B, 5 ; A, 1 ; B, 5 ; A, 2 ; B, 5 ; A, 2 ; B, 3. A is now forced to play 1, and B wins by playing 1.

A slightly different form of the game has also been sug-

* S. Loyd, *Tit-Bits*, London, July 17, Aug. 7, 1897.

gested. In this there are put on the table an agreed number of cards—say, for example, the four aces, twos, threes, fours, fives, and sixes of a pack of cards—twenty-four cards in all. Each player in turn takes a card. The score at any time is the sum of the pips on all the cards taken, whether by A or B. He wins who first selects a card which makes the score equal, say to 50, and a player who is forced to go beyond 50 loses.

Thus, suppose they play as follows. A takes a 6, and scores 6; B takes a 2, and scores 8; A takes a 5, and scores 13; B takes a 2, and scores 15; A takes a 5, and scores 20; B takes a 2, and scores 22; A takes a 5, and scores 27; B takes a 2, and scores 29; A takes a 5, and scores 34; B takes a 6, and scores 40; A takes a 1, and scores 41; B takes a 4, and scores 45; A takes a 3, and scores 48; B now must take 1, and thus score 49; and A takes a 1, and wins.

In these variations the object of each player is to get to one of the key numbers, provided there are sufficient available remaining numbers to let him retain the possession of each subsequent key number. The number of cards used, the points on them, and the number to be reached can be changed at will; and the higher the number to be reached, the more difficult it is to forecast the result and to say whether or not it is an advantage to begin.

Fourth Example. The following medieval problem is somewhat more elaborate. Suppose that three people, P, Q, R, select three things, which we may denote by a, e, i respectively, and that it is desired to find by whom each object was selected.*

Place 24 counters on a table. Ask P to take one counter, Q to take two counters, and R to take three counters. Next, ask the person who selected a to take as many counters as he has already, whoever selected e to take twice as many counters as he has already, and whoever selected i to take four times as many counters as he has already. Note how many counters remain on the table. There are only six ways of distributing the three things among P, Q, and R; and the number of

* Bachet, problem xxv, p. 187.

counters remaining on the table is different for each way. The remainders may be 1, 2, 3, 5, 6, or 7. Bachet summed up the results in the mnemonic line *Par fer* (1) *César* (2) *jadis* (3) *devint* (5) *si grand* (6) *prince* (7). Corresponding to any remainder is a word or words containing two syllables : for instance, to the remainder 5 corresponds the word *devint*. The vowel in the first syllable indicates the thing selected by P, the vowel in the second syllable indicates the thing selected by Q, and of course R selected the remaining thing.

Extension. M. Bourlet, in the course of a very kindly notice * of the second edition of this work, gave a much neater solution of the above question, and has extended the problem to the case of n people, P_0, P_1, P_2 ..., P_{n-1}, each of whom selects one object, out of a collection of n objects, such as dominoes or cards. It is required to know which domino or card was selected by each person.

Let us suppose the dominoes to be denoted or marked by the numbers 0, 1, ..., $n - 1$, instead of by vowels. Give one counter to P_1, two counters to P_2, and generally k counters to P_k. Note the number of counters left on the table. Next ask the person who had chosen the domino 0 to take as many counters as he had already, and generally whoever had chosen the domino h to take n^h times as many dominoes as he had already : thus if P_h had chosen the domino numbered h, he would take $n^h k$ counters. The total number of counters taken is $\Sigma n^h k$. Divide this by n, then the remainder will be the number on the domino selected by P_0 ; divide the quotient by n, and the remainder will be the number on the domino selected by P_1 ; divide this quotient by n, and the remainder will be the number on the domino selected by P_2 ; and so on. In other words, if the number of counters taken is expressed in the scale of notation whose radix is n, then the $(h + 1)$th digit from the right will give the number on the domino selected by P_h.

* *Bulletin des Sciences Mathématiques*, Paris, 1893, vol. xvii, pp. 105—107.

Thus in Bachet's problem with 3 people and 3 dominoes, we should first give one counter to Q, and two counters to R, while P would have no counters; then we should ask the person who had selected the domino marked 0 or a to take as many counters as he had already, whoever had selected the domino marked 1 or e to take three times as many counters as he had already, and whoever had selected the domino marked 2 or i to take nine times as many counters as he had already. By noticing the original number of counters, and observing that 3 of these had been given to Q and R, we should know the total number taken by P, Q, and R. If this number were divided by 3, the remainder would be the number of the domino chosen by P; if the quotient were divided by 3 the remainder would be the number of the domino chosen by Q; and the final quotient would be the number of the domino chosen by R.

Exploration Problems. Another common question is concerned with the maximum distance into a desert which could be reached from a frontier settlement by the aid of a party of n explorers, each capable of carrying provisions that would last one man for a days. The answer is that the man who reaches the greatest distance will occupy $na/(n+1)$ days before he returns to his starting-point. If in the course of their journey they may make depôts, the longest possible journey will occupy $\frac{1}{2}a(1 + \frac{1}{2} + \frac{1}{3} + \ldots + 1/n)$ days.

The Josephus Problem. Another of these antique problems consists in placing men round a circle so that if every mth man is killed, the remainder shall be certain specified individuals. Such problems can be easily solved empirically.

Hegesippus * says that Josephus saved his life by such a device. According to his account, after the Romans had captured Jotapat, Josephus and forty other Jews took refuge in a cave. Josephus, much to his disgust, found that all except himself and one other man were resolved to kill themselves, so as not to fall into the hands of their conquerors.

* *De Bello Judaico*, bk. III, chaps. 16—18.

Fearing to show his opposition too openly he consented, but declared that the operation must be carried out in an orderly way, and suggested that they should arrange themselves round a circle and that every third person should be killed until but one man was left, who must then commit suicide. It is alleged that he placed himself and the other man in the 31st and 16th place respectively.

The medieval question was usually presented in the following form. A ship, carrying as passengers 15 Turks and 15 Christians, encountered a storm, and, in order to save the ship and crew, one-half of the passengers had to be thrown into the sea. Accordingly the passengers were placed in a circle, and every ninth man, reckoning from a certain point, was cast overboard. It is desired to find an arrangement by which all the Christians should be saved.* In this case we must arrange the men thus :
$C\ C\ C\ C\ T\ T\ T\ T\ T\ C\ C\ T\ C\ C\ C\ T\ C\ T\ T\ C\ C\ T\ T\ T\ C\ T\ T\ C\ C\ T$,
where C stands for a Christian and T for a Turk. The order can be recollected by the positions of the vowels in the following line : *From numbers' aid and art, never will fame depart*, where a stands for 1, e for 2, i for 3, o for 4, and u for 5. Hence the order is o Christians, u Turks, etc.

If every tenth man were cast overboard, a similar mnemonic line is *Rex paphi cum gente bona dat signa serena*. An oriental setting of this decimation problem runs somewhat as follows. Once upon a time, there lived a rich farmer who had 30 children, 15 by his first wife who was dead, and 15 by his second wife. The latter woman was eager that her eldest son should inherit the property. Accordingly one day she said to him, " Dear Husband, you are getting old. We ought to settle who shall be your heir. Let us arrange our 30 children in a circle, and counting from one of them, remove every tenth child until there remains but one, who shall succeed to your estate." The proposal seemed reasonable. As the process of selection went on, the farmer grew more and more astonished as he

---

* Bachet, problem XXIII, p. 174. The same problem had been previously enunciated by Tartaglia.

D

noticed that the first 14 to disappear were children by his first wife, and he observed that the next to go would be the last remaining member of that family. So he suggested that they should see what would happen if they began to count backwards from this lad. She, forced to make an immediate decision, and reflecting that the odds were now 15 to 1 in favour of her family, readily assented. Who became the heir?

In the general case n men are arranged in a circle which is closed up as individuals are picked out. Beginning anywhere, we continually go round, picking out each mth man until only r are left. Let one of these be the man who originally occupied the pth place. Then had we begun with $n + 1$ men, he would have originally occupied the $(p + m)$th place when $p + m$ is not greater than $n + 1$, and the $(p + m - n - 1)$th place when $p + m$ is greater than $n + 1$. Thus, provided there are to be r men left, their original positions are each shifted forwards along the circle m places for each addition of a single man to the original group.*

Now suppose that with n men the last survivor $(r = 1)$ occupied originally the pth place, and that with $(n + x)$ men the last survivor occupied the yth place. Then, if we confine ourselves to the lowest value of x which makes y less than m, we have $y = (p + mx) - (n + x)$.

Based on this theorem we can, for any specified value of n, calculate rapidly the position occupied by the last survivor of the company. In effect, Tait found the values of n for which a man occupying a given position p, which is less than m, would be the last survivor, and then, by repeated applications of the proposition, obtained the position of the survivor for intermediate values of n.

For instance, take the Josephus problem in which $m = 3$. Then we know that the final survivor of 41 men occupied originally the 31st place. Suppose that when there had been

* P. G. Tait, *Collected Scientific Papers*, Cambridge, vol. II, 1900, pp. 432—435.

$(41 + x)$ men, the survivor occupied originally the yth place. Then, if we consider only the lowest value of x which makes y less than m, we have $y = (31 + 3x) - (41 + x) = 2x - 10$. Now, we have to take a value of x which makes y positive and less than m—that is, in this case equal to 1 or 2. This is $x = 6$, which makes $y = 2$. Hence, had there been 47 men, the man last chosen would have originally occupied the second place. Similarly had there been $(47 + x)$ men, the man would have occupied originally the yth place, where, subject to the same conditions as before, we have $y = (2 + 3x) - (47 + x) = 2x - 45$. If $x = 23$, $y = 1$. Hence, with 70 men the man last chosen would have occupied originally the first place. Continuing the process, it is easily found that if n does not exceed 2000000 the last man to be taken occupies the first place when $n = 4$, 6, 9, 31, 70, 105, 355, 799, 1798, 2697, 9103, 20482, 30723, 69127, 155536, 233304, 349956, 524934, or 787401; and the second place when $n = 2$, 3, 14, 21, 47, 158, 237, 533, 1199, 4046, 6069, 13655, 46085, 103691, 1181102, or 1771653. From these results, by repeated applications of the proposition, we find, for any intermediate values of n, the position originally occupied by the man last taken. Thus with 1000 men, the 604th place; with 100000 men, the 92620th place; and with 1000000 men, the 637798th place are those which would be selected by a prudent mathematician in a company subjected to trimation.

Similarly if a set of 100 men were subjected to decimation, the last to be taken would be the man originally in the 26th place. Hence, with 227 men the last to be taken would be the man originally in the first place.

Modifications of the original problem have been suggested. For instance,* let 5 Christians and 5 Turks be arranged round a circle thus, $T\ C\ T\ C\ C\ T\ C\ T\ C\ T$. Suppose that, if beginning at the ath man, every hth man is selected, all the Turks will be picked out for punishment; but if beginning at the bth man, every kth man is selected, all the Christians will be picked out

* H. E. Dudeney, *Tit-Bits*, London, Oct. 14 and 28, 1905.

for punishment. The problem is to find a, b, h, and k. A solution is $a = 1$, $h = 11$, $b = 9$, $k = 29$.

I suggest as a similar problem, to find an arrangement of c Turks and c Christians arranged in a circle, so that if beginning at a particular man, say the first, every hth man is selected, all the Turks will be picked out, but if, beginning at the same man, every kth man is selected, all the Christians will be picked out. This makes an interesting question because it is conceivable that the operator who picked out the victims might get confused and take k instead of h, or vice versa, and so consign all his friends to execution instead of those whom he had intended to pick out. The problem is, for any given value of c, to find an arrangement of the men and the corresponding suitable values of h and k. Obviously if $c = 2$, then for an arrangement like $T \, C \, C \, T$ a solution is $h = 4$, $k = 3$. If $c = 3$, then for an arrangement like $T \, C \, T \, C \, C \, T$ a solution is $h = 7$, $k = 8$. If $c = 4$, then for an arrangement like $T \, C \, T \, T \, C \, T \, C \, C$ a solution is $h = 9$, $k = 5$. And generally, as first pointed out by Mr. Swinden, with $2c$ men, c of them, occupying initially the consecutive places numbered c, $c + 1$, ..., $2c - 1$, will be picked out, if h is the L.C.M. of $c + 1$, $c + 2$, ..., $2c - 1$; and the other c will be picked out if $k = h + 1$, though it may well be that there is a simpler solution for another initial arrangement. It may be impossible to arrange the men so that n specified individuals shall be picked out in a defined order.

THE GAME OF NIM [*]

Here is a game which has a complete mathematical analysis. Suppose that any number of counters are divided arbitrarily into several heaps. Two people play alternately. Each, when his turn comes, may select any one heap, and remove from it all the counters in it or as many of them as he pleases (but at least one). The player drawing the last counter (or counters) wins.

[*] C. L. Bouton, *Annals of Mathematics*, 1902, series 2, vol. III, pp. 35–39.

Suppose that the counters are dealt by the player A, and that the other player B, draws first. If A deals only one heap, B may win at once by drawing all the counters. Such a deal is thus an *unsafe combination* (*i.e.*, unsafe for A, who dealt it). On the other hand, if A deals two equal heaps, B cannot help making them unequal, and A must eventually win if at each stage he makes them equal again. Such a deal is therefore a *safe combination* for A. The fact is, that every combination is either safe or unsafe, in the sense that *every unsafe combination by a suitable draw may be made safe*, while *every safe combination by every draw is made unsafe*. Thus, if A deals a safe combination, B by drawing cannot avoid making it unsafe, A by drawing suitably makes it safe again, and so on, until finally B is obliged to leave a single heap, when A wins. On the other hand, if A deals an unsafe combination, B by drawing suitably makes it safe, and then the game proceeds as before, until B finally wins.

It is soon found that heaps containing $1, 2n, 2n + 1$ counters, or $n, 7 - n, 7$ counters, or $2, 3, 4, 5$ counters, are safe combinations; and that two separate safe combinations make a safe combination. These facts are usually sufficient for playing with a novice, but Bouton has shown them to be special cases of a general rule, enabling the Mathematician to beat the Gambler practically every time.

Suppose there are a_r counters in the rth heap. Express a_r in the binary scale, and denote the coefficient of 2^p in it by d_{rp} ($= 0$ or 1). Thus $a_r = d_{r0} + 2d_{r1} + 2^2 d_{r2} + 2^3 d_{r3} + \ldots$. Do this for each heap, and let s_p be the sum of the coefficients of 2^p thus determined, so that $s_p = d_{1p} + d_{2p} + d_{3p} + \ldots$. We shall see that the combination is safe or unsafe according as $S_0, S_1, S_2, \ldots$ are all even or not all even.

If $S_0, S_1, S_2, \ldots$ are not all even, let S_q be the last one of them that is odd. Then $d_{rq} = 1$ for at least one value of r. The next player should operate on this rth heap, reducing it in such a way as to alter d_{rp} for just those values of p which make S_p odd. This operation naturally has the effect of making S_0, S_1, S_2, ... all even. Since the other player must take at least one counter, he cannot help changing one of the S's by 1, and so making it odd.

For instance, (2, 3, 4, 5) is a safe combination, because these numbers, in the binary scale, are 10, 11, 100, 101, so that $S_2 = S_1 = S_0 = 2$. If the number of counters in the largest heap is less than 2^{10}, the computation is easily carried out with the fingers. For each a_r in turn, raise or lower those fingers which correspond to digits 1 in the binary number. (This is a kind of " addition without carrying," which I will mention again in the next chapter, page 73.)

If the rules of the game are changed to the extent of making that player *lose* who takes the last counter, the procedure is unaltered, save at the end. You merely have to remember that a number of heaps, each consisting of a single counter, makes a safe or unsafe combination according as the number is odd or even, instead of *vice versa*.

Moore's " Nim$_k$". E. H. Moore [*] has proposed the following generalization. The rules for " Nim$_k$ " are the same as for Nim itself (which is " Nim$_1$ "), save that in each draw the player may take at will from any number of heaps not exceeding k. It is clear that, if A deals fewer than $k + 1$ heaps, B may win at once by drawing all the counters. Such a deal is therefore an unsafe combination. As an instance of a safe combination, consider $k + 1$ equal heaps.

Defining a_r, d_{rp}, and S_p as before, we easily see that a given combination is safe if, and only if, S_0, S_1, S_2, ... are all divisible by $k + 1$.

Wythoff's Game. W. A. Wythoff [†] has invented a similar game, where there are just two heaps. In each draw the player may take counters at will from either one or both heaps, but in the latter case he must take the same number from each heap. That player wins who takes the last counter.

---

* *Annals of Mathematics*, 1910, series 2, vol. XI, pp. 90—94.
† *Nieuw Archief voor Wiskunde*, 1907, p. 199.

The safe combinations are now (1, 2), (3, 5), (4, 7), (6, 10), (8, 13), (9, 15), (11, 18), (12, 20), ...

The first pair of numbers differ by 1, the second by 2, the third by 3, and so on. In fact, the rth pair is ($[r\tau]$, $[r\tau^2]$), where $\tau = \frac{1}{2}(\sqrt{5} + 1)$, $\tau^2 = \frac{1}{2}(\sqrt{5} + 3)$, and $[x]$ means the greatest integer not exceeding x. It is interesting to observe that every positive integer appears just once in this list; in other words, every interval between two consecutive positive integers contains just one multiple of either τ or τ^2.

Kayles. Perhaps some of my readers will feel inspired to complete the following preliminary analysis of the game of Kayles,* which differs from Nim and Wythoff's game in that the number of heaps is apt to increase as the game progresses. Thirteen counters are arranged in a row, touching one another successively, and then the second one is removed, leaving a row of eleven and one isolated counter.

o ooooooooooo

Two people play alternately, removing any counter or any two that touch one another. The player drawing the last counter (or pair) wins. As in Nim, there are safe and unsafe combinations, two equal sets make a safe combination, and two safe combinations make a safe combination. The initial combination is unsafe; it can be made safe by removing the fourth (or eighth) of the eleven counters, so as to leave (1, 3, 7). Other safe combinations are (1, 4), (1, 8), (2, 7), (3, 6), (1, 2, 3), (2, 3, 4).

When the game is extended to more than twelve counters, the number of safe combinations may overtax one's memory. Michael Goldberg has worked out all the safe combinations that involve numbers from 1 to 20; they are exhibited in the accompanying diagram. Each circle contains one or more numbers, and the circles are joined by straight lines. The safe combinations are as follows: (i) two numbers in any circle, such as (8, 13) or (5, 12); (ii) three numbers, one from

* H. E. Dudeney, *The Canterbury Puzzles*, London, 1919, pp. 118, 220.

each of three circles which lie along a straight line, such as
(8, 11, 15) or (4, 6, 7); (iii) four numbers, one from each of
four circles which lie along two straight lines, excluding the
circle at their intersection, such as (1, 2, 5, 15) or (1, 3, 5, 11).
We must remember also that two equal sets make a safe
combination, as also do two separate safe combinations.

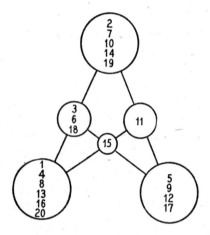

ADDENDUM

Note. Page 15. Solutions of the ten-digit problems are $35/70 + 148/296 = 1$ or $\cdot 01234 + \cdot 98765 = 1$, and $50 + 49 + 1/2 + 38/76 = 100$. A solution of the nine-digit problem is $1 \cdot 234 + 98 \cdot 765 = 100$ or $97 + 8/12 + 4/6 + 5/3 = 100$; but a neater solution (due to Perelman *) is $1 + 2 + 3 + 4 + 5 + 6 + 7 + 8 \times 9 = 100$, where the digits occur in their natural order.

Note. Page 28. There are several solutions of the division of 24 ounces under the conditions specified. One of these solutions is as follows:

	24 oz.	13 oz.	11 oz.	5 oz.
The vessels can contain . .	24 oz.	13 oz.	11 oz.	5 oz.
Their contents originally are .	24 ,,	0 ,,	0 ,,	0 ,,
First, make their contents . .	0 ,,	8 ,,	11 ,,	5 ,,
Second, make their contents .	16 ,,	8 ,,	0 ,,	0 ,,
Third, make their contents . .	16 ,,	0 ,,	8 ,,	0 ,,
Fourth, make their contents .	3 ,,	13 ,,	8 ,,	0 ,,
Fifth, make their contents . .	3 ,,	8 ,,	8 ,,	5 ,,
Lastly, make their contents .	8 ,,	8 ,,	8 ,,	0 ,,

* *L'Arithmétique Récréative*, pp. 20, 44, 74. For several hundred other solutions, see *Sphinx*, 1935, pp. 95, 111, 112, 124, 125.

CHAPTER II

ARITHMETICAL RECREATIONS (*continued*)

I DEVOTE this chapter to the description of some arithmetical fallacies, a few additional problems, and notes on one or two problems in higher arithmetic.

ARITHMETICAL FALLACIES

I begin by mentioning some instances of demonstrations* leading to arithmetical results which are obviously impossible. I include algebraical proofs as well as arithmetical ones. Some of the fallacies are so patent that in preparing the first and second editions I did not think such questions worth printing, but, as some correspondents expressed a contrary opinion, I give them for what they are worth.

First Fallacy. One of the oldest of these—and not a very interesting specimen—is as follows. Suppose that $a = b$, then

$$ab = a^2. \quad \therefore ab - b^2 = a^2 - b^2. \quad \therefore b\,(a - b) = (a + b)(a - b).$$
$$\therefore b = a + b. \quad \therefore b = 2b. \quad \therefore 1 = 2.$$

Second Fallacy. Another example, the idea of which is due to John Bernoulli, may be stated as follows. We have

* Of the fallacies given in the text, the first and second are well known; the third is not new, but the earliest work in which I recollect seeing it is my *Algebra*, Cambridge, 1890, p. 430; the fourth is given in G. Chrystal's *Algebra*, Edinburgh, 1889, vol. II, p. 159; the sixth is due to G. T. Walker, and, I believe, has not appeared elsewhere than in this book; the seventh is due to D'Alembert; and the eighth to F. Galton. It may be worth recording (i) that a mechanical demonstration that $1 = 2$ was given by R. Chartres in *Knowledge*, July, 1891; and (ii) that J. L. F. Bertrand pointed out that a demonstration that $1 = -1$ can be obtained from the proposition in the Integral Calculus that, if the limits are constant, the order of integration is indifferent; hence the integral to x (from $x = 0$ to $x = 1$) of the integral to y (from $y = 0$ to $y = 1$) of a function ϕ should be equal to the integral to y (from $y = 0$ to $y = 1$) of the integral to x (from $x = 0$ to $x = 1$) of ϕ, but if $\phi = (x^2 - y^2)/(x^2 + y^2)^2$, this gives $\frac{1}{4}\pi = -\frac{1}{4}\pi$.

$(-1)^2 = 1$. Take logarithms, $\therefore$ $2 \log (-1) = \log 1 = 0$. $\therefore \log(-1) = 0$. $\therefore -1 = e^0$. $\therefore -1 = 1$.

The same argument may be expressed thus. Let x be a quantity which satisfies the equation $e^x = -1$. Square both sides,

$$\therefore e^{2x} = 1. \quad \therefore 2x = 0. \quad \therefore x = 0. \quad \therefore e^x = e^0.$$

But $e^x = -1$ and $e^0 = 1$, $\therefore -1 = 1$.

The error in each of the foregoing examples is obvious, but the fallacies in the next examples are concealed somewhat better.

Third Fallacy. As yet another instance, we know that

$$\log (1 + x) = x - \tfrac{1}{2}x^2 + \tfrac{1}{3}x^3 - \dots.$$

If $x = 1$, the resulting series is convergent; hence we have

$$\log 2 = 1 - \tfrac{1}{2} + \tfrac{1}{3} - \tfrac{1}{4} + \tfrac{1}{5} - \tfrac{1}{6} + \tfrac{1}{7} - \tfrac{1}{8} + \tfrac{1}{9} - \dots.$$
$$\therefore 2 \log 2 = 2 - 1 + \tfrac{2}{3} - \tfrac{1}{2} + \tfrac{2}{5} - \tfrac{1}{3} + \tfrac{2}{7} - \tfrac{1}{4} + \tfrac{2}{9} - \dots.$$

Taking those terms together which have a common denominator, we obtain

$$2 \log 2 = 1 + \tfrac{1}{3} - \tfrac{1}{2} + \tfrac{1}{5} + \tfrac{1}{7} - \tfrac{1}{4} + \tfrac{1}{9} \dots$$
$$= 1 - \tfrac{1}{2} + \tfrac{1}{3} - \tfrac{1}{4} + \tfrac{1}{5} - \dots$$
$$= \log 2.$$

Hence $2 = 1$.

Fourth Fallacy. This fallacy is very similar to that last given. We have

$$\log 2 = 1 - \tfrac{1}{2} + \tfrac{1}{3} - \tfrac{1}{4} + \tfrac{1}{5} - \tfrac{1}{6} + \dots$$
$$= (1 + \tfrac{1}{3} + \tfrac{1}{5} + \dots) - (\tfrac{1}{2} + \tfrac{1}{4} + \tfrac{1}{6} + \dots)$$
$$= \{(1 + \tfrac{1}{3} + \tfrac{1}{5} + \dots) + (\tfrac{1}{2} + \tfrac{1}{4} + \tfrac{1}{6} + \dots)\}$$
$$\qquad\qquad - 2(\tfrac{1}{2} + \tfrac{1}{4} + \tfrac{1}{6} + \dots)$$
$$= \{1 + \tfrac{1}{2} + \tfrac{1}{3} + \dots\} - (1 + \tfrac{1}{2} + \tfrac{1}{3} + \dots)$$
$$= 0.$$

Fifth Fallacy. We have

$$\sqrt{a} \times \sqrt{b} = \sqrt{ab}.$$

Hence $\sqrt{-1} \times \sqrt{-1} = \sqrt{(-1)(-1)}$,

therefore, $(\sqrt{-1})^2 = \sqrt{1}$, that is, $-1 = 1$.

Sixth Fallacy. The following demonstration depends on the fact that an algebraical identity is true whatever be the symbols used in it, and it will appeal only to those who are familiar with this fact. We have, as an identity,

$$\sqrt{x-y} = i\sqrt{y-x} \quad . \quad . \quad . \quad . \quad \text{(i)},$$

where i stands either for $+\sqrt{-1}$ or for $-\sqrt{-1}$. Now an identity in x and y is necessarily true whatever numbers x and y may represent. First put $x = a$ and $y = b$,

$$\therefore \sqrt{a-b} = i\sqrt{b-a} \quad . \quad . \quad . \quad \text{(ii)}.$$

Next put $x = b$ and $y = a$,

$$\therefore \sqrt{b-a} = i\sqrt{a-b} \quad . \quad . \quad . \quad \text{(iii)}.$$

Also since (i) is an identity, it follows that in (ii) and (iii) the symbol i must be the same, that is, it represents $+\sqrt{-1}$ or $-\sqrt{-1}$ in both cases. Hence, from (ii) and (iii), we have

$$\sqrt{a-b}\,\sqrt{b-a} = i^2\sqrt{b-a}\,\sqrt{a-b},$$
$$\therefore 1 = i^2,$$

that is, $$1 = -1.$$

Seventh Fallacy. The following fallacy is due to D'Alembert.[*] We know that if the product of two numbers is equal to the product of two other numbers, the numbers will be in proportion, and from the definition of a proportion it follows that if the first term is greater than the second, then the third term will be greater than the fourth: thus, if $ad = bc$, then $a : b = c : d$, and if in this proportion $a > b$, then $c > d$. Now if we put $a = d = 1$ and $b = c = -1$ we have four numbers which satisfy the relation $ad = bc$ and such that $a > b$; hence, by the proposition, $c > d$, that is, $-1 > 1$, which is absurd.

Eighth Fallacy. The mathematical theory of probability leads to various paradoxes : of these I will give a few specimens. Suppose † three coins to be thrown up and the fact whether

* *Opuscules Mathématiques*, Paris, 1761, vol. I, p. 201.

† See *Nature*, Feb. 15, March 1, 1894, vol. XLIX, pp. 365—366, 413.

each comes down head or tail to be noticed. The probability that all three coins come down head is clearly $(1/2)^3$, that is, is $1/8$; similarly the probability that all three come down tail is $1/8$; hence the probability that all the coins come down alike (*i.e.* either all of them heads or all of them tails) is $1/4$. But, of three coins thus thrown up, at least two must come down alike : now the probability that the third coin comes down head is $1/2$ and the probability that it comes down tail is $1/2$, thus the probability that it comes down the same as the other two coins is $1/2$: hence the probability that all the coins come down alike is $1/2$. I leave to my readers to say whether either of these conflicting conclusions is right, and, if so, which is correct.

The Paradox of the Second Ace. Suppose that a player at bridge or whist asserts that an ace is included among the thirteen cards dealt to him, and let p be the probability that he has another ace among the other cards in his hand. Suppose, however, that he asserts that the ace of hearts is included in the thirteen cards dealt to him; then the probability, q, that he has another ace among the other cards in his hand is greater than was the probability p in the first case. For,[*] the number of hands containing an ace is $\binom{52}{13} - \binom{48}{13}$, whereas the number of hands containing two or more aces is $\binom{52}{13} - \binom{48}{13} - 4\binom{48}{12}$; therefore $p = 1 - 4\binom{48}{12}/\{\binom{52}{13} - \binom{48}{13}\} = \frac{5359}{14498}$. But the number of hands containing the ace of hearts is $\binom{51}{12}$, whereas the number of hands containing this and another ace is $\binom{51}{12} - \binom{48}{12}$; therefore $q = 1 - \binom{48}{12}/\binom{51}{12} = \frac{11686}{20825}$. Thus $p < \frac{1}{2} < q$, which at first sight appears to be absurd.

The St. Petersburg Paradox.[†] The following example is a famous one. A penny is tossed until it comes down head. If this happens at the first throw, the bank pays the player £1. Otherwise, the player throws again. If head appears at the second throw, the bank pays £2; if at the third throw, £4; and so on, doubling every time. Thus, if the coin does

[*] This argument is due to D. B. De Lury.

[†] Cf. E. Kamke, *Einführung in die Wahrscheinlichkeitstheorie*, Leipzig, 1932, pp. 82—89.

not come down head till the nth throw, the player then receives £2^{n-1}. What should the player pay the bank for the privilege of playing this game?

There is a probability 1/2 that the player will receive the £1, a probability 1/4 that he will receive the £2, and so on. Hence the total number of pounds that he may reasonably expect to receive is

$$\tfrac{1}{2}.1 + \tfrac{1}{4}.2 + \ldots + (\tfrac{1}{2})^n 2^{n-1} + \ldots = \tfrac{1}{2} + \tfrac{1}{2} + \tfrac{1}{2} + \ldots,$$

i.e. it is infinite.

Among various ways of modifying the problem to make the answer finite, perhaps the most satisfactory is that of T. C. Fry,* who supposes that the bank's wealth is limited, say to £1000000. There is then a probability $(1/2)^n$ that the player will receive £2^{n-1} at the nth throw, only as long as $2^{n-1} < 1000000$; thereafter, he will receive merely £1000000.

Since

$$\sum_{1}^{20} (\tfrac{1}{2})^n 2^{n-1} + \sum_{21}^{\infty} (\tfrac{1}{2})^n 1000000 = 10 + (\tfrac{1}{2})^{20} 1000000$$
$$= 10.9536\ldots,$$

the player's expectation is about £10 19s. 1d.—a reasonable amount.

OTHER QUESTIONS ON PROBABILITY

Here is a result (due to H. Davenport) which many people find surprising. If you know more than 23 people's birthdays, it is more likely than not that two of them are the same (as to day and month). Consider the probability that n people's birthdays are all different, *i.e.* that in a random selection of n days out of 365 there shall be no day counted more than once. The total number of possible selections is 365^n, and the number of selections in which no day is counted more than once is $365 . 364 \ldots (365 - n + 1)$. The probability is therefore †

* *Probability and its Engineering Uses*, New York, 1928, pp. 197—198.

† As a check on the working, note that this correctly gives 0 when $n = 366$. (For simplicity, I have ignored the possibility of a birthday falling on Feb. 29; that does not affect the result, save in this extreme case.)

$365 . 364 \ldots (365 - n + 1)/365^n$. The occurrence is as likely as not if this expression is equal to $1/2$, *i.e.* if

$$\left(1 - \frac{1}{365}\right)\left(1 - \frac{2}{365}\right) \cdots \left(1 - \frac{n-1}{365}\right) = \frac{1}{2}.$$

By taking logarithms, we obtain approximately

$$\frac{1}{365} + \frac{2}{365} + \cdots + \frac{n-1}{365} = \log_e 2,$$

or $n(n - 1) = 506$, whence $n = 23$.

Derangements. The following problem * is somewhat similar. Suppose you have written a letter to each of n different friends, and addressed the n corresponding envelopes. In how many ways can you make the regrettable mistake of putting *every* letter into a wrong envelope? Let X_n denote the number of ways. Suppose the first letter is placed in the ath envelope, and the bth letter in the first envelope. If $a = b$, there remain $n - 2$ letters to be placed in wrong envelopes, which can be done in X_{n-2} ways. Since $a (= b)$ may take any value from 2 to n, this possibility covers $(n - 1)X_{n-2}$ cases. In every other case, $a \neq b$. For the moment, let us fix b (and let a run over all values from 2 to n, except b). In the $n - 1$ envelopes other than the first, we have to place the $n - 1$ letters other than the bth, but the first letter must not be placed in the bth envelope. The number of ways in which this can be done is just X_{n-1}, since the situation is equivalent to that of the original problem with $n - 1$ letters, if we imagine the bth envelope to be the proper one for the first letter. Letting b vary, this accounts for $(n - 1)X_{n-1}$ cases. Hence $X_n = (n - 1)(X_{n-1} + X_{n-2})$. This relation † gives the successive numbers readily. Obviously $X_1 = 0$ and $X_2 = 1$; therefore $X_3 = 2$, $X_4 = 9$, $X_5 = 44$, $X_6 = 265$, and so on. The explicit formula is

* Cf. De Montmort, *Essai d'analyse sur les jeux de hasard*, Paris, 1713, p. 132; J. L. Coolidge, *An Introduction to Mathematical Probability*, Oxford, 1925, p. 24; Durell and Robson, *Advanced Algebra*, London, 1937, p. 459.

† A still simpler relation is $X_n = nX_{n-1} + (-1)^n$ $(X_1 = 0)$.

$$X_n = n! \left(1 - \frac{1}{1!} + \frac{1}{2!} - \frac{1}{3!} + \cdots \pm \frac{1}{n!}\right)$$

(" sub-factorial n ").

Since n given letters can be placed in n given envelopes in $n!$ ways altogether, the probability of this unhappy occurrence is

$$\frac{X_n}{n!} = 1 - \frac{1}{1!} + \frac{1}{2!} - \frac{1}{3!} + \cdots \pm \frac{1}{n!}.$$

Now this is the beginning of the series for e^{-1} ($= 0 \cdot 367879 \ldots$), so we may say that the probability is approximately $1/e$. The error is less than $1/(n + 1)!$, which, when $n = 6$, is about $0 \cdot 0002$.

If we compare two packs of cards (one of them having been well shuffled), card by card, what is the probability that we shall get right through the packs without finding a single coincidence? This is merely another form of the same problem; the answer is $1/e$ (with an error of less than 10^{-69}, for packs of 52 cards). Many people are prepared to bet that no coincidence will occur, so an unscrupulous gambler might profit by knowing that $e > 2$.

Miscellaneous Problems. To the above examples I may add the following standard questions, or recreations.

The first of these questions is as follows. Two clerks, *A* and *B*, are engaged, *A* at a salary commencing at the rate of (say) £100 a year with a rise of £20 every year, *B* at a salary commencing at the same rate of £100 a year with a rise of £5 every half-year, in each case payments being made half-yearly; which has the larger income? The answer is *B*; for in the first year *A* receives £100, but *B* receives £50 and £55 as his two half-yearly payments and thus receives in all £105. In the second year *A* receives £120, but *B* receives £60 and £65 as his two half-yearly payments and thus receives in all £125. In fact *B* will always receive £5 a year more than *A*.

Another simple arithmetical problem is as follows. A hymn-board in a church has four grooved rows on which the numbers of four hymns chosen for the service are placed. The hymn-book in use contains 700 hymns. What is the smallest number of plates, each carrying one digit, which must be kept in stock so that the numbers of any four different hymns selected can be displayed; and how will the result be affected if an inverted 6 can be used for a 9? The answers are 86 and 81. What are the answers if a digit is painted on each side of each plate?

As another question take the following. A man bets 1/nth of his money on an even chance (say tossing heads or tails with a penny): he repeats this again and again, each time betting 1/nth of all the money then in his possession. If, finally, the number of times he has won is equal to the number of times he has lost, has he gained or lost by the transaction? He has, in fact, lost.

Here is another simple question to which I have frequently received incorrect answers. One tumbler is half-full of wine, another is half-full of water: from the first tumbler a tea-spoonful of wine is taken out and poured into the tumbler containing the water: a teaspoonful of the mixture in the second tumbler is then transferred to the first tumbler. As the result of this double transaction, is the quantity of wine removed from the first tumbler greater or less than the quantity of water removed from the second tumbler? In my experience the majority of people will say it is greater, but this is not the case.

PERMUTATION PROBLEMS

Many of the problems in permutations and combinations are of considerable interest. As a simple illustration of the very large number of ways in which combinations of even a few things can be arranged, I may note that there are 500,291833 different ways in which change for a sovereign can be given in current coins,* including therein the obsolescent double-florin, and crown; also that as many as 19,958400

* *The Tribune,* September 3, 1906.

distinct skeleton cubes can be formed with twelve differently coloured rods of equal length ; * while there are no less than $(52!)/(13!)^4$, that is, 53644,737765,488792,839237,440000 possible different distributions of hands at bridge or whist with a pack of fifty-two cards.

Voting Problems. As a simple example on combinations I take the cumulative vote as affecting the representation of a minority. If there are p electors each having r votes of which not more than s may be given to one candidate, and n men are to be elected, then the least number of supporters who can secure the election of a candidate must exceed $pr/(ns + r)$.

The Knights of the Round Table. A far more difficult permutation problem consists in finding as many arrangements as possible of n people in a ring so that no one has the same two neighbours more than once. It is a well-known proposition that n persons can be arranged in a ring in $(n-1)!/2$ different ways. The number of these arrangements in which all the persons have different pairs of neighbours on each occasion cannot exceed $(n-1)(n-2)/2$, since this gives the number of ways in which any assigned person may sit between every possible pair selected from the rest. But in fact it is always possible to determine $(n-1)(n-2)/2$ arrangements in which no one has the same two neighbours on any two occasions.

Solutions for various values of n have been given. Here, for instance $(n = 8)$, are 21 arrangements † of eight persons. Each arrangement may be placed round a circle and no one has the same two neighbours on any two occasions.

* *Mathematical Tripos*, Cambridge, Part I, 1894.

† Communicated to me by Mr. E. G. B. Bergholt, May, 1906, see *The Secretary* and *The Queen*, August, 1906. Mr. Dudeney had given the problem for the case when $n = 6$ in 1905, and informs me that the problem has been solved by Mr. E. D. Bewley when n is even, and that he has a general method applicable when n is odd. Various memoirs on the subject have appeared in the mathematical journals.

E

1.2.3.4.5.6.7.8;   1.2.5.6.8.7.4.3;   1.2.7.8.4.3.5.6;
1.3.5.2.7.4.8.6;   1.3.7.4.6.8.2.5;   1.3.8.6.2.5.7.4;
1.4.2.6.3.8.5.7;   1.4.3.8.7.5.6.2;   1.4.5.7.6.2.3.8;
1.5.6.4.3.7.8.2;   1.5.7.3.8.2.6.4;   1.5.8.2.4.6.3.7;
1.6.2.7.5.3.8.4;   1.6.3.5.8.4.2.7;   1.6.4.8.2.7.3.5;
1.7.4.2.5.8.6.3;   1.7.6.3.2.4.5.8;   1.7.8.5.6.3.4.2;
1.8.2.3.7.6.4.5;   1.8.4.5.3.2.7.6;   1.8.6.7.4.5.2.3.

The methods of determining these arrangements are lengthy, and far from easy.

The Ménage Problem.* Another difficult permutation problem is concerned with the number x of possible arrangements of n married couples, seated alternately man and woman, round a table, the n wives being in assigned positions, and the n husbands so placed that a man does not sit next to his wife.

The solution involves the theory of discordant permutations,† and is far from easy. I content myself with noting the results when n does not exceed 10. When $n = 3$, $x = 1$; when $n = 4$, $x = 2$; when $n = 5$, $x = 13$; when $n = 6$, $x = 80$; when $n = 7$, $x = 579$; when $n = 8$, $x = 4738$; when $n = 9$, $x = 43387$; and when $n = 10$, $x = 439792$.

BACHET'S WEIGHTS PROBLEM ‡

It will be noticed that a considerable number of the easier problems given in the last chapter either are due to Bachet or were collected by him in his classical *Problèmes*. Among the more difficult problems proposed by him was the determination of the least number of weights which would serve to weigh any integral number of pounds from 1 lb. to 40 lbs. inclusive. Bachet gave two solutions : namely, (i) the series of weights of 1, 2, 4, 8, 16, and 32 lbs.; (ii) the series of weights of 1, 3, 9, and 27 lbs.

If the weights may be placed in only one of the scale-pans,

* *Théorie des Nombres*, by E. Lucas, Paris, 1891, pp. 215, 491—495.

† See P. A. MacMahon, *Combinatory Analysis*, vol. I, Cambridge, 1915, pp. 253—256.

‡ Bachet, Appendix, problem v, p. 215.

the first series gives a solution, as had been pointed out in 1556 by Tartaglia.*

Bachet, however, assumed that any weight might be placed in either of the scale-pans. In this case the second series gives the least possible number of weights required. His reasoning is as follows. To weigh 1 lb. we must have a 1-lb. weight. To weigh 2 lbs. we must have in addition either a 2-lb. weight or a 3-lb. weight; but, whereas with a 2-lb. weight we can weigh 1 lb., 2 lbs., and 3 lbs., with a 3-lb. weight we can weigh 1 lb., $(3 - 1)$ lbs., 3 lbs., and $(3 + 1)$ lbs. Another weight of 9 lbs. will enable us to weigh all weights from 1 lb. to 13 lbs.; and we get thus a greater range than is obtainable with any weight less than 9 lbs. Similarly weights of 1, 3, 9, and 27 lbs. suffice for all weights up to 40 lbs., and weights of 1, 3, 3^2, ..., 3^{n-1} lbs. enable us to weigh any integral number of pounds from 1 lb. to $(1 + 3 + 3^2 + \ldots 3^{n-1})$ lbs.—that is, to $\frac{1}{2}(3^n - 1)$ lbs.

To determine the arrangement of the weights to weigh any given mass we have only to express the number of pounds in it as a number in the ternary scale of notation, except that in finding the successive digits we must make every remainder either 0, 1 or -1 : to effect this a remainder 2 must be written as $3 - 1$—that is, the quotient must be increased by unity, in which case the remainder is -1. This is explained in most text-books on algebra.

Bachet's argument does not prove that his result is unique or that it gives the least possible number of weights required. These omissions have been supplied by Major MacMahon, who has discussed the far more difficult problem (of which Bachet's is a particular case) of the determination of all possible sets of weights, not necessarily unequal, which enable us to weigh any integral number of pounds from 1 to n inclusive, (i) when the weights may be placed in only one scale-pan, and (ii) when any weight may be placed in either scale-pan. He

* *Trattato de' numeri e misure*, Venice, 1556, vol. II, bk. I, chap. XVI, art. 32.

has investigated also the modifications of the results which are necessary when we impose either or both of the further conditions (a) that no other weighings are to be possible, and (b) that each weighing is to be possible in only one way, that is, is to be unique.*

The method for case (i) consists in resolving $1 + x + x^2 + \ldots + x^n$ into factors, each factor being of the form $1 + x^a + x^{2a} + \ldots + x^{ma}$; the number of solutions depends on the composite character of $n + 1$. The method for case (ii) consists in resolving the expression $x^{-n} + x^{-n+1} + \ldots + x^{-1} + 1 + x + \ldots + x^{n-1} + x^n$ into factors, each factor being of the form $x^{-ma} + \ldots + x^{-a} + 1 + x^a + \ldots + x^{ma}$; the number of solutions depends on the composite character of $2n + 1$.

Bachet's problem falls under case (ii), $n = 40$. Mac-Mahon's analysis shows that there are eight such ways of factorizing $x^{-40} + x^{-39} + \ldots + 1 + \ldots + x^{39} + x^{40}$. First, there is the expression itself in which $a = 1$, $m = 40$. Second, the expression is equal to $(1 - x^{81})/x^{40}(1 - x)$, which can be resolved into the product of $(1 - x^3)/x(1 - x)$ and $(1 - x^{81})/x^{39}(1 - x^3)$; hence it can be resolved into two factors of the form given above, in one of which $a = 1$, $m = 1$, and in the other $a = 3$, $m = 13$. Third, similarly, it can be resolved into two such factors, in one of which $a = 1$, $m = 4$, and in the other $a = 9$, $m = 4$. Fourth, it can be resolved into three such factors, in one of which $a = 1$, $m = 1$, in another $a = 3$, $m = 1$, and in the other $a = 9$, $m = 4$. Fifth, it can be resolved into two such factors, in one of which $a = 1$, $m = 13$, and in the other $a = 27$, $m = 1$. Sixth, it can be resolved into three such factors, in one of which $a = 1$, $m = 1$, in another $a = 3$, $m = 4$, and in the other $a = 27$, $m = 1$. Seventh, it can be resolved into three such factors, in one of which $a = 1$, $m = 4$, in another $a = 9$, $m = 1$, and in the other $a = 27$, $m = 1$. Eighth, it can be resolved into four

* See his article in the *Quarterly Journal of Mathematics*, 1886, vol. XXI, pp. 367—373. An account of the method is given in *Nature*, Dec. 4, 1890, vol. XLII, pp. 113—114.

such factors, in one of which $a = 1$, $m = 1$, in another $a = 3$, $m = 1$, in another $a = 9$, $m = 1$, and in the other $a = 27$, $m = 1$.

These results show that there are eight possible sets of weights with which any integral number of pounds from 1 to 40 can be weighed subject to the conditions (ii), (a), and (b). If we denote p weights each equal to w by w^p, these eight solutions are 1^{40}; 1, 3^{13}; 1^4, 9^4; 1, 3, 9^4; 1^{13}, 27; 1, 3^4, 27; 1^4, 9, 27; 1, 3, 9, 27. The last of these is Bachet's solution : not only is it that in which the least number of weights are employed, but it is also the only one in which all the weights are unequal.

The Decimal Expression for $1/n$

E. Schiffner has invented a remarkable technique for expressing certain fractions $1/n$ as recurring decimals. The first few digits have to be calculated in the ordinary way, say by long division ; but after a certain stage we pass from division by n to division by a power of 2 or of 5. The ordinary division is continued until the remainder happens to be of the form 5^m or 2^m (mod n). (Such a remainder will always arise when the decimal has the longest possible period, namely $n - 1$ digits ; also in many other cases.) Suppose that at this stage k digits have been found. We write the first $m + 1$ of these in a row from left to right, and the rest in a column below the $(m + 1)$th. The new divisor (for the rest of the process) is 2^m or 5^m, according as the above-mentioned remainder is 5^m or 2^m. By this we divide the number formed by the first $m + 1$ digits, placing the quotient * below the kth digit (since it is in fact the $(k + 1)$th), and the remainder to the left of the $(m + 2)$th digit. Then we divide the number so formed, placing the quotient below the $(k + 1)$th digit, and the remainder beside the $(m + 3)$th. The successive quotients and remainders can now be written down quite rapidly.

When $n = 7$, for example, we find a remainder 2 after obtaining (by ordinary division) the digits 14. Thus $m = 1$,

* If this quotient $\geqslant 10$, we write only its unit-digit.

and the new divisor is 5. Dividing 14 by 5, we obtain the
quotient 2, which we place below the 4, and the remainder 4,
which we place to the left of the 2. We next divide 42 by 5,
and so on.

14	011	0212
42	4	47
28	9	76
35	4	45
07	2	9
21	5	. . .

Again, when $n = 87$, we find a remainder 25 after obtaining
the digits 01149425. Thus $m = 2$, and the new divisor is 4.
Accordingly, we arrange the digits in a column, as above,
and divide 11 by 4, placing the quotient (2) below the 5, and
the remainder (3) beside the first 4. We then divide 34 by 4,
placing the quotient below the 2 and the remainder beside the
9. By this means, the period

0 1 1 4 9 4 2 5 2 8 7 3 5 6 3 2 1 8 3 9 0 8 0 4 5 9 7 7

can be written down in a few seconds.

When $n = 47$, after obtaining the digits 0 2 1 2 7 we find
a remainder 31, which is congruent to 125. The next digit is
6, since this is the unit-digit of the quotient when 212 is divided
by 8.

For an explanation, see Schiffner's article.*

DECIMALS AND CONTINUED FRACTIONS

Every positive number can be expressed in just one way
as a decimal. If the number is rational (*i.e.*, expressible
as a vulgar fraction), its decimal expression will either terminate or (after a certain stage) recur. Otherwise, as in the
case of $\sqrt{2} = 1 \cdot 41421356 \ldots$, or of $\pi = 3 \cdot 14159265 \ldots$,
it will neither terminate nor recur. If another scale of nota-
tion is used, the sequence of digits will, of course, be quite

* *Sphinx*, 1937, p. 115. For a modified form of this method, see *Sphinx*,
1938, p. 206.

different. The " decimal " for a rational number may terminate in one scale and recur in another; thus, in the scale of seven, $\frac{1}{7} = 0\cdot1$, instead of the familiar $0\cdot\dot{1}4285\dot{7}$. Given an integer, expressed in the ordinary (denary) scale, we can express it in the scale of p by dividing by p again and again, noting the successive remainders. These remainders, when read backwards, are the digits of the required new expression. The rule for a fraction is different. There we *multiply* by p again and again, operating only on the fractional part at each stage. The successive integral parts are the digits of the required new expression (in their proper order). For instance, in the binary scale,

$$\sqrt{2} (= \sqrt{10}) = 1\cdot0\,1\,1\,0\,1\,0\,1\,0\,0\,0\,0\,0\,1\,0\,0\,1\,1\,1\,1\,0\,0\ldots,$$
$$\pi = 1\,1\cdot0\,0\,1\,0\,0\,1\,0\,0\,0\,0\,1\,1\,1\,1\,1\,1\,0\,1\,1\,0\,1\ldots.$$

The actual computation proceeds thus :

1·41421356	3·14159265
0·82842712	0·28318530
1·65685424	0·56637060
1·3137085	1·1327412
0·6274170	0·2654824
1·2548340	0·5309648
0·509668	1·061930
etc.	etc.

The sequence of five zeros makes $1\cdot0110101$ a particularly good approximation for $\sqrt{2}$. In fact, working in the binary scale, we easily find that $(1\cdot0110101)^2 = 1\cdot11111111111001$. As a good approximation for π, we note $11\cdot0\dot{0}\dot{1} = 3\frac{1}{7}$.

Somewhat analogously, every positive number can be expressed in just one way as a *regular continued fraction*

$$a_0 + \cfrac{1}{a_1 + \cfrac{1}{a_2 + \cfrac{1}{a_3 + \ldots}}} = a_0 + \frac{1}{a_1} + \frac{1}{a_2} + \frac{1}{a_3} + \cdots$$

where the a's are positive integers, save that a_0 may be zero. Thus *

$$\sqrt{2} = 1 + \frac{1}{2} + \frac{1}{2} + \frac{1}{2} + \cdots,$$

$$e = 2 + \frac{1}{1} + \frac{1}{2} + \frac{1}{1} + \frac{1}{1} + \frac{1}{4} + \frac{1}{1} + \frac{1}{1} + \frac{1}{6} + \frac{1}{1} + \frac{1}{1} + \frac{1}{8} + \frac{1}{1} + \cdots,$$

$$\pi = 3 + \frac{1}{7} + \frac{1}{15} + \frac{1}{1} + \frac{1}{292} + \frac{1}{1} + \frac{1}{1} + \frac{1}{1} + \frac{1}{2} + \frac{1}{1} + \frac{1}{3} + \frac{1}{1} + \cdots.$$

This kind of expression excels the decimal in three respects : (i) the continued fraction terminates whenever the number is rational, and recurs whenever it is quadratically irrational ; (ii) it does not depend on any particular scale of notation (except trivially, in writing the a's) ; (iii) it leads to rational approximations which are " best possible " in a sense that will be illustrated geometrically in the next chapter (page 87).

The rational approximations

$$\frac{b_1}{c_1} = \frac{a_0}{1}, \ \frac{b_2}{c_2} = \frac{1 + a_0 a_1}{a_1}, \ \frac{b_3}{c_3} = \frac{a_0 + a_0 a_1 a_2 + a_2}{1 + a_1 a_2}, \ \cdots,$$

obtained by stopping the continued fraction at each successive stage, are called *convergents*, and have many remarkable properties. They are given successively by the formulae

$$b_{n+1} = b_{n-1} + a_n b_n, \ c_{n+1} = c_{n-1} + a_n c_n.$$

For instance, the first half-dozen convergents to $\sqrt{2}$, e and π are $\frac{1}{1}, \frac{3}{2}, \frac{7}{5}, \frac{17}{12}, \frac{41}{29}, \frac{99}{70}$; $\frac{2}{1}, \frac{3}{1}, \frac{8}{3}, \frac{11}{4}, \frac{19}{7}, \frac{87}{32}$; $\frac{3}{1}, \frac{22}{7}, \frac{333}{106}, \frac{355}{113}, \frac{103993}{33102}, \frac{104348}{33215}$.

The simplest of all irrational continued fractions is

$$\tau = 1 + \frac{1}{1} + \frac{1}{1} + \frac{1}{1} + \cdots,$$

which satisfies the equation $\tau = 1 + 1/\tau$, whence, being

---

* Although the " partial quotients " ($a_1, a_2, \ldots$) for $\sqrt{2}$ and e obey simple laws, no law has yet been found for π. The fourth quotient 292 is still the largest known, the runner-up being $a_{73} = 161$. According to D. H. Lehmer, the arithmetic mean of the first hundred quotients is 10·2; 41 of them are equal to unity. See *Sphinx*, 1938, pp. 185—187.

obviously positive, $\tau = \frac{1}{2}(\sqrt{5} + 1)$. (Cf. Wythoff's Game, on page 38.) Its convergents are $\frac{1}{1}$, $\frac{2}{1}$, $\frac{3}{2}$, $\frac{5}{3}$, $\frac{8}{5}$, $\frac{13}{8}$, ..., both numerators and denominators being formed from the sequence of *Fibonacci numbers*

$$1, 1, 2, 3, 5, 8, 13, 21, 34, 55, 89, 144, 233, 377, \ldots.$$

Each of these numbers is equal to the sum of the preceding two. The ratios of alternate Fibonacci numbers are said * to measure the fraction of a turn between successive leaves on the stalk of a plant: $\frac{1}{2}$ for grasses, $\frac{1}{3}$ for sedges, $\frac{2}{5}$ for the apple, cherry, etc., $\frac{3}{8}$ for the common plantain, $\frac{5}{13}$ for the leek, and so on. These are the convergents to

$$\frac{1}{\tau^2} = \frac{1}{2} + \frac{1}{1} + \frac{1}{1} + \frac{1}{1} + \cdots$$

The number τ is intimately connected with the metrical properties of the pentagon, decagon, dodecahedron and icosahedron, since it is equal to $2 \cos \frac{1}{5}\pi$. A line-segment is said to be divided according to the *golden section* if one part is τ times the other, or $1/\tau$ of the whole. The nth Fibonacci number is

$$\{\tau^n - (-\tau)^{-n}\}/\sqrt{5}.$$

RATIONAL RIGHT-ANGLED TRIANGLES

If the sides of a right-angled triangle are in rational ratios, we may take them to be integers without a common factor. By Pythagoras' Theorem, the sides, x, y, z, of such a " primitive " triangle satisfy the equation $x^2 + y^2 = z^2$, z being the hypotenuse. The general solution (apart from the obvious possibility of interchanging x and y) is †

$$x = b^2 - c^2, \quad y = 2bc, \quad z = b^2 + c^2,$$

where b and c are arbitrary co-prime integers, one even and one odd, with $b > c$. The values $b = 2$, $c = 1$ give the familiar 3, 4, 5 triangle.‡ The numbers x and z are always odd, and

---

* H. E. Licks, *Recreations in Mathematics*, New York, 1936, p. 107.

† G. Chrystal, *Algebra*, Edinburgh, 1889, vol. II, p. 531.

‡ E. T. Bell, *Numerology*, Baltimore, 1933, p. 26 ff.

y is divisible by 4. Either x or y is divisible by 3, and one of x, y, z by 5. Consequently, xy is divisible by 12, and xyz by 60.

b	c	x	y	z	$x + y + z$ $= 2b(b+c)$	b	c	x	y	z	$x + y + z$ $= 2b(b+c)$
2	1	3	4	5	12	5	4	9	40	41	90
3	2	5	12	13	30	7	2	45	28	53	126
4	1	15	8	17	40	6	5	11	60	61	132
4	3	7	24	25	56	8	1	63	16	65	144
5	2	21	20	29	70	7	4	33	56	65	154
6	1	35	12	37	84	8	3	55	48	73	176

The first twelve primitive triangles are tabulated above. These are all that have $z < 80$, and all that have $x + y + z < 180$. D. N. Lehmer has proved [*] that the number of primitive triangles with hypotenuse less than X is approximately $X/2\pi$, and that the number with perimeter less than X is approximately $(X \log 2)/\pi^2$. We observe that $80/2\pi = 12 \cdot 73 \ldots$, while $(180 \log 2)/\pi^2 = 12 \cdot 64 \ldots$

If $b - c = 1$, then $z - y = 1$, as in the first, second, fourth, seventh and ninth of the above triangles. If c and b are consecutive terms of the sequence 1, 2, 5, 12, 29, 70, ..., *i.e.*[†] if b/c is a convergent to the continued fraction

$$\sqrt{2} + 1 = 2 + \frac{1}{2} + \frac{1}{2} + \frac{1}{2} + \cdots,$$

then $|x - y| = 1$, as in the first and fifth triangles.

F. Hoppenot has pointed out that the sum of the squares of $n + 1$ consecutive integers, of which the greatest is $2n(n + 1)$, is equal to the sum of the squares of the next n integers; thus $10^2 + 11^2 + 12^2 = 13^2 + 14^2$, $21^2 + 22^2 + 23^2 + 24^2 = 25^2 + 26^2 + 27^2$, and so on. As another analogue of the identity $3^2 + 4^2 = 5^2$, observe that $3^3 + 4^3 + 5^3 = 6^3$. The equation $x^3 + y^3 = z^3$ has no solutions in integers; nor

* *American Journal of Mathematics*, 1900, vol. XXII, p. 38.

† M. Kraïtchik, *La Mathématique des Jeux*, Brussels, 1930, p. 106.

has $x^4 + y^4 = z^4$. Euler * has conjectured a corresponding result for the equation $x^4 + y^4 + z^4 = v^4$; if any solution exists, v must exceed 1040. On the other hand, $x^4 + y^4 = z^4 + v^4$ has infinitely many solutions.†

TRIANGULAR AND PYRAMIDAL NUMBERS ‡

The *triangular numbers*

1, 3, 6, 10, 15, 21, 28, 36, 45, 55, 66, ..., $\frac{1}{2}n(n + 1)$, ...

are the sums of consecutive integers, beginning with 1. Hence, as their name indicates, they are the numbers of dots (or equal circles) that can be arranged in triangular formation : one at the top, two below it, three below them, and so on. The numbers 1, 36, 1225, 41616, 1413721, 48024900, ... are simultaneously triangular and square; the general formula for such a number is b^2c^2, where b/c is any convergent to the continued fraction for $\sqrt{2}$.

The sums of consecutive triangular numbers are the *tetrahedral numbers*

1, 4, 10, 20, 35, 56, 84, 120, ..., $\frac{1}{6}n(n + 1)(n + 2)$, ...

These are the numbers of equal spheres that can be piled in tetrahedral formation. Similarly, the sums of consecutive squares are the *pyramidal numbers*

1, 5, 14, 30, 55, 91, 140, 204, ..., $\frac{1}{6}n(n + 1)(2n + 1)$, ...

The sums of consecutive cubes (from 1 up) are the squares of the triangular numbers; the sums of consecutive *pairs* of triangular numbers are the square numbers, and the sums of consecutive pairs of tetrahedral numbers are the pyramidal numbers.

* *Commentationes Arithmeticae Collectae*, Petrograd, 1849, vol. I, pp. 473—476; vol. II, pp. 450—456. A somewhat similar unproved theorem is that the sum of n numbers of the form x^k cannot be of the form u^k if n is less than k.

† See *Sphinx*, 1937, p. 98.

‡ Cf. H. E. Dudeney, *Amusements in Mathematics*, London, 1917, pp. 26, 167.

The *only* number (> 1) which is simultaneously square and pyramidal is 4900. This result [*] was conjectured by Lucas in 1875, and proved by Watson in 1918. The proof is by no means elementary.

AUTOMORPHIC NUMBERS [†]

If two numbers, x and y, differ by a multiple of p, we say that they are congruent modulo p, and write

$$x \equiv y \pmod{p}, \text{ or } x - y \equiv 0 \pmod{p}.$$

If these numbers are expressed in the scale of p, they will have the same unit-digit.

A number is said to be *automorphic* if its n digits are the last n digits of its square, and consequently of its cube and higher powers too. Thus 25 and 76 are automorphic (in the denary scale), since $25^2 = 625$ and $76^2 = 5776$. In the scale of p, a number x is automorphic if $x^2 \equiv x \pmod{p^n}$. The numbers 0 and 1 are trivially automorphic, and need hardly be mentioned; but if p is a prime, or a power of a prime, there are no others. Thus $p = 6$ and $p = 10$ are the first significant cases. In the scale of six, the last seven digits of an automorphic number must be either 1350213 or 4205344. (The last six digits of the former are the same as the last six digits of 3^{16}.) In the scale of ten, the last sixteen digits of an automorphic number must be either

6259918212890625 or 3740081787109376.

(The last five digits of the former are the same as the last five digits of $5^8 = 390625$.)

FINITE ARITHMETICS

The numbers 0, 1, 2, ..., $p - 1$ are called *residues* modulo p; every integer is congruent to just one of them. There is an arithmetic of residues, closely analogous to the arithmetic

[*] E. Lucas, *Nouvelles Annales de Math.* (2), vol. XIV, p. 336. G. N Watson, *Messenger of Mathematics* (new series), vol. XLVIII, pp. 1—22.

[†] Kraïtchik, p. 66. *Sphinx*, 1935, pp. 1—4.

of ordinary numbers. In it, we can obviously add, subtract and multiply. Thus, when $p = 6$, we have $3 + 4 \equiv 1$, $3 - 4 \equiv 5$, $3 \times 4 \equiv 0$. If p is a *prime* number (as we shall suppose, for the rest of this chapter), we can also divide (by any residue except 0). Thus, when $p = 7$, we have $\frac{3}{4} \equiv 3 \times \frac{1}{4} \equiv 3 \times \frac{8}{4} \equiv 6$; or, briefly, $3/4 \equiv 24/4 \equiv 6$.

It follows that every numerical problem whose solutions are rational leads to a corresponding problem in the finite arithmetic modulo p, with solutions which are congruent to those of the original problem. For instance, the equation $x^2 - x - 2 = 0$ has the roots 2, -1, and the congruence $x^2 - x - 2 \equiv 0 \pmod{p}$ has the roots 2, $p - 1$. If we can solve a problem in the finite arithmetic for each of a number of different moduli p, then the solutions of the corresponding unrestricted problem are known to within a multiple of the product of all the moduli.

LEHMER'S MACHINE

This is the underlying principle of D. H. Lehmer's Photo-electric Number-Sieve,* which factorizes large numbers with almost miraculous rapidity. (It took only three seconds to factorize

$$2^{93} + 1 = 3^2 \times 529{,}510939 \times 715{,}827883 \times 2903{,}110321.)$$

This wonderful machine consists essentially of thirty parallel cog-wheels, which, in certain positions, allow a beam of light to pass through small holes in all of them. Their numbers of cogs are convenient multiples of the primes from 2 to 113, respectively; and there is a hole opposite each cog, at a uniform distance from the periphery. These holes are numbered from 0 to $p - 1$; and a problem (such as that of finding a positive integer x for which $4787532864x^2 + 171576027618912x + 10553711710905$ is a square †) is presented to the machine by plugging up, in each wheel, all the holes except those which give solutions of the corresponding

* *American Mathematical Monthly*, 1933, vol. XL, pp. 401—406.

† This problem arises quite naturally in seeking to factorize $2^{93} + 1$.

problem in the arithmetic modulo p. The wheels are made to turn rapidly, all with the same peripheral speed, *i.e.* so that the number of holes that pass the beam of light in a second is the same for all and is about 5000. The beam can pass through all the holes only when their positions correspond to a number which is congruent to a solution in every one of the finite arithmetics. When this happens, the light actuates a photo-electric cell, and the induced current (after enormous amplification) stops the machine.

THE DISTRIBUTION OF PRIMES

A *prime* (or *prime number*) is a positive integer which has no divisors save 1 and itself.* The twenty-six primes less than 100 are 1, 2, 3, 5, 7, 11, 13, 17, 19, 23, 29, 31, 37, 41, 43, 47, 53, 59, 61, 67, 71, 73, 79, 83, 89, 97. Euclid † proved that there are infinitely many primes, arguing somewhat as follows. Consider the product $P = 2 \cdot 3 \cdot 5 \cdot 7 \ldots p$ of all the primes up to a particular one. Clearly, $P + 1$ is not divisible by any of these primes. Therefore it has a prime divisor greater than p (including, as a possibility, itself). Thus there is a prime greater than any given prime.

The best attempt that has ever been made towards an explicit formula for primes is Euler's ‡ quadratic form $x^2 + x + 41$, which represents primes for $x = 0, 1, 2, 3, \ldots$, 39. D. H. Lehmer has shown § that if there is a form $x^2 + x + A$, with $A > 41$, which represents primes for $A - 1$ consecutive values of x, then A must exceed 1250,000000, and there is at most one such form.

It is clearly desirable to be able to tell whether a given number N is prime or composite without having to test every prime less than $\sqrt{N}$ as a possible divisor. I will mention two criteria.

---

* Some authors prefer to exclude 1 from the list of primes. See, for instance, A. E. Ingham, *The Distribution of Prime Numbers*, Cambridge, 1932

† *Elementa*, IX, 20.

‡ *Nouveaux Mémoires de l'Académie Royale des Sciences*, Berlin, 1772, p. 36.

§ *Sphinx*, 1936, pp. 212—214.

Sir J. Wilson discovered (1770) and Lagrange proved (1773) that N is prime *if, and only if,* $(N - 1)! + 1$ is divisible by N. For instance, $(7 - 1)! + 1 = 721$ is divisible by 7, but $(9 - 1)! + 1 = 40321$ is not divisible by 9. Wilson's Theorem is a theoretical rather than practical test for primality, since, if N is large enough for its primality to be in doubt, it is more laborious to find whether $(N - 1)! + 1$ is or is not divisible by N than to test every prime less than $\sqrt{N}$ as a possible factor of N.

Fermat discovered (1640) and Euler proved (1736) that, if p is prime and a is not divisible by p, then $a^{p-1} - 1$ is divisible by p. The case when $a = 2$ was known to the Chinese as early as 500 B.C.; they stated also the converse proposition: if N divides $2^{N-1} - 1$ then N is a prime. This proposition was rediscovered and " proved " by Leibniz in 1680. However, it is false; it fails for $N = 341 = 11 \times 31$ and for an infinity of other N's. Modern tests for primality are based on the following converse of Fermat's Theorem, due to Lucas : * if $a^x - 1$ is divisible by N when $x = N - 1$, but not when x is a proper divisor of $N - 1$, then N is a prime. Modifications of this converse both as to hypothesis and conclusion are necessary before the actual modern tests emerge.†

The numbers up to 10^7 have all been factorized.‡ They include 664580 primes. In order to see how larger numbers behave, Hoppenot and Kraïtchik § have tabulated the smallest prime factor of every number from $10^{12} - 10^4$ to $10^{12} + 10^4$. By an ingenious process, due to Meissel,‖ it is possible to calculate the number of primes less than X without finding the primes themselves and counting them.

* *Théorie des Nombres*, Paris, 1891, pp. 423, 441. For an interesting discussion of Fermat's Theorem, see E. T. Bell's *Numerology*, Baltimore, 1933, pp. 182—185.

† See *Bulletin of the American Mathematical Society*, 1927, vol. XXXIII, pp. 327—340.

‡ D. N. Lehmer, *Factor Table for the First Ten Millions*, Washington, 1909.

§ *Sphinx*, 1936, p. 164; 1938, p. 84.

‖ *Mathematische Annalen*, 1870, vol. II, p. 636; 1871, vol. III, p. 523.

If X is large, and x is comparatively small, the number of primes between X and $X + x$ (or between $X - x$ and X) is approximately * $x/\log X$. For the number of primes between 10,000000 and 10,005000, this formula gives $5000/(7 \log 10)$ $= \frac{5000}{7} \log_{10} e = 310 \cdot 210 \ldots$; the exact number is known to be 305. Again, according to the Hoppenot–Kraïtchik table, there are exactly 336 primes between $10^{12} - 10^4$ and 10^{12}, whereas the approximate formula gives $10^4/(12 \log 10)$ $= 361 \cdot 912 \ldots$

For the number of primes less than X, Riemann has given an approximate formula (too complicated to reproduce here †) which is so close that its error is only 24 when $X = 10^9$. (According to Meissel, the number of primes less than 10^9 is exactly 50,847479.)

A. de Polignac ‡ has conjectured that every even number is the difference of two consecutive primes in infinitely many ways. Taking the even number to be 2, this means that there are infinitely many pairs of primes that are consecutive odd numbers, such as 5, 7; 11, 13; 17, 19; 29, 31; 41, 43; 59, 61; 71, 73. This conjecture has not been proved or disproved. As evidence in its favour, the Hoppenot–Kraïtchik table shows that the interval from $10^{12} - 10^4$ to 10^{12} contains fifteen such pairs,§ of which the largest is the pair $999999,999960 \pm 1$. Since $10^4/(12 \log 10)^2 = (3 \cdot 61912 \ldots)^2$ $= 13 \cdot 097 \ldots$, we may guess that the number of prime pairs between $X - x$ and X is approximately $x/(\log X)^2$.

It can be proved quite easily that the sum of the reciprocals of all the primes less than X increases without limit as X increases. If, however, we consider only the sum of the reciprocals of those primes less than X which differ by 2, then this sum remains bounded as X increases. This fact, due to Brun,

---

* De la Vallée Poussin, *Mémoires Couronnés de l'Académie Royale de Belgique*, 1889, vol. LIX, pp. 1—74.

† See the fascinating Introduction to D. N. Lehmer's *List of Prime Numbers from 1 to 10,006721*, Washington, 1914.

‡ *Nouvelles Annales de Math.*, 1849, vol. VIII, p. 428.

§ There are also twenty pairs in the interval from 10^{12} to $10^{12} + 10^4$.

shows that there are not " too many " primes which differ by 2.

A somewhat similar conjecture is *Goldbach's Theorem*, that every even number can be expressed as the sum of two primes. Haussner has verified this for all even numbers up to 10000, and others have verified it for small ranges of very large numbers and for many isolated large numbers.* Vinogradoff † has proved that every sufficiently large odd number is the sum of three primes, and Estermann ‡ has made precise the statement that *almost all* even numbers are sums of two primes.

MERSENNE'S NUMBERS

A curious assertion (only partially correct) about the prime or composite character of numbers of the form $2^p - 1$ is to be found in Mersenne's *Cogitata Physico-Mathematica*, published in 1644. In the preface to that work a statement is made about perfect numbers, which implies that the only values of p not greater than 257 which make $2^p - 1$ prime are 1, 2, 3, 5, 7, 13, 17, 19, 31, 67, 127, and 257. Some years ago I gave reasons for thinking that 67 was a misprint for 61. Until 1911, no error in this corrected statement was established, and it was gradually verified for all except sixteen values of p. In 1911 and 1914, however, R. E. Powers § discovered that $2^{89} - 1$ and $2^{107} - 1$ are prime; and in 1922, M. Kraïtchik ‖ found $2^{257} - 1$ to be composite : three facts at variance with Mersenne's statement.

The modern technique was established by Lucas ¶ in 1877,

* For the latest work on the verification of Goldbach's Theorem, see Pipping, *Finska Vetenskaps Societeten, Commentationes Physico-Math.*, 1927, vol. IV, Nos. 4, 10, 25.

† *C. R. Acad. Sci., U.R.S.S.*, 1937, pp. 169—172.

‡ *Proceedings of the London Mathematical Society* (Second Series), 1938, vol. XLIV, pp. 307—314.

§ *American Mathematical Monthly*, 1911, vol. XVIII, pp. 195—197. *Proceedings of the London Mathematical Society*, 1919, Ser. 2, vol. XIII, p. 39.

‖ See *Sphinx*, 1931, p. 31.

¶ *American Journal of Mathematics*, 1878, vol. I, p. 316.

F

and used by him to verify Mersenne's assertion that $2^{127} - 1$

$$(= 170{,}141183{,}460469{,}231731{,}687303{,}715884{,}105727)$$

is prime. (This still remains the largest known prime, in spite of eight attempts to find a larger one.) Lucas considered the sequences

$$3,\ 7,\ 47,\ 2207,\ 4870847,\ \ldots,\ u_n,\ \ldots;$$
$$4,\ 14,\ 194,\ 37634,\ 1416317954,\ \ldots,\ v_n,\ \ldots;$$

in which each term is the square of the preceding term, diminished by 2. His rule is that $2^p - 1$ is prime if it divides u_{p-1} ($p = 4k - 1$) or v_{p-1} ($p = 4k + 1$). D. H. Lehmer * has recently shown that the sequence v_n could be used in both cases, and that $2^p - 1$ is composite if it fails to divide v_{p-1}. For instance, $2^{257} - 1$ is composite, since the division of v_{256} by $2^{257} - 1$ leaves a remainder †
21044,788566,116177,742020,115097,384196,442185,967503,-553765,065760,419861,415332,100776.

The most recent results have supported Mersenne's conjecture. Lehmer and Powers,‡ respectively, have shown $2^{149} - 1$ and $2^{241} - 1$ to be composite. The present state of knowledge is as follows. §

$2^p - 1$ is known to be prime in thirteen cases :
$p = 1, 2, 3, 5, 7, 13, 17, 19, 31, 61, 89, 107, 127.$

The complete factorization is known in thirteen cases :
$p = 11, 23, 29, 37, 41, 43, 47, 53, 59, 67, 71, 73, 79.$

Two or more prime factors are known in five other cases :
$p = 113, 151, 179, 239, 251.$

One prime factor is known in eleven other cases :
$p = 83, 97, 131, 163, 173, 181, 191, 197, 211, 223, 233.$

The composite character has been established, although no factor is known, in eight cases :
$p = 101, 103, 109, 137, 139, 149, 241, 257.$

---

* *Sphinx*, 1931, p. 164.   † *Sphinx*, 1931, p. 32.
‡ *Sphinx*, 1931, p. 163; 1935, p. 57.
§ Cf. the ninth edition of this book, p. 336, and R. C. Archibald, *Scripta Mathematica*, 1935, vol. III, pp. 112—119.

There remain six cases in which nothing is yet known :
$p = 157, 167, 193, 199, 227, 229.$

Perfect Numbers *

The theory of *perfect numbers* depends directly on that of
Mersenne's Numbers. A number is said to be perfect if it
is equal to the sum of all its proper divisors. Thus 6
and 28 are perfect numbers, since $6 = 1 + 2 + 3$ and
$28 = 1 + 2 + 4 + 7 + 14.$ These numbers have had a
strong appeal for mystics, since the Creation took 6 days,
and there are 28 days in a lunar month.

Euclid proved that $2^{p-1}(2^p - 1)$ is perfect whenever $2^p - 1$
is prime. In fact, the divisors of $2^{p-1}(2^p - 1)$ (including
itself) are then 2^n and $2^n(2^p - 1)$, for $n = 0, 1, \ldots, p - 1$;
and we know that $1 + 2 + 2^2 + \ldots + 2^{p-1} = 2^p - 1.$

Euler showed that this formula includes all *even* perfect
numbers. The following simplified proof has been given
by Dickson.† Let $2^n q$ be perfect, where q is odd and $n > 0$.
Then $2^{n+1} q = (2^{n+1} - 1)s$, where s is the sum of all the divisors
of q. Thus $s = q + d$, where $d = q/(2^{n+1} - 1)$. Hence d
is a divisor of q, so that q and d are the only divisors of q.
Hence $d = 1$ and $q = 2^{n+1} - 1$ is a prime.

There is reason to believe—though a rigid demonstration
is wanting—that an odd number cannot be perfect; at any
rate no odd number less than 2,000000 can be perfect. According to J. J. Sylvester,‡ an odd perfect number must have at
least six distinct prime factors.

The values $p = 2, 3, 5, 7, 13, 17, 19, 31$ give the Mersenne
primes 3, 7, 31, 127, 8191, 131071, 524287, 2147483647, and

---

* On the theory of perfect numbers, see bibliographical references by
H. Brocard, *L'Intermédiaire des Mathématiciens*, Paris, 1895, vol. II, pp. 52—
54; and 1905, vol. XII, p. 19. The first volume of the second edition of the
French translation of this book contains (pp. 280—294) a summary of the
leading investigation on Perfect Numbers, as also some remarks on Amicable
Numbers. See also L. E. Dickson, *History of the Theory of Numbers*, vol. I,
Washington, 1919.

† *American Mathematical Monthly*, 1911, vol. XVIII, p. 109.

‡ *Collected Mathematical Papers*, 1912, vol. IV, p. 588.

the perfect numbers 6, 28, 496, 8128, 33550336, 8589869056, 137438691328, 2305843008139952128. It is easy to show that the two final digits of an even perfect number are necessarily either 28 or (apart from 6 itself) 6 preceded by an *odd* digit. Of the twelve known perfect numbers, six end in 28, and the rest (after 6 itself) end in 96, 36, 56, 76, 16, respectively.

Fermat's Theorem on Binary Powers

Fermat enriched mathematics with a multitude of new propositions. With one exception all these have been proved or are believed to be true. This exception is his *theorem on binary powers*, in which he asserted that all numbers of the form $2^m + 1$, where $m = 2^n$, are primes,* but he added that, though he was convinced of the truth of this proposition, he could not obtain a valid demonstration.

It may be shown that $2^m + 1$ is composite if m is not a power of 2, but of course it does not follow that $2^m + 1$ is a prime if m is a power of 2, say 2^n. As a matter of fact the theorem is not true. In 1732 Euler † showed that if $n = 5$ the formula gives 4294,967297, which is equal to $641 \times 6,700417$: curiously enough, these factors can be deduced at once from Fermat's remark on the possible factors of numbers of the form $2^m \pm 1$, from which it may be shown that the prime factors (if any) of $2^{32} + 1$ must be primes of the form $64k + 1$.

Kraïtchik ‡ has shown how the divisibility of $2^{32} + 1$ by 641 may be verified without actual division. We have $641 = 2^4 + 5^4 = 1 + 5 \cdot 2^7$, whence, in the finite arithmetic modulo 641,

$$2^7 \equiv -\tfrac{1}{5}, \ 2^8 \equiv -\tfrac{2}{5}, \ 2^{32} \equiv (-\tfrac{2}{5})^4 \equiv 2^4/5^4 \equiv -1.$$

---

* Letter of Oct. 18, 1640, *Opera*, Toulouse, 1679, p. 162 : or Brassinne's *Précis*, p. 143.

† *Commentarii Academiae Scientiarum Petropolitanae*, Petrograd, 1738, vol. vi, p. 104; see also *Novi Comm. Acad. Sci. Petrop.*, Petrograd, 1764, vol. ix, p. 101 : or *Commentationes Arithmeticae Collectae*, Petrograd, 1849, vol. i, pp. 2, 357.

‡ *Théorie des Nombres*, vol. ii, p. 221.

G. T. Bennett has suggested a variant of this proof, which has the advantage of giving both factors. Let $a = 2^7$ and $b = 5$, so that $a - b^3 = 3$ and $ab - b^4 = 3b = 2^4 - 1$. Then
$2^{32} + 1 = 2^4a^4 + 1 = (ab - b^4 + 1)a^4 + 1$

$$= (ab + 1)\{a^4 - (ab - 1)(a^2b^2 + 1)\}$$
$$= (ab + 1)(3a^3 + a^2b^2 - ab + 1).$$

Let $F_n = 2^{2^n} + 1$, so that $F_0 = 3$, $F_1 = 5$, $F_2 = 17$, $F_3 = 257$, $F_4 = 65537$ (all primes) and $F_5 = 641 \times 6700417$. In 1880, F. Landry showed that $F_6 = 274177 \times 67{,}280421{,}310721$. In 1909, Morehead and Western proved that F_7 and F_8 are composite (although no factors have yet been found).[*] By that time, it was already known that F_9 is divisible by $37 . 2^{16} + 1$, F_{11} by $(39 . 2^{13} + 1)(119 . 2^{13} + 1)$, F_{12} by $(7 . 2^{14} + 1)(397 . 2^{16} + 1)(973 . 2^{16} + 1)$, F_{18} by $13 . 2^{20} + 1$, F_{23} by $5 . 2^{25} + 1$, F_{36} by $5 . 2^{39} + 1$, F_{38} by $3 . 2^{41} + 1$, and F_{73} by $5 . 2^{75} + 1$. (F_{73} is one of the largest numbers that have ever been investigated. Its digits are so numerous that, if it were printed in full with the type and number of pages used in this book, many more volumes would be required than are contained in all the public libraries in the world.) More recently, Kraïtchik showed that F_{15} is divisible by $579 . 2^{21} + 1$. Thus it may well be true that Fermat was *completely* wrong, *i.e.*, that F_n is in fact composite whenever $n > 4$.

FERMAT'S LAST THEOREM

I pass now to another assertion made by Fermat which hitherto has not been proved. This, which is sometimes known as *Fermat's Last Theorem*, is to the effect † that no in-

---

* For bibliographical references, see A. J. C. Cunningham and A. E. Western, *Transactions of the London Mathematical Society*, 1903, series 2, vol. I, p. 175; and J. C. Morehead and A. E. Western, *Bulletin of the American Mathematical Society*, 1909, vol. XVI, pp. 1—6.

† Fermat's enunciation will be found in his edition of *Diophantus*, Toulouse, 1670, bk. II, qu. 8, p. 61; or Brassinne's *Précis*, Paris, 1853, p. 53. For bibliographical references, see L. E. Dickson, *History of the Theory of Numbers*, Washington, 1920, vol. II, ch. 26; see also L. J. Mordell, *Fermat's Last Theorem*, Cambridge, 1921.

tegral values of x, y, z can be found to satisfy the equation $x^n + y^n = z^n$, if n is an integer greater than 2. This proposition has acquired extraordinary celebrity from the fact that no general demonstration of it has been given, but there is no reason to doubt that it is true.

Fermat seems to have discovered its truth first * for the case $n = 3$, and then for the case $n = 4$. His proof for the former of these cases is lost, but that for the latter is extant,† and a similar proof for the case of $n = 3$ was outlined by Euler.‡ These proofs depend upon showing that, if three integral values of x, y, z can be found which satisfy the equation, then it will be possible to find three other and smaller integers which also satisfy it : in this way finally we show that the equation must be satisfied by three values which obviously do not satisfy it. Thus no integral solution is possible. This method is inapplicable to the general case.

Fermat's discovery of the general theorem was made later. A proof can be given on the assumption that every number can be resolved into the product of powers of primes in only one way. The assumption is true of rational integers, but is not necessarily true for algebraic integers—an algebraic integer being defined as a root of an equation

$$x^n + a_1 x^{n-1} + \ldots + a_n = 0,$$

whose coefficients, a, are arithmetical integers ; for instance, $a + b\sqrt{-m}$, where a, b, and m are arithmetical integers, is an algebraic integer. Thus, admitting the use of these generalized integers, 21 can be expressed in three ways as the product of primes, namely, of 3 and 7, or of $4 + \sqrt{-5}$ and $4 - \sqrt{-5}$, or of $1 + 2\sqrt{-5}$ and $1 - 2\sqrt{-5}$; and similarly, there are values of n for which Fermat's equation leads to expressions which can be factorized in more than one way. It is possible

* See a Letter from Fermat quoted in my *History of Mathematics*, London, chapter xv.

† Fermat's *Diophantus*, note on p. 339; or Brassinne's *Précis*, p. 127.

‡ Euler's *Algebra* (English trans. 1797), vol. ii, chap. xv, p. 247 : one point was overlooked by Euler, but the omission can be supplied.

that Fermat's argument rested on the above erroneous supposition, but this is an unsupported conjecture. At any rate he asserted definitely that he had a valid proof—*demonstratio mirabilis sane*—and the fact that no theorem on the subject which he stated he had proved has been subsequently shown to be false must weigh strongly in his favour; the more so because in making the one incorrect statement in his writings (namely, that about binary powers) he added that he could not obtain a satisfactory demonstration of it.

It must be remembered that Fermat was a mathematician of quite the first rank who had made a special study of the theory of numbers. The subject is in itself one of peculiar interest and elegance, but its conclusions have little practical importance, and for long it was studied by only a few mathematicians. This is the explanation of the fact that it took more than a century before some of the simpler results which Fermat had enunciated were proved, and thus it is not surprising that a proof of the theorem which he succeeded in establishing only towards the close of his life should involve great difficulties.

In 1823 Legendre * obtained a proof for the case of $n = 5$; in 1832 Lejeune Dirichlet † gave one for $n = 14$; and in 1840 Lamé and Lebesgue ‡ gave proofs for $n = 7$.

To prove the proposition when $n > 4$, obviously it is sufficient to confine ourselves to cases where n is a prime. In 1849, Kummer § proved it for all "regular" primes. (A prime p is said to be regular if it does not divide any of the numerators of the Bernoulli numbers ‖ $B_1, B_2, \ldots, B_{\frac{1}{2}(p-3)}$.)

---

* Reprinted in his *Théorie des Nombres*, Paris, 1830, vol. II, pp. 361—368: see also pp. 5, 6.

† *Crelle's Journal*, 1832, vol. IX, pp. 390—393.

‡ *Liouville's Journal*, 1841, vol. V, pp. 195—215, 276—279, 348—349.

§ References to Kummer's Memoirs are given by H. S. Vandiver, *Transactions of the American Mathematical Society*, 1929, vol. XXXI, pp. 613—642.

‖ The Bernoulli numbers appear in the series

$$\frac{x}{2} \cot \frac{x}{2} = 1 - \frac{B_1}{2!}\, x \;-\; \frac{B_2}{4!}\, x^4 - \frac{B_3}{6!}\, x^6 - \ldots$$

The values of the first eight are $\frac{1}{6}, \frac{1}{30}, \frac{1}{42}, \frac{1}{30}, \frac{5}{66}, \frac{691}{2730}, \frac{7}{6}, \frac{3617}{510}$.

Kummer found that 37, 59, 67, 101, 103, 131, 149, 157 are the only " irregular " primes less than 164, and H. S. Vandiver * found that 233, 257, 263, 271, 283, 293, 307, 311, 347, 353, 379, 401, 409, 421, 433, 461, 463, 467, 491, 523, 541, 547, 557, 577, 587, 593, 607 are the only irregular primes between 164 and 616. The theorem can, by other arguments,* be proved for these thirty-five cases. Other tests have been established; for instance, A. Wieferich † has shown that if the equation is soluble in integers prime to n, where n is an odd prime, then $2^{n-1} - 1$ is divisible by n^2. This restricted problem has been pushed as far as $n = 41{,}000000$ and $250{,}000000$ by J. B. Rosser and D. H. Lehmer,‡ respectively. A prize § of 100,000 marks has been offered for a general proof, to be given before 2007. (Of course this is now worthless, on account of the German inflation.)

Even though Fermat's problem remains unsolved, it has been of great importance for the theory of numbers, because many of the modern methods have been developed in connection with it, and the theories which have arisen in this connection are perhaps more important than a proof of the theorem itself would have been. Naturally there has been much speculation as to how Fermat arrived at the result. Such of his proofs as are extant involve nothing more than elementary geometry and algebra, and indeed some of his arguments do not involve any symbols. This has led some writers to think that Fermat used none but elementary algebraic methods. This may be so, but the following remark, which I believe is not generally known, rather points to the opposite conclusion. He had proposed, as a problem to the English mathematicians, to show that there was only one integral solution of the equation $x^2 + 2 = y^3$: the solution evidently being $x = 5$, $y = 3$. On this he has a note ‖ to the

* *Duke Mathematical Journal*, 1937, vol. III, pp. 569—584.
† *Crelle's Journal*, 1909, vol. CXXXVI, pp. 293—302.
‡ *Bulletin of the American Mathematical Society*, 1940, vol. XLVI, p. 299.
§ *L'Intermédiaire des Mathématiciens*, vol. XV, pp. 217–218.
‖ Fermat's *Diophantus*, bk. VI, prop. 19, p. 320; or Brassinne's *Précis*, p. 122.

effect that there was no difficulty in finding a solution in rational fractions, but that he had discovered an entirely new method—*sane pulcherrima et subtilissima*—which enabled him to solve such questions in integers. It was his intention to write a work * on his researches in the theory of numbers, but it was never completed, and we know but little of his methods of analysis. I venture, however, to add my private suspicion that continued fractions played a not unimportant part in his researches, and as strengthening this conjecture I may note that some of his more recondite results—such as the theorem that a prime of the form $4n + 1$ is expressible as the sum of two squares †—may be established with comparative ease by properties of such fractions.

GALOIS ARITHMETICS ‡

In analysing the game of Nim (page 36), we considered the numbers of counters in the various heaps, expressed in the scale of 2, and added all the unit-digits, then all the next digits, and so on, noting whether each sum was even or odd. This process is essentially the same as writing the binary numbers below one another, as in an ordinary addition-sum, and adding them (in the scale of 2) *without carrying*. In other words, we add each column of digits as in the finite arithmetic modulo 2. The given numbers of counters form a " safe combination " if the result is 0 (in every column), as in the second of the following examples.

$$
\begin{array}{cc}
10 & 10 \\
10 & 11 \\
11 & 100 \\
101 & 101 \\
\hline
110 & 000 \\
\end{array}
$$

* Fermat's *Diophantus*, bk. IV, prop. 31, p. 181; or Brassinne's *Précis*, p. 82.

† Fermat's *Diophantus*, bk. III, prop. 22, p. 127; or Brassinne's *Précis*, p. 65.

‡ Cf. L. E. Dickson, *History of the Theory of Numbers*, vol. I, Washington, 1919, p. viii.

In Moore's " Nim_k," we write out the binary numbers as before, and add them without carrying, but in the scale of $k + 1$ instead of the scale of 2. The process is familiar in the addition of polynomials by the method of detached coefficients ; the only new feature is that the coefficients (or " digits ") now belong to a finite arithmetic.

10	x
11	$x + 1$
100	x^2
110	$x^2 + x$
111	$x^2 + x + 1$
012 (mod 3)	$x + 2$

The notion of adding without carrying has many other applications. The entities which are added, not being ordinary numbers, may be called " marks." Their digits belong to a finite arithmetic whose modulus (previously denoted by $k + 1$) is most usefully taken to be a prime, p. The rules for svbtraction, and for multiplication by an ordinary number (of the finite arithmetic), are immediate consequences of the rule for addition, namely that the digits of each rank are added modulo p. If we restrict consideration to the p^n marks that have not more than n digits, these operations will not take us outside that field.

But the multiplication of one mark by another might increase the number of digits. In order to avoid this complication, we introduce a second modulus, namely a particular mark of $n + 1$ digits which is "prime" (or irreducible) in the sense of not being the product of two marks, each of more than one digit. (It is always possible to find such a " prime " mark.) Two marks are then regarded as identical if they differ by a multiple of this particular mark. For instance, if $p^n = 3^3$, we take the second modulus 1021, and a typical multiplication-sum proceeds as follows : $112 \times 21 \equiv 2210 + 112 \equiv 2022 \equiv 2022 + 1021 \equiv 10$. Division is possible too, since in fact every mark has a reciprocal.

Most properties of the ordinary finite arithmetics continue to hold in these "Galois Arithmetics." In the ordinary arithmetic modulo 7, every number except 0 is a power of 3, since $3^2 \equiv 2$, $3^3 \equiv 6$, $3^4 \equiv 4$, $3^5 \equiv 5$, and $3^6 \equiv 1$. Analogously, in the Galois arithmetic with moduli 2 and 1011 ($p^n = 2^3$), every mark except 0 is a power of 10, since $10^2 \equiv 100$, $10^3 \equiv 11$, $10^4 \equiv 110$, $10^5 \equiv 111$, $10^6 \equiv 101$, and $10^7 \equiv 1$. Again, in the arithmetic modulo 7 (or any other odd prime), just half the numbers other than 0 are squares. Thus $1^2 \equiv 6^2 \equiv 1$, $2^2 \equiv 5^2 \equiv 4$, and $3^2 \equiv 4^2 \equiv 2$ (mod 7). It is the same in any Galois arithmetic with $p > 2$. For instance, if $p^n = 3^2$ and the second modulus is 101, we have $1^2 \equiv 2^2 \equiv 1$, $10^2 \equiv 20^2 \equiv 2$, $11^2 \equiv 22^2 \equiv 20$, and $12^2 \equiv 21^2 \equiv 10$.

CHAPTER III

IN this chapter and the next one I propose to enumerate
certain geometrical questions, puzzles, and games, the discussion of which will not involve necessarily any considerable
use of algebra or arithmetic. Most of this chapter is devoted
to questions which are of the nature of formal propositions :
the next chapter contains a description of various amusements.

In accordance with the rule I laid down for myself in the
preface, I exclude the detailed discussion of theorems which
involve advanced mathematics. Moreover (with one or two
exceptions) I exclude any mention of the numerous geometrical
paradoxes which depend merely on the inability of the eye
to compare correctly the dimensions of figures when their
relative position is changed. This apparent deception does
not involve the conscious reasoning powers, but rests on the
inaccurate interpretation by the mind of the sensations
derived through the eyes, and I do not consider such paradoxes
as coming within the domain of mathematics.

GEOMETRICAL FALLACIES

Most educated Englishmen are acquainted with the series
of logical propositions in geometry associated with the name
of Euclid, but it is not known so generally that these propositions were supplemented originally by certain exercises. Of
such exercises Euclid issued three series : two containing
easy theorems or problems, and the third consisting of geometrical fallacies, the errors in which the student was required
to find.

The collection of fallacies prepared by Euclid is lost, and

tradition has not preserved any record as to the nature of the erroneous reasoning or conclusions; but, as an illustration of such questions, I append a few demonstrations, leading to obviously impossible results. Perhaps they may amuse anyone to whom they are new. I leave the discovery of the errors to the ingenuity of my readers.

First Fallacy.* *To prove that a right angle is equal to an angle which is greater than a right angle.* Let $ABCD$ be a rectangle. From A draw a line AE outside the rectangle, equal to AB or DC and making an acute angle with AB, as indicated in the

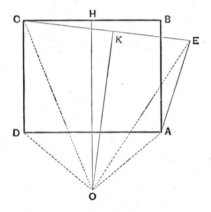

diagram. Bisect CB in H, and through H draw HO at right angles to CB. Bisect CE in K, and through K draw KO at right angles to CE. Since CB and CE are not parallel the lines HO and KO will meet (say) at O. Join OA, OE, OC, and OD.

The triangles ODC and OAE are equal in all respects. For, since KO bisects CE and is perpendicular to it, we have $OC = OE$. Similarly, since HO bisects CB and DA and is perpendicular to them, we have $OD = OA$. Also, by construction, $DC = AE$. Therefore the three sides of the triangle

---

* I believe that this and the fourth of these fallacies were first published in this book. They particularly interested Mr. C. L. Dodgson; see the *Lewis Carroll Picture Book*, London, 1899, pp. 264, 266, where they appear in the form in which I originally gave them.

ODC are equal respectively to the three sides of the triangle
OAE. Hence, by Euc. I. 8, the triangles are equal; and therefore the angle *ODC* is equal to the angle *OAE*.

Again, since *HO* bisects *DA* and is perpendicular to it, we
have the angle *ODA* equal to the angle *OAD*.

Hence the angle *ADC* (which is the difference of *ODC* and
ODA) is equal to the angle *DAE* (which is the difference of
OAE and *OAD*). But *ADC* is a right angle, and *DAE* is
necessarily greater than a right angle. Thus the result is
impossible.

Second Fallacy.* *To prove that a part of a line is equal to
the whole line.* Let *ABC* be a triangle; and, to fix our ideas,
let us suppose that the triangle is scalene, that the angle *B*

is acute, and that the angle *A* is greater than the angle *C*.
From *A* draw *AD* making the angle *BAD* equal to the angle *C*,
and cutting *BC* in D. From *A* draw *AE* perpendicular to
BC.

The triangles *ABC*, *ABD* are equiangular; hence, by Euc.
VI. 19,

$$\triangle\, ABC : \triangle\, ABD = AC^2 : AD^2.$$

Also the triangles *ABC*, *ABD* are of equal altitude; hence
by Euc. VI. 1,

$$\triangle\, ABC : \triangle\, ABD = BC : BD,$$
$$\therefore AC^2 : AD^2 = BC : BD.$$
$$\therefore \frac{AC^2}{BC} = \frac{AD^2}{BD}.$$

---

* See a note by M. Coccoz in *L'Illustration*, Paris, Jan. 12, 1895.

Hence, by Euc. II. 13,

$$\frac{AB^2 + BC^2 - 2BC \cdot BE}{BC} = \frac{AB^2 + BD^2 - 2BD \cdot BE}{BD};$$

$$\therefore \frac{AB^2}{BC} + BC - 2BE = \frac{AB^2}{BD} + BD - 2BE.$$

$$\therefore \frac{AB^2}{BC} - BD = \frac{AB^2}{BD} - BC.$$

$$\therefore \frac{AB^2 - BC \cdot BD}{BC} = \frac{AB^2 - BC \cdot BD}{BD}.$$

$$\therefore BC = BD,$$

a result which is impossible.

Third Fallacy.* *To prove that the sum of the lengths of two sides of any triangle is equal to the length of the third side.*

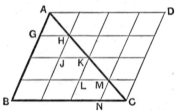

Let ABC be a triangle. Complete the parallelogram of which AB and BC are sides. Divide AB into $n + 1$ equal parts, and through the points so determined draw n lines parallel to BC. Similarly, divide BC into $n + 1$ equal parts, and through the points so determined draw n lines parallel to AB. The parallelogram $ABCD$ is thus divided into $(n + 1)^2$ equal and similar parallelograms.

I draw the figure for the case in which n is equal to 3, then, taking the parallelograms of which AC is a diagonal, as indicated in the diagram, we have

$$AB + BC = AG + HJ + KL + MN$$
$$+ GH + JK + LM + NC.$$

A similar relation is true however large n may be. Now let n increase indefinitely. Then the lines AG, GH, etc. will

* *The Canterbury Puzzles*, by H. E. Dudeney, London, 1907, pp. 26—28.

get smaller and smaller. Finally the points G, J, L, ... will approach indefinitely near the line AC, and ultimately will lie on it; when this is the case the sum of AG and GH will be equal to AH, and similarly for the other similar pairs of lines. Thus, ultimately,

$$AB + BC = AH + HK + KM + MC$$
$$= AC,$$

a result which is impossible.

Fourth Fallacy. *To prove that every triangle is isosceles.* Let ABC be any triangle. Bisect BC in D, and through D draw DO perpendicular to BC. Bisect the angle BAC by AO.

First. If DO and AO do not meet, then they are parallel. Therefore AO is at right angles to BC. Therefore $AB = AC$.

Second. If DO and AO meet, let them meet in O. Draw OE perpendicular to AC. Draw OF perpendicular to AB. Join OB, OC.

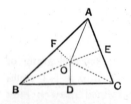

Let us begin by taking the case where O is inside the triangle, in which case E falls on AC and F on AB.

The triangles AOF and AOE are equal, since the side AO is common, angle OAF = angle OAE, and angle OFA = angle OEA. Hence $AF = AE$. Also, the triangles BOF and COE are equal. For since OD bisects BC at right angles, we have $OB = OC$; also, since the triangles AOF and AOE are equal, we have $OF = OE$; lastly, the angles at F and E are right angles. Therefore, by Euc. I. 47 and I. 8, the triangles BOF and COE are equal. Hence $FB = EC$.

Therefore $AF + FB = AE + EC$, that is, $AB = AC$.

The same demonstration will cover the case where DO and AO meet at D, as also the case where they meet outside BC but so near it that E and F fall on AC and AB and not on AC and AB produced.

Next take the case where DO and AO meet outside the triangle, and E and F fall on AC and AB produced. Draw OE perpendicular to AC produced. Draw OF perpendicular to AB produced. Join OB, OC.

Following the same argument as before, from the equality of the triangles AOF and AOE, we obtain $AF = AE$; and, from the equality of the triangles BOF and COE, we obtain $FB = EC$. Therefore $AF - FB = AE - EC$, that is, $AB = AC$.

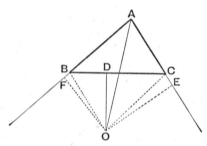

Thus in all cases, whether or not DO and AO meet, and whether they meet inside or outside the triangle, we have $AB = AC$: and therefore every triangle is isosceles, a result which is impossible.

Fifth Fallacy.* *To prove that $\pi/4$ is equal to $\pi/3$.* On the hypotenuse, BC, of an isosceles right-angled triangle, DBC, describe an equilateral triangle ABC, the vertex A being on the same side of the base as D is. On CA take a point H so that $CH = CD$. Bisect BD in K. Join HK and let it cut CB (produced) in L. Join DL. Bisect DL at M, and through M draw MO perpendicular to DL. Bisect HL at N, and through N draw NO perpendicular to HL. Since DL and HL intersect, therefore MO and NO will also intersect; moreover, since BDC is a right angle, MO and NO both slope away from DC and therefore they will meet on the side of DL remote from A. Join OC, OD, OH, OL.

* This ingenious fallacy is due to Captain Turton : it appeared for the first time in the third edition of this work.

G

The triangles OMD and OML are equal, hence $OD = OL$. Similarly the triangles ONL and ONH are equal, hence $OL = OH$. Therefore $OD = OH$. Now in the triangles OCD and OCH, we have $OD = OH$, $CD = CH$ (by construction), and OC common, hence (by Euc. I. 8) the angle OCD is equal to the angle OCH. Hence the angle BCD is equal to the angle BCH, that is, $\pi/4$ is equal to $\pi/3$, which is absurd.

Sixth Fallacy.[*] *To prove that, if two opposite sides of a quadrilateral are equal, the other two sides must be parallel.* Let $ABCD$ be a quadrilateral such that AB is equal to DC. Bisect AD in M, and through M draw MO at right angles to AD. Bisect BC in N, and draw NO at right angles to BC.

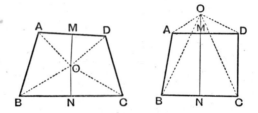

If MO and NO are parallel, then AD and BC (which are at right angles to them) are also parallel.

If MO and NO are not parallel, let them meet in O; then O must be either inside the quadrilateral as in the left-hand diagram or outside the quadrilateral as in the right-hand diagram. Join OA, OB, OC, OD.

Since OM bisects AD and is perpendicular to it, we have $OA = OD$, and the angle OAM equal to the angle ODM. Similarly $OB = OC$, and the angle OBN is equal to the angle OCN. Also by hypothesis $AB = DC$, hence, by Euc. I. 8, the triangles OAB and ODC are equal in all respects, and therefore the angle AOB is equal to the angle DOC.

Hence in the left-hand diagram the sum of the angle AOM, AOB is equal to the sum of the angles DOM, DOC; and in the right-hand diagram the difference of the angles AOM, AOB is equal to the difference of the angles DOM,

* *Mathesis*, October, 1893, series 2, vol. III, p. 224.

DOC; and therefore in both cases the angle MOB is equal to the angle MOC, *i.e.* OM (or OM produced) bisects the angle BOC. But the angle NOB is equal to the angle NOC, *i.e.* ON bisects the angle BOC; hence OM and ON coincide in direction. Therefore AD and BC, which are perpendicular to this direction, must be parallel. This result is not universally true, and the above demonstration contains a flaw.

Seventh Fallacy. The following argument is taken from a text-book on electricity, published in 1889 by two distinguished mathematicians, in which it was presented as valid. A given vector OP of length l can be resolved in an infinite number of ways into two vectors OM, MP, of lengths l', l'', and we can make l'/l'' have any value we please from nothing to infinity. Suppose that the system is referred to rectangular axes Ox, Oy; and that OP, OM, MP make respectively angles θ, θ', θ'' with Ox. Hence, by projection on Oy and on Ox, we have

$$l \sin \theta = l' \sin \theta' + l'' \sin \theta'',$$
$$l \cos \theta = l' \cos \theta' + l'' \cos \theta''.$$
$$\therefore \tan \theta = \frac{n \sin \theta' + \sin \theta''}{n \cos \theta' + \cos \theta''},$$

where $n = l'/l''$. This result is true whatever be the value of n. But n may have any value (*e.g.*, $n = \infty$, or $n = 0$), hence $\tan \theta = \tan \theta' = \tan \theta''$, which obviously is impossible.

Eighth Fallacy.* Here is a fallacious investigation of the value of π: it is founded on well-known quadratures. The area of the semi-ellipse bounded by the minor axis is (in the usual notation) equal to $\frac{1}{2}\pi ab$. If the centre is moved off to an indefinitely great distance along the major axis, the ellipse degenerates into a parabola, and therefore in this particular limiting position the area is equal to two-thirds of the circumscribing rectangle. But the first result is true whatever be the dimensions of the curve.

$$\therefore \tfrac{1}{2}\pi ab = \tfrac{2}{3}a \times 2b,$$
$$\therefore \pi = 8/3,$$

a result which obviously is untrue.

* This was communicated to me by Mr. R. Chartres.

Ninth Fallacy. *Every ellipse is a circle.* The focal distance of a point on an ellipse is given (in the usual notation) in terms of the abscissa by the formula $r = a + ex$. Hence $dr/dx = e$. From this it follows that r cannot have a maximum or minimum value. But the only closed curve in which the radius vector has not a maximum or minimum value is a circle. Hence, every ellipse is a circle, a result which obviously is untrue.

Geometrical Paradoxes

To the above examples I may add the following questions, which, though not exactly fallacious, lead to results which at a hasty glance appear impossible.

First Paradox. The first is a problem sent to me by Mr. W. Renton, to rotate a plane lamina (say, for instance, a sheet of paper) through four right angles so that the effect is equivalent to turning it through only one right angle.

Second Paradox. As in arithmetic, so in geometry, the theory of probability lends itself to numerous paradoxes. Here is a very simple illustration. A stick is broken at random into three pieces. It is possible to put them together into the shape of a triangle provided the length of the longest piece is less than the sum of the other two pieces (*cf.* Euc. i. 20), that is, provided the length of the longest piece is less than half the length of the stick. But the probability that a fragment of a stick shall be less than half the original length of the stick is $1/2$. Hence the probability that a triangle can be constructed out of the three pieces into which the stick is broken would appear to be $1/2$. This is not true, for actually the probability is $1/4$.

Third Paradox. The following example illustrates how easily the eye may be deceived in demonstrations obtained by actually dissecting the figures and re-arranging the parts. In fact proofs by superposition should be regarded with considerable distrust unless they are supplemented by mathematical reasoning. The well-known proofs of the propositions Euclid i. 32 and Euclid i. 47 can be so supplemented and are valid.

On the other hand, as an illustration of how deceptive a non-mathematical proof may be, I here mention the familiar paradox that a square of paper, subdivided like a chessboard into 64 small squares, can be cut into four pieces which being put together form a figure containing 65 such small squares.* This is effected by cutting the original square into four pieces in the manner indicated by the thick lines in the first figure. If these four pieces are put together in the shape of a rectangle in the way shown in the second figure it will appear as if this rectangle contains 65 of the small squares.

This phenomenon, which in my experience non-mathematicians find perplexing, is due to the fact that the edges of

the four pieces of paper, which in the second figure lie along the diagonal AB, do not coincide exactly in direction. In reality they include a small lozenge or diamond-shaped figure, whose area is equal to that of one of the 64 small squares in the original square, but whose length AB is much greater than its breadth. The diagrams show that the angle between the two sides of this lozenge which meet at A is $\tan^{-1}\frac{2}{5} - \tan^{-1}\frac{3}{8}$, that is, is $\tan^{-1}\frac{1}{46}$, which is less than $1\frac{1}{4}°$. To enable the eye to distinguish so small an angle as this the dividing lines in the first figure would have to be cut with extreme accuracy and the pieces placed together with great care.

* I do not know who discovered this paradox. It is given in various books, but I cannot find an earlier reference to it than one in the *Zeitschrift für Mathematik und Physik*, Leipzig, 1868, vol. XIII, p. 162. Some similar paradoxes were given by Ozanam, 1803 edition, vol. I, p. 299.

This paradox depends upon the relation $5 \times 13 - 8^2 = 1$. Similar results can be obtained from the formulae

$$13 \times 34 - 21^2 = 1, \; 34 \times 89 - 55^2 = 1, \ldots;$$

or from the formulae

$$5^2 - 3 \times 8 = 1, \; 13^2 - 8 \times 21 = 1, \; 34^2 - 21 \times 55 = 1, \ldots.$$

These relations connect sets of three consecutive Fibonacci numbers (see p. 57). The general formula

$$b_n c_{n+1} - c_n b_{n+1} = (-1)^n$$

holds for two adjacent convergents to any continued fraction.

CONTINUED FRACTIONS AND LATTICE POINTS *

Consider a board, divided into a large number of equal squares, with small pegs sticking up at the vertices of all the squares. Let us regard the lines of pegs nearest to two

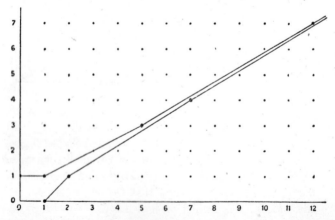

adjacent edges of the board as axes of co-ordinates, so that every peg has co-ordinates which are non-negative integers. If y/x is a fraction in its lowest terms, a stretched string joining the pegs $(0, 0)$ and (x, y) will not touch any other pegs. This string being fastened at (x, y), let us move it from the other end without allowing it to jump over any pegs. If the string is

* Cf. F. Klein, *Elementary Mathematics*, New York, 1932, p. 44.

stretched taut, with its free end at (1, 0), it will, in general, press against certain pegs (x_1, y_1), (x_2, y_2), ... between (1, 0) and (x, y). If its free end is held at (0, 1) instead of (1, 0), it will press against other pegs (x_1', y_1'), (x_2', y_2'), ... It can be proved that the fractions y_1/x_1, y_2/x_2, ... are alternate convergents to y/x, while y_1'/x_1', y_2'/x_2', ... are the remaining convergents. (The convergent y_r'/x_r' comes just before or just after y_r/x_r according as y/x is less or greater than 1.)

This construction shows clearly the manner in which the convergents approximate to y/x, alternately by excess and defect. The fraction y/x measures the *gradient* of the string in its original position. There is no difficulty in extending these notions to the case of a string of irrational gradient, firmly attached " at infinity." The case when the gradient is

$$\frac{1}{e-1} = \frac{1}{1} + \frac{1}{1} + \frac{1}{2} + \frac{1}{1} + \frac{1}{1} + \frac{1}{4} + \cdots$$

is shown above. Observe that the string from (1, 1) to (5, 3) touches (without " pressing against ") the peg (3, 2). The fraction $\frac{2}{3}$ is one of the *intermediate convergents* which, together with the ordinary or *principal* convergents ($\frac{0}{1}$, $\frac{1}{1}$, $\frac{1}{2}$, $\frac{3}{5}$, $\frac{4}{7}$, $\frac{7}{12}$, ...), make up the set of fractions of best approximation.

If b_{n-1}/c_{n-1}, b_n/c_n, b_{n+1}/c_{n+1} are three consecutive (principal) convergents to any continued fraction, we know that

$$b_n/c_n = (b_{n+1} - b_{n-1})/(c_{n+1} - c_{n-1}).$$

Geometrically, this means that the line from (0, 0) to (c_n, b_n) is parallel to the line from (c_{n-1}, b_{n-1}) to (c_{n+1}, b_{n+1}).

GEOMETRICAL DISSECTIONS

Problems requiring the division by straight lines of a given plane rectilinear figure into pieces which can be put together in some other assigned form are well known. A class of geometrical recreations is concerned with such constructions.

Pythagorean Extension. A familiar instance is found in many text-books in a dissection proof of the Pythagorean property of a right-angled triangle. In fact, however, if we are given any two squares we can always by three cuts divide them into five pieces which can be put together to make a square. There are various solutions. Here are two which answer the purpose.*

The first of these is as follows : Place the larger and smaller squares AG and CE side by side as in figure i below, and take AB equal to CD. Then a cut BH and a cut BE (*i.e.* a cut BJ on the larger square and another cut JE on the smaller square) will divide the squares into five pieces which can be put together to make one square of which BH and BE are sides.

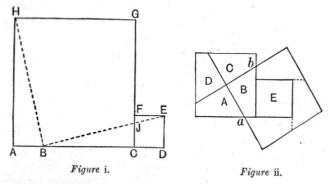

Figure i.   *Figure* ii.

A more symmetrical, though less simple, five-part solution (made up of the smaller square together with a four-part division of the larger square) can be effected as follows. Place the larger square (denoted by the letters A, B, C, D) next the smaller square (denoted by E), as in figure ii, with their bases in the same line. Bisect this line in one point a, and on their common side take another point b whose distance above their bases is half the sum of their sides. Through these points draw lines perpendicular to each other, crossing in the centre of the larger square, and terminating in its sides. This divides the larger square into four equal parts A, B, C, D. Produce the two lines drawn through a and b for half their length

* H. Perigal, *Messenger of Mathematics*, 1873, vol. II, N.S., pp. 103—106; H. E. Dudeney, *Amusements*, London, 1917, p. 32.

beyond the common base and side of the squares, and through their extremities draw two other lines perpendicular to them. These four lines will form another square inclosing the small square within four segments equal and similar to the four quarters of the larger of the given squares, and consequently equal in area to the two together.

Montucla's Dissection. Demonstrations of a few similar propositions had long been current, but towards the close of the eighteenth century attention was recalled to this kind of solution by Montucla, who proposed and solved the problem of dividing a rectangle so that the parts could be put together in the form of a square; he also solved the converse problem. Later, other solutions of this problem were given by P. Busschop and de Coatpont who made respectively eight-part and seven-part dissections. The former also had constructions for making a square from a five-part division of a regular hexagon, and from a seven-part division of a regular pentagon.*

Polygonal Dissections. The more general problem of the dissection of a given polygon of any number of sides, and the rearrangement of the parts in the form of another polygon of equal area, had been raised by Bolyai, and a method of solution indicated by Gerwien. The question continued to attract occasional attention. In particular a solution for the case of a polygon and a triangle was given by Euzet in 1854, and the wider problem of two polygons was discussed by E. Guitel in 1895, by E. Holst in 1896,† and more recently by A. Mineur.‡

Consider first the dissection of a given triangle to form a rectangle of given base. In figure iii, a line *DE*, parallel to the

* G. G. F. Montucla, Ozanam's *Récréations Mathématiques*, 1803, English edition, vol. I, pp. 292—298; 1840 edition, pp. 127—129; Paul Busschop, *Nouvelle Correspondance Mathématique*, Brussels, 1875, vol. II, p. 83; de Coatpont, *ibid.*, 1876, vol. III, p. 116.

† P. Gerwien, *Crelle's Journal*, 1833, p. 228; M. Euzet, *Nouvelles Annales de Mathématiques*, 1854, vol. XIII, pp. 114—115; E. Guitel, *Association Française pour l'Avancement des Sciences*, 1895, pp. 264—267; E. Holst, *L'Intermédiaire des Mathématiciens*, 1896, vol. III, pp. 91—92.

‡ See *Mathesis*, 1931, pp. 150—152. The following treatment is due to Michael Goldberg.

base BC of the given triangle ABC and bisecting the sides, cuts the triangle into two parts which may be assembled into a parallelogram $BCFD$. Now with B as centre and with the

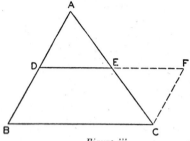

Figure iii.

given base as radius draw an arc. Make a cut CH tangent to this arc and a cut BG perpendicular to CH. The point G may fall inside the parallelogram, as in figure iv, or outside, as in

Figure iv.

figure v. In the latter case, locate J (on CH) so that $CJ = HG$, and make the cut JL parallel to BG. Then the pieces may be

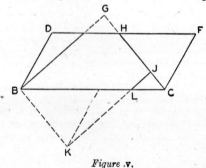

Figure .v.

assembled into the desired rectangle $BGJK$. If the base BG is too long or too short to follow this procedure directly, it will be necessary first to change the proportions of the parallelogram $BCFD$ by cutting it into three pieces and rearranging these as in figure vi (where $E'F = BC' \gg \frac{1}{2}BC$). Of course, if the

Figure vi.

base of the rectangle had been chosen to be the side of the square equivalent to the triangle, the given triangle would have been converted into a square.

Every polygon can be cut into triangles by drawing a sufficient number of diagonals. Therefore every polygon can be transformed into a square or rectangle by transforming the component triangles into rectangles all having the same base and then stacking the rectangles into a column.

We can always use a rectangle as an intermediate stage in the transformation of one polygon into another. Given the dissections which transform the given polygon and the desired polygon each into the same rectangle, we go from the given polygon to the rectangle by using the first transformation and then to the desired polygon by reversing the second transformation.

Minimum Dissections. The above-mentioned writers aimed only at finding a solution, and did not in general trouble themselves with considering the smallest number of pieces required. In 1905, the special cases of a four-part dissection of a pair of triangles, a four-part dissection of a triangle and parallelogram, and dissections of a pair of parallelograms were given by H. M. Taylor,* and he recognized the desirability of finding the smallest necessary number of cuts.

* *Messenger of Mathematics*, vol. xxxv, pp. 81—101.

Henceforth the explicit determination of the number of pieces in which a figure has to be cut to give a solution was regarded as an essential feature of the problem, and it is accepted that that solution is to be preferred in which the number of pieces is smallest. I have no doubt that Taylor's solutions do in fact give the minimum number of pieces required in those cases.

Puzzle Dissections. Of late years H. E. Dudeney has propounded various ingenious puzzles of this kind, in all cases the number of parts being specified.* His reputation has served to attract attention to this class of problems. As illustrating his results and as geometrical recreations of this

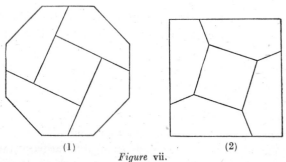

(1)   (2)

Figure vii.

type, I pick out his problems, (*a*) to divide, by two straight lines, a Greek cross, that is, one made up of five equal squares, into four pieces all of the same shape and size which can be put together to make a square; (*b*) to divide an isosceles right-angled triangle into four pieces which can be put together to make a Greek cross; (*c*) to divide a regular pentagon into six pieces which can be put together to make a square; (*d*) to divide an equilateral triangle into four pieces which can be put together to make a square. The reader interested in the subject will like to compare Dudeney's solution of the last question with that given by Taylor already mentioned, and that by Macaulay referred to below.

* For instance, see his *Amusements in Mathematics*, London, 1917, p. 27 *et seq.*

A. H. Wheeler has divided a regular pentagon into six pieces which can be put together to make an equilateral triangle; and J. Travers * has divided a regular octagon into five pieces which can be put together to make a square. (See figure vii.)

Macaulay's Four-part Dissections. The theory of four-part dissections of pairs of rectilinear figures of equal area has been discussed by W. H. Macaulay.† He has treated four-part dissections of pairs of triangles, of a triangle and a parallelo-gram, of pairs of quadrilaterals, of pairs of pentagons each with two sides equal and parallel, and of pairs of certain related hexagons. His results are projective and all of them are deducible from his hexagon dissections. This is an interesting generalization.

Dissecting a Square into Different Squares. Z. Moroń ‡ has ob-served that nine different squares can be fitted together to make a rectangle 32×33. A general theory of such arrangements has been developed,§ whereby W. T. Tutte has solved the prob-lem of fitting together 26 different squares to make a *square*.

Volume Dissections. It is natural to ask whether every polyhedral solid can be divided, by a finite number of plane cuts, into pieces which will fit together to form any other polyhedral solid of the same volume. The answer is No; it was proved by M. Dehn ‖ that it is impossible to transform any tetrahedron by dissections into a prism. This annihilates any hopes for a general method of volume dissections analogous to polygonal dissections, although special volume dissections are quite possible.

The Duplication of the Cube. Here is a variant of the "Delian Problem" (which we shall consider in Chapter XII):

---

* *Education Outlook*, 1933, p. 145.

† *Mathematical Gazette*, 1914, vol. VII, p. 381; vol. VIII, 1915, pp. 72, 109; *Messenger of Mathematics*, vol. XLVIII, 1919, p. 159; vol. XLIX, 1919, p. 111.

‡ *Przeglad Mat.-Fiz.*, 1925, vol. III, pp. 152—153.

§ By R. L. Brooks, C. A. B. Smith, A. H. Stone, and W. T. Tutte, *Duke Mathematical Journal*, 1940, vol. VI.

‖ *Nachr. der k. Gesellschaft der Wissensch, zu Göttingen*, 1900.

given a line of length $2^{1/3}$ (or $\sqrt[3]{2}$), divide two cubes of unit edge, by plane cuts, into pieces which can be assembled into a single cube. This problem can be solved by two applications of the transformation of a given rectangle into a rectangle of given base. The " minimum " dissection is obtained by using the method of figure vi, rather than that of figure iv.

First place the two equal cubes together to form a square prism $2 \times 1 \times 1$. Then mark on one of the rectangular faces (2×1) the cuts necessary to transform it into a rectangle of base $2^{1/3}$, which is equal to the edge of the duplicated cube. Through these lines pass planes perpendicular to this face, cutting the prism into three parts.

Assemble these parts to form the new prism $2^{1/3} \times 2^{2/3} \times 1$. Then, on either of the faces $2^{2/3} \times 1$, mark the cuts necessary to transform this rectangle into a square of side $2^{1/3}$. Through these lines pass planes perpendicular to this face, and assemble the three parts into the desired cube. The original prism $2 \times 1 \times 1$ has been divided into seven irregular solids by these cuts. If the pieces are disarranged, the task of assembling them to form the cube or the prism is not an easy puzzle.

This problem was proposed by W. F. Cheney, Jr., and solved thus by A. H. Wheeler.*

CYCLOTOMY

At the age of nineteen, Gauss † proved that the solution of the " cyclotomic equation " $x^p = 1$, where p is a prime, can be reduced to the solution of a succession of quadratic equations if, and only if, $p - 1$ is a power of 2. So far as we know, the only such primes (greater than 2) are the first five Fermat Numbers : 3, 5, 17, 257, 65537 (see page 69). Since the roots of the cyclotomic equation are

$$\cos (2r\pi/p) + i \sin (2r\pi/p) \quad (r = 0, 1, \ldots, p-1),$$

it follows that a regular n-gon, where n is odd, can be drawn by

* *American Mathematical Monthly*, 1935, vol. XLII, p. 509.
† *Disquisitiones Arithmeticae*, 1801.

a Euclidean construction (*i.e.* with ruler and compasses) if, and only if, n is such a prime, or a product of several such primes without repetition. It is sufficient to consider odd values of n, since the construction of a $(2^k n)$-gon involves that of an n-gon followed by k angle-bisections.

If we assume that all Fermat Numbers after Γ_4 are composite, it follows * that n must be a divisor of $3 . 5 . 17 . 257 . 65537 = 2^{32} - 1 = 4294,967295$. If a polygon with a larger odd number of sides can be drawn with ruler and compasses, this larger number must have at least 309 digits, since the first Fermat Number whose composite character is in doubt is F_{10} ($= 2^{1024} + 1$).

Constructions for the triangle and pentagon are familiar. A construction for the 15-gon follows immediately, since $\frac{4}{5}\pi - \frac{2}{3}\pi = \frac{2}{15}\pi$; you merely have to inscribe in one circle both a triangle and a pentagon. The following construction for the 17-gon is due to H. W. Richmond, who gave also an analogous construction for the pentagon to compare with it.

The problem is to inscribe, in a given circle, a regular 17-gon with one vertex at P_0 (see figure viii). Let OB be a radius,

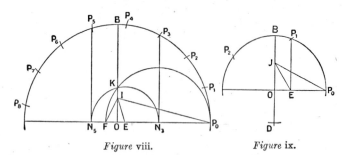

Figure viii.   *Figure* ix.

perpendicular to the diameter through P_0. Find a point I on OB so that $OI = \frac{1}{4}OB$. Join IP_0, and find points E, F on OP_0 so that angle $OIE = \frac{1}{4}OIP_0$ and angle $FIE = \frac{1}{4}\pi$. Let the circle on FP_0 as diameter cut OB in K, and let the circle with centre E and radius EK cut OP_0 in N_3 (between O and P_0)

* Kraïtchik, *La Mathématique des Jeux*, Brussels, 1930, p. 99.

and N_5. Let lines $N_3 P_3$, $N_5 P_5$, parallel to OB, cut the original circle in P_3, P_5. Then the arcs $P_0 P_3$, $P_0 P_5$ will be $\frac{3}{17}$ and $\frac{5}{17}$ of the circumference.

The proof* involves repeated application of the principle that the roots of the equation $x^2 + 2x \cot 2C = 1$ are $\tan C$ and $-\cot C$.

For the pentagon† (figure ix), define B as before, bisect OB at J, and find E on OP_0 so that JE bisects the angle OJP_0. If the line through E parallel to OB cuts the circle in P_1 the arc $P_0 P_1$ will be $\frac{1}{5}$ of the circumference.

Constructions for polygons of 51, 85 and 255 sides follow immediately; so do constructions for polygons whose numbers of sides are these numbers multiplied by any power of 2.

Compass Problems

It is well known that Euclid in his *Elements* confined his constructions to those which could be made with ungraduated rulers and compasses. The use of a ruler is, however, unnecessary.‡ Mascheroni § established a connected series of propositions by constructions made with compasses alone. Of course, the logical sequence is very different from that with which we are familiar.

As an instance which will illustrate the subject, I select the problem to find a point midway between two given points A and B. Of this fundamental proposition Mascheroni gave five solutions (prop. 66). Here are two of them : they rest on the assumption that we can draw a semicircle whose centre and one extremity are given, a result he had previously established.

* *Quarterly Journal of Mathematics*, 1893, vol. XXVI, p. 206.

† A slightly simpler construction for the pentagon has been suggested by H. E. Dudeney, *Amusements in Mathematics*, p. 38. With centre J and radius JP_0, draw an arc to cut BO (produced) in D. Then an arc with centre P_0 and radius $P_0 D$ will cut the original circle in P_1.

‡ Michael Goldberg, *School Science and Mathematics*, 1925, vol. XXV, pp. 961—965.

§ His work was published at Pavia in 1797. However, it has recently become known that he was largely anticipated by G. Mohr, whose *Euclides Danicus* was published at Amsterdam in 1672 (and at Copenhagen in 1928).

In each case the demonstration is straightforward. Other solutions of this proposition have been given, some of which evade the use of a semicircle.

One of his constructions is as follows. With B as centre, and a radius BA, describe a semicircle of which A and C are the extremities. With centres A and C, and radii AB and CA, describe circles which cut in P and Q. With centres P and Q, and a radius equal to AB, describe circles. These will cut in a point midway between A and B.

Here is another of his solutions, which for some purposes he preferred. With B as centre, and radius BA, describe a semicircle of which A and C are the extremities. With A and C as centres, and a radius equal to AB, describe circles which cut the semicircle in H and K respectively. With A and C as centres, and a radius equal to AC, describe circles which cut the last-mentioned circles (above AC) in Q and P respectively. With centres P and C, and radii PA and PQ, describe circles. These will cut in a point midway between A and B.

Numerous geometrical recreations of this kind can be made by any one, for all that is necessary is to select at random one of Euclid's propositions, and see how it can be established by using only circles. As instances, I select the construction on a given line of a triangle similar to a given triangle (prop. 125); and the construction of a regular pentagon of given dimensions (prop. 137). Whatever be the solution obtained, it is always interesting to turn to Mascheroni's book, and see how the question is tackled there.

THE FIVE DISC PROBLEM

The problem of completely covering a fixed red circular space by placing over it, one at a time, five smaller equal circular tin discs is familiar to frequenters of English fairs. Its effectiveness depends on making the tin discs as small as possible, and therefore leads to the interesting geometrical question of finding the size of the smallest tin discs which can be used for the purpose.

H

The problem is soluble if the radius of each tin disc is just greater than three-fifths of the radius of the red circle. Of course, in a show the visitor is not allowed to move the discs when once he has put them down, and it is only rarely, very rarely, that he succeeds empirically in placing them correctly.

The rule works out thus. If O is the centre of the red circle, a its radius, and AOB a diameter of it, we take on OA a point P such that approximately $OP = a/40$. We then place the first tin disc with its centre on OB, and so that P is on its edge : suppose that its edge meets the edge of the red circle in C and C', points on opposite sides of AB. Place the next two discs so that in each case AP is a chord of the disc. Suppose that these discs meet the edge of the red circle in D and D' respectively, C and D being on the same side of AB. Then if we place the two remaining discs so that CD and $C'D'$ are chords of them, the problem will be solved. The minimum discs are not obtained, as one might at first guess, by the overlapping of five discs placed at the vertices of an inscribed pentagon.

In practice and for simplicity it is desirable to make the tin discs a trifle larger than the theory requires, and to treat P as coincident with O.

The mathematical discussion on this problem is too technical and long to insert here. Probably a bare statement of the results such as is given above is all that most readers will want. Should closer approximations be desired, here they are.* If the radius of the red circle be taken as one foot, the critical radius for the discs, below which the problem is impossible, is ·609418 foot. Also $OP =$ ·028545 foot, hence O lies very near but not quite on the circumference of the first disc which is put down. If three of the discs are placed so that their edges pass through O, the radius of each of them must exceed ·6099578 foot, a length practically indistinguishable from that of the radius of the minimum disc. If the discs are

---

* See *Solutions of Numerical Functional Equations*, by E. H. Neville, *Proceedings of the London Mathematical Society*, 1915, second series, vol. XIV, pp. 308—326.

put with their centres at the vertices of an inscribed pentagon and their edges passing through O, the radius of each of them must exceed ·6180340 foot. It follows that unless the discs are cut with extreme accuracy the problem may be solved by making the circumference of each disc pass through O; the possibility of using this inaccurate rule is a serious defect in the problem when used as the foundation of a puzzle.

I believe that the discs used in fairs are generally large enough to allow of the employment of the inaccurate rule, though even then it is safer to use the correct method. In an example made for myself I put a minute faint mark near the centre of the red circle but just far enough away to ensure failure for those who make that point lie on the edge of each disc. Notwithstanding their neglect or ignorance of the correct rule showmen seem to find that the game is profitable, and obviously this is an excellent test of its merits from their point of view.

BESICOVITCH'S MINIMAL PROBLEM

Here is an unsolved problem about covering an area. The *diameter* of any figure may be defined as the longest straight line that can be drawn so as to join two points of the figure. Besicovitch's problem is the determination of *the plane lamina of least area which, when suitably oriented, will cover any given plane figure of unit diameter*.

A circle of unit diameter is too small, since, although it will cover a square of unit diagonal, it will not cover an equilateral triangle of unit side. On the other hand, a square of unit side is unnecessarily large. Thus the required area is greater than $\frac{1}{4}\pi$ but less than 1. Its precise value, and the shape, have never been determined. Of course, there is no reason to expect any kind of symmetry.

KAKEYA'S MINIMAL PROBLEM

A somewhat similar problem * is the determination of the least area swept over by a straight line of unit length which is

* S. Kakeya, *Tôhoku Science Reports*, 1917, vol. VI, pp. 71—78; G. D. Birkhoff, *The Origin, Nature, and Influence of Relativity*, 1925, p. 4.

reversed in direction by a continuous motion during which it takes every possible orientation in the plane. Kakeya's problem had assumed the proportions of a famous unsolved problem although its complete solution was published only ten years after it was proposed. Osgood and Kubota suggested the deltoid (or three-cusped hypocycloid) as a possible solution, the area in this case being just half that of the circle of unit diameter. (See figure x.)

Besicovitch showed * that there is no smallest area, that the area can be made as small as we please ! This astounding fact is difficult to believe, so I proceed to give a very brief outline of his elegant demonstration.

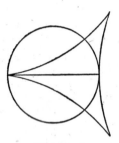

Figure x.

Consider a right-angled isosceles triangle whose hypotenuse is of length 2. Then it is obvious that the line of unit length can be rotated continuously through a right angle within this triangle of unit area. Besicovitch cuts up the triangle into a large number of small pieces, certain sets of which he shifts by translation, making them overlap. He thus obtains a number of regions, of rather complicated shape, in each of which the line can be rotated through a definite small angle. On account of the overlapping, the sum of the areas of these regions is less than $1/k$ for any value of k, previously assigned. He then shows how the line may be moved from each one of these regions into the next in such a way that the total area swept out in such processes can be

* A. S. Besicovitch, *Mathematische Zeitschrift*, 1928, vol. XXVII, p. 312.

made as small as we please. Finally, since the given line has
been moved continuously through a right angle, we can just
as readily repeat the process through another right angle
(thus reversing the direction of the line) and still make the
total area as small as we please.

Physical Configuration of a Country

The theory of the representation of the physical configuration
of a country by means of lines drawn on a map was discussed
by Cayley and Clerk Maxwell.* They showed that a certain
relation exists between the number of hills, dales, passes, etc.
which can co-exist on the earth or on an island. I proceed to
give a summary of their nomenclature and conclusions.

All places whose heights above the mean sea level are equal
are on the same level. The locus of such points on a map is
indicated by a *contour-line*. Roughly speaking, an island is
bounded by a contour-line. It is usual to draw the successive
contour-lines on a map so that the difference between the
heights of any two successive lines is the same, and thus the
closer the contour-lines the steeper is the slope; but the
heights are measured dynamically by the amount of work to
be done to go from one level to the other, and not by linear
distances.

A contour-line in general will be a closed curve. This
curve may enclose a region of elevation : if two such regions
meet at a point, that point will be a crunode (*i.e.* a real double
point) on the contour-line through it, and such a point is
called a *pass*. The contour-line may enclose a region of depression : if two such regions meet at a point, that point will
be a crunode on the contour-line through it, and such a
point is called a *fork* or bar. As the heights of the corresponding level surfaces become greater, the areas of the regions

* Cayley on ' Contour and Slope Lines,' *Philosophical Magazine*, London,
October, 1859, series 4, vol. XVIII, pp. 264—268; *Collected Works*, vol. IV,
pp. 108—111. J. Clerk Maxwell on ' Hills and Dales,' *Philosophical Magazine*,
December, 1870, series 4, vol. XL, pp. 421—427; *Collected Works*, vol. II,
pp. 233—240.

of elevation become smaller, and at last become reduced to points : these points are the *summits* of the corresponding mountains. Similarly as the level surface sinks the regions of depression contract, and at last are reduced to points : these points are the *bottoms*, or immits, of the corresponding valleys.

Lines drawn so as to be everywhere at right angles to the contour-lines are called *lines of slope*. If we go up a line of slope generally we shall reach a summit, and if we go down such a line generally we shall reach a bottom : we may come, however, in particular cases either to a pass or to a fork. Districts whose lines of slope run to the same summit are *hills*. Those whose lines of slope run to the same bottom are *dales*. A *watershed* is the line of slope from a summit to a pass or a fork, and it separates two dales. A *watercourse* is the line of slope from a pass or a fork to a bottom, and it separates two hills.

If $n + 1$ regions of elevation or of depression meet at a point, the point is a multiple point on the contour-line drawn through it ; such a point is called a pass or a fork of the nth order, and must be counted as n separate passes (or forks). If one region of depression meets another in several places at once, one of these must be taken as a fork and the rest as passes.

Having now a definite geographical terminology we can apply geometrical propositions to the subject. Let h be the number of hills on the earth (or an island), then there will be also h summits ; let d be the number of dales, then there will be also d bottoms ; let p be the whole number of passes, p_1 that of single passes, p_2 of double passes, and so on; let f be the whole number of forks, f_1 that of single forks, f_2 of double forks, and so on ; let w be the number of watercourses, then there will be also w watersheds. Hence, by the theorems of Cauchy and Euler,

$$h = 1 + p_1 + 2p_2 + \ldots,$$
$$d = 1 + f_1 + 2f_2 + \ldots,$$

and
$$w = 2(p_1 + f_1) + 3(p_2 + f_2) + \ldots$$

ADDENDUM

Note. Page 84. The required rotation of the lamina can be effected thus. Suppose that the result is to be equivalent to turning it through a right angle about a point O. Describe on the lamina a square $OABC$. Rotate the lamina successively through two right angles about the diagonal OB as axis and through two right angles about the side OA as axis, and the required result will be attained.

Note. Page 93. The sides of Tutte's twenty-six squares are: 1, 5, 7, 11, 20, 27, 34, 41, 42, 43, 44, 61, 85, 95, 108, 113, 118, 123, 136, 168, 172, 183, 194, 205, 209, 231. These make a single square of side 608. To solve this unusual jigsaw puzzle, use the packer's rule of placing the largest parts first. The arrangement is not quite unique, since certain blocks of squares form rectangles which can be turned around or reflected.

CHAPTER IV

GEOMETRICAL RECREATIONS (*continued*)

LEAVING now the question of formal geometrical propositions, I proceed to enumerate a few games or puzzles which
depend mainly on the relative position of things, but I postpone
to Chapter X the discussion of such amusements of this
kind as necessitate any considerable use of arithmetic or
algebra. Some writers regard draughts, solitaire, chess, and
such-like games as subjects for geometrical treatment in the
same way as they treat dominoes, backgammon, and games
with dice in connection with arithmetic : but these discussions
require too many artificial assumptions to correspond with the
games as actually played or to be interesting.

The amusements to which I refer are of a more trivial
description, and it is possible that a mathematician may like to
omit this chapter. In some cases it is difficult to say whether
they should be classified as mainly arithmetical or geometrical,
but the point is of no importance.

STATICAL GAMES OF POSITION

Of the innumerable statical games involving geometry of
position I shall mention only three or four.

Three-in-a-row. First, I may mention the games of three-
in-a-row, of which noughts and crosses, one form of merrilees,
and go-bang are well-known examples. These games are
played on a board—generally in the form of a square containing n^2 small squares or cells. The common practice is for
one player to place a white counter or piece or to make a cross
on each small square or cell which he occupies : his opponent
similarly uses black counters or pieces or makes a nought on
each cell which he occupies. Whoever first gets three (or any

other assigned number) of his pieces in three adjacent cells and in a straight line wins. There is no difficulty in giving the complete analysis for boards of 9 cells and of 16 cells : but it is lengthy, and not particularly interesting. Most of these games were known to the ancients,* and it is for that reason I mention them here.

Three-in-a-row. Extension. I may, however, add an elegant but difficult extension which has not previously found its way, so far as I am aware, into any book of mathematical recreations. The problem is to place n counters on a plane so as to form as many rows as possible, each of which shall contain three, and only three, counters.†

It is easy to arrange the counters in a number of rows equal to the integral part of $(n-1)^2/8$. This can be effected by the following construction. Let P be any point on a cubic. Let the tangent at P cut the curve again in Q. Let the tangent at Q cut the curve in A. Let PA cut the curve in B, QB cut it in C, PC cut it in D, QD cut it in E, and so on. Then the counters must be placed at the points $P, Q, A, B. \ldots$ Thus 9 counters can be placed in 8 such rows ; 10 counters in 10 rows ; 15 counters in 24 rows ; 81 counters in 800 rows ; and so on.

Sylvester found that, by a suitable choice of the initial point P, the number of rows can be increased to the integral part of $(n-1)(n-2)/6$. Thus 9 counters can be arranged in 9 rows ; 10 counters in 12 rows ; 15 counters in 30 rows ; 81 counters in 1053 rows ; and so on.

These, however, are inferior limits, and may be exceeded— for instance, Sylvester stated that 9 counters can be placed in 10 rows, each containing three counters ; I do not know how he placed them, but one way of so arranging them is by putting them at points whose co-ordinates are $(2, 0)$, $(2, 2)$, $(2, 4)$, $(4, 0)$, $(4, 2)$, $(4, 4)$, $(0, 0)$, $(3, 2)$, $(6, 4)$; another way

---

* Becq de Fouquières, *Les Jeux des Anciens*, second edition, Paris, 1873, chap. XVIII.

† *Educational Times Reprints*, 1868, vol. VIII, p. 106 ; *ibid.*, 1886, vol. XLV, pp. 127—128.

is by putting them at the points (0, 0), (0, 2), (0, 4), (2, 1), (2, 2), (2, 3), (4, 0), (4, 2), (4, 4); more generally, the angular points of a regular hexagon and the three points (at infinity) of intersection of opposite sides form such a group, and therefore any projection of that figure will give a solution. At present it is not possible to say what is the maximum number of rows of three which can be formed from n counters placed on a plane.

Extension to p-in-a-row. The problem mentioned above at once suggests the extension of placing n counters so as to form as many rows as possible, each of which shall contain p and only p counters. Such problems can be often solved immediately by placing at infinity the points of intersection of some of the lines, and (if it is so desired) subsequently projecting the diagram thus formed so as to bring these points to a finite distance. One instance of such a solution is given above.

As examples I may give the arrangement of 10 counters in 5 rows, each containing 4 counters; the arrangement of 16 counters in 15 rows, each containing 4 counters; the arrangement of 18 counters in 9 rows, each containing 5 counters; and the arrangement of 19 counters in 10 rows, each containing 5 counters. These problems I leave to the ingenuity of my readers (see p. 127).

Tessellation. Another of these statical recreations is known as tessellation, and consists in the formation of geometrical designs or mosaics covering a plane area by the use of tiles of given geometrical forms.

If the tiles are regular polygons, the resulting forms can be found by analysis. For instance, if we confine ourselves to the use of like tiles, each of which is a regular polygon of n sides, we are restricted to the use of equilateral triangles, squares, or hexagons. For suppose that to fill the space round a point where one of the angles of the polygon is situated we require m polygons. Each interior angle of the polygon is equal to $(n-2)\pi/n$. Hence $m(n-2)\pi/n = 2\pi$. Therefore $(m-2)(n-2) = 4$. Now, from the nature of the problem m is greater than 2, and so is n. If $m = 3$, $n = 6$. If $m > 3$, then $n < 6$, and since $n > 2$, we have in this case only to consider the values $n = 3$, $n = 4$, and $n = 5$. If $n = 3$ we have $m = 6$. If $n = 4$ we have $m = 4$. If $n = 5$, m is non-integral, and this is impossible. Thus the only solutions are $m = 3$ and $n = 6$, $m = 4$ and $n = 4$, $m = 6$ and $n = 3$.* It is convenient to use the symbols 6^3, 4^4, 3^6 to denote these regular tessellations.

If, however, we allow the use of unlike regular tiles (triangles, squares, etc.), we can construct numerous geometrical designs covering a plane area. If at each point the same number and kind of polygons are used, in the same (or the

opposite) cyclic order, analysis similar to the above † shows that we can get eight possible arrangements—namely,

$$3.12^2, \quad 4.6.12, \quad 4.8^2, \quad (3.6)^2, \quad 3.4.6.4, \quad 3^3.4^2, \quad 3^2.4.3.4, \quad 3^4.6.$$

The tessellation $3^4.6$ (with four triangles and a hexagon at each vertex) has the peculiarity of existing in two enantio-

* The analogous problem for polygons covering the surface of a sphere is equivalent to the construction of regular polyhedra (see page 130). For an application of 6^3 to the voting system known as Proportional Representation, see G. Pólya, *L'Enseignement Mathématique*, 1918, vol. **xx**, p. 367.

† See Kraïtchik, pp. 272—282, Figs. 421—423, 425, 426, 432, 433, 440.

morphous forms; *i.e.*, it is not superposable with its image in a mirror (unless we allow the whole plane to be turned over).

When every edge of such a tessellation is replaced by a perpendicular line, joining the centres of two adjacent tiles, we obtain a *reciprocal* tessellation, whose tiles are all alike (though not necessarily regular). In this sense, 6^3 is reciprocal to 3^6 (and *vice versa*), while 4^4 is self-reciprocal (or rather, reciprocal to another equal 4^4). The tessellation $(3.6)^2$ and its reciprocal are drawn above.

Anallagmatic Pavements. The use of colours introduces new considerations. One formation of a pavement by the employment of square tiles of two colours is illustrated by the common chess-board; in this the cells are coloured alternately white and black. Another variety of a pavement made with square tiles of two colours was invented by Sylvester,* who termed it anallagmatic. In the ordinary chess-board, if any two rows or any two columns are placed in juxtaposition, cell to cell, the cells which are side by side are either all of the same colour or all of different colours. In an anallagmatic arrangement the cells are so coloured (with two colours) that when any two columns or any two rows are placed together side by side, half the cells next to one another are of the same colour and half are of different colours.

Anallagmatic pavements composed of m^2 cells or square tiles cannot be constructed if m is odd or oddly-even. It has been conjectured that they exist whenever m is a multiple of 4. The first doubtful case is when $m = 92$.

If solutions when $m = a$ and when $m = b$ are known, a solution when $m = ab$ can be deduced at once; we merely have to replace every black cell of the a-pavement by the whole b-pavement, and every white cell of the a-pavement by the b-pavement with its colours reversed. Repeated application of this principle gives a solution whenever m is a power

* See *Mathematical Questions from the Educational Times*, London, vol. x, 1868, pp. 74—76; vol. LVI, 1892, pp. 97—99. The results are closely connected with theorems in the theory of equations.

of 2. The case when $m = 8$ is shown in the first of the following drawings.

∞	∞	∞	∞	∞	∞	∞	∞
6	0	1	2	3	4	5	∞
5	6	0	1	2	3	4	∞
4	5	6	0	1	2	3	∞
3	4	5	6	0	1	2	∞
2	3	4	5	6	0	1	∞
1	2	3	4	5	6	0	∞
0	1	2	3	4	5	6	∞

When $m = p + 1$, where p is a prime (of the form $4k - 1$), an anallagmatic tessellation can be derived from the addition-table for the finite arithmetic modulo p (see page 60). In the bottom row and left-hand column of this table we write the numbers $0, 1, \ldots, p - 1$, and ∞, the last of these being an artificially introduced "number" which is unchanged when any number is added to it. The rest of the table is completed by adding (mod p) the numbers which thus define the columns and rows. Each cell is then coloured white or black according as its number is or is not a square, with the (somewhat artificial*) convention that ∞ is *not* a square. The case when $p = 7$ is illustrated above; the squares are then $0, 1, 2 \; (\equiv 9)$ and 4.

When $m = p^n + 1$ (where p^n is of the form $4k - 1$), we make a precisely analogous use of the addition-table for a Galois arithmetic of p^n marks (page 74), with an extra mark ∞ (which is unchanged when any mark is added to it). The case when $m = 28$ (and the two moduli are 3 and 1021) is illustrated below. In the bottom row and left-hand column of the addition-table we write the 28 marks $0, 1, 2, 10, 11, 12, 20, \ldots,$ $221, 222, \infty$. The squares are $0, 1, 20, 21, 22, 100, 102, 110,$ $111, 120, 121, 202, 211, 221$. These (apart from 0) are most easily calculated as being alternate terms in the sequence of powers of 10 (namely $1, 10, 100, 12, 120, \ldots, 201$).

* One would naturally expect ∞ to be its own square, like 0. I avoid using the words "quadratic residues," because 0 is undeniably a square, although it is not included among the quadratic residues.

The underlying theory is due to H. Davenport and R. E. A. C. Paley.* The latter gave also a more complicated rule to cover the case when $m = 2(p^n + 1)$ where p^n is of the form $4k + 1$. By combining these methods, he showed how an anallagmatic tessellation of m^2 cells can be constructed whenever m is divisible by 4 and of the form $2^k(p^n + 1)$, where p

An Anallagmatic Pavement, $m = 28$.

is an odd prime. (The first multiple of 4 which is not of this form is 92.)

In all these cases the pavement has one completely black row and column; consequently every other row or column is half black and half white. When m is a power of 4, it is possible† to construct an anallagmatic pavement which is

---

* *Journal of Mathematics and Physics* (Cambridge, Mass.), 1933, vol. XII, pp. 311—320. Actually, Paley used subtraction instead of addition; but the consequent changes are quite trivial. An interesting application of this theory (to m-dimensional geometry) has been made by J. A. Barrau, *Nieuw Archief voor Wiskunde*, series 2, vol. VII. He gives tessellations, different from Paley's, for the cases $m = 16$, 28 and 36.

† *Mathematical Questions from the Educational Times*, 1868, vol. X, p. 112.

" isochromatic " in the sense that half the rows (and columns) have $\sqrt{m}$ more black than white tiles, while the rest have $\sqrt{m}$ more white than black. Previous editions of this book show such a pavement with $m = 16$.

Tessellation with Super-Dominoes. A novel form of tessellation problem was suggested in 1921 by Major MacMahon.* The object is to fill, according to certain rules, a prescribed area with wood or cardboard super-dominoes. The shape of an ordinary domino is a rectangle, the breadth of which is immaterial, with two ends or faces on which numbers or pips can be inscribed, and, if we like, each number may be taken to

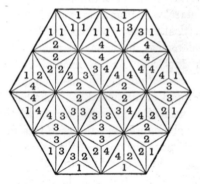

indicate a particular colour; by using n numbers we can get $n(n + 1)/2$ different linear dominoes. If our dominoes are triangular in shape, and from the centres of the triangles we draw lines to the angular points, we get dominoes with three faces on each of which numbers or pips can be inscribed, and, as before, each number may be taken to indicate a particular colour: by using n colours we can get $n(n^2 + 2)/3$ different triangular dominoes. Similarly, by using n colours we can get $n(n + 1)(n^2 - n + 2)/4$ different square dominoes, $n(n^4 + 1)/5$ different pentagonal dominoes, and so on. With each of these sets we can make up puzzles.

A particular case will illustrate the kind of questions

* P. A. MacMahon, *New Mathematical Pastimes*, Cambridge, 1921.

treated. Take the case of equilateral triangular dominoes. If four colours are used we get a set of twenty-four different dominoes, and these can be put together (preferably in a shallow box cut to the right size) to make a regular hexagon. Innumerable conditions may be imposed. For example, we may suppose that it is required to fit the dominoes into the box so that the colours of adjoining faces of the dominoes shall be the same, as also those of all the exterior faces. Here is the solution of this problem. A consideration of what conditions may be imposed naturally arises, and leads to various other problems. If our dominoes are right-angled triangles we get a hexagonal arrangement of a different shape. Further, we can play with sets selected from a particular full set and arranged in other geometrical figures. Similar problems arise from the use of square dominoes, hexagonal dominoes, etc.

Colour-Cube Problem. As an example of a recreation analogous to tessellation I will mention the colour-cube problem.* Stripped of mathematical technicalities the problem may be enunciated as follows. A cube has six faces, and if six colours are chosen we can paint each face with a different colour. By permuting the order of the colours we can obtain thirty such cubes, no two of which are coloured alike. Take any one of these cubes, K, then it is desired to select eight out of the remaining twenty-nine cubes, such that they can be arranged in the form of a cube (whose linear dimensions are double those of any of the separate cubes) coloured like the cube K, and placed so that where any two cubes touch each other the faces in contact are coloured alike.

Only one collection of eight cubes can be found to satisfy these conditions. These eight cubes can be determined by the following rule. Take any face of the cube K: it has four angles, and at each angle three colours meet. By permuting the colours cyclically we can obtain from each angle two other

* P. A. MacMahon, *London Mathematical Society Proceedings*, vol. XXIV, 1893, pp. 145—155; and *New Mathematical Pastimes*, Cambridge, 1921, pp. 42—46. See also F. Winter, *Die Spiele der 30 bunten Würfel*, Leipzig, 1934.

cubes, and the eight cubes so obtained are those required. A little consideration will show that these are the required cubes, and that the solution is unique.

For instance, suppose that the six colours are indicated by the letters a, b, c, d, e, f. Let the cube K be put on a table, and to fix our ideas suppose that the face coloured f is at the bottom, the face coloured a is at the top, and the faces coloured b, c, d, and e front respectively the east, north, west, and south points of the compass. I may denote such an arrangement by $(f; a; b, c, d, e)$. One cyclical permutation of the colours which meet at the north-east corner of the top face gives the cube $(f; c; a, b, d, e)$, and a second cyclical permutation gives the cube $(f; b; c, a, d, e)$. Similarly cyclical permutations of the colours which meet at the north-west corner of the top face of K give the cubes $(f; d; b, a, c, e)$ and $(f; c; b, d, a, e)$. Similarly from the top south-west corner of K we get the cubes $(f; e; b, c, a, d)$ and $(f; d; b, c, e, a)$: and from the top south-east corner we get the cubes $(f; e; a, c, d, b)$ and $(f; b; e, c, d, a)$.

The eight cubes being thus determined, it is not difficult to arrange them in the form of a cube coloured similarly to K, and subject to the condition that faces in contact are coloured alike; in fact they can be arranged in two ways to satisfy these conditions. One such way, taking the cubes in the numerical order given above, is to put the cubes 3, 6, 8, and 2 at the SE, NE, NW, and SW corners of the bottom face; of course, each placed with the colour f at the bottom, while 3 and 6 have the colour b to the east, and 2 and 8 have the colour d to the west: the cubes 7, 1, 4, and 5 will then form the SE, NE, NW, and SW corners of the top face; of course, each placed with the colour a at the top, while 7 and 1 have the colour b to the east, and 5 and 4 have the colour d to the west. If K is not given, the difficulty of the problem is increased. Similar puzzles in two dimensions can be made.

Tangrams. The formation of designs by means of seven pieces of wood—namely, a square, a rhombus, and five triangles, known as tans, of fixed traditional shapes—is one of the oldest amusements in the East. Many hundreds of figures representing men, women, birds, beasts, fish, houses, boats, domestic objects, designs, etc., can be made, but the recreation is not mathematical, and I reluctantly content myself with a bare mention of it.

DYNAMICAL GAMES OF POSITION

Games which are played by moving pieces on boards of various shapes—such as merrilees, fox and geese, solitaire, backgammon, draughts, and chess—present more interest. In general, possible movements of the pieces are so numerous that mathematical analysis is not practicable, but in a few games the possible movements are sufficiently limited as to permit of mathematical treatment; one or two of these are given later : here I shall confine myself mainly to puzzles and simple amusements.

Shunting Problems. The first I will mention is a little puzzle which I bought some years ago, and which was described as the " Great Northern Puzzle." It is typical of a good many problems connected with the shunting of trains, and though it rests on a most improbable hypothesis, I give it as a specimen of its kind.

The puzzle shows a railway, *DEF*, with two sidings, *DBA* and *FCA*, connected at *A*. The portion of the rails at *A*

which is common to the two sidings is long enough to permit of a single wagon, like *P* or *Q*, running in or out of it; but is too short to contain the whole of an engine, like *R*. Hence,

IV] GEOMETRICAL RECREATIONS

if an engine runs up one siding, such as DBA, it must come back the same way.

Initially a small block of wood, P, coloured to represent a wagon, is placed at B; a similar block, Q, is placed at C; and a longer block of wood, R, representing an engine, is placed at E. The problem is to use the engine R to interchange the wagons P and Q, without allowing any flying shunts.

Another shunting puzzle, on sale in the streets in 1905, under the name of the "Chifu-Chemulpo Puzzle," is made as follows. A loop-line BGE connects two points B and E on a railway track AF, which is supposed blocked at both ends, as shown in the diagram. In the model, the track AF is 9 inches long, $AB = EF = 1\frac{5}{8}$ inches, and $AH = FK = BC = DE = \frac{1}{4}$ inch.

On the track and loop are eight wagons, numbered successively 1 to 8, each 1 inch long and one-quarter of an inch broad, and an engine, e, of the same dimensions. Originally the wagons are on the track from A to F and in the order 1, 2, 3, 4, 5, 6, 7, 8, and the engine is on the loop. The construction and the initial arrangement ensure that at any one time there cannot be more than eight vehicles on the track. Also if eight vehicles are on it, only the penultimate vehicle at either end can be moved on to the loop, but if less than eight are on the track, then the last two vehicles at either end can be moved on to the loop. If the points at each end of the loop-line are clear, it will hold four, but not more than four, vehicles. The object is to reverse the order of the wagons on the track, so that from A to F they will be numbered successively 8 to 1: and to do this by means which will involve as few transferences of the engine or a wagon to or from the loop as is possible.

Twenty-six moves are required, and there is more than one solution in 26 moves (see p. 127).

Other shunting problems are not uncommon, but these two examples will suffice.

Ferry-Boat Problems.   Everybody is familiar with the story of the showman who was travelling with a wolf, a goat, and a basket of cabbages; and for obvious reasons was unable to leave the wolf alone with the goat, or the goat alone with the cabbages.   The only means of transporting them across a river was a boat so small that he could take in it only one of them at a time.   The problem is to show how the passage could be effected.*

A somewhat similar problem is to arrange for the passage of a river by three men and three boys who have the use of a boat which will not carry at one time more than one man or two boys.   Fifteen passages are required.†

Problems like these were proposed by Alcuin, Tartaglia, and other medieval writers.   The following is a common type of such questions.   Three ‡ beautiful ladies have for husbands three men, who are young, gallant, and jealous.   The party are travelling, and find on the bank of a river over which they have to pass, a small boat which can hold no more than two persons.   How can they cross the river, it being agreed that, in order to avoid scandal, no woman shall be left in the society of a man unless her husband is present ?   Eleven passages are required.   With two married couples five passages are required.   The similar problem with four married couples is insoluble.

Another similar problem is the case of n married couples who have to cross a river by means of a boat which can be rowed by one person and will carry $n - 1$ people, but not more, with the condition that no woman is to be in the society of a man unless her husband is present.   Alcuin's problem given

* Ozanam, 1803 edition, vol. I, p. 171; 1840 edition, p. 77.
† H. E. Dudeney, *The Tribune*, October 4, 1906.
‡ Bachet, Appendix, problem IV, p. 212.

above is the case of $n = 3$. Let y denote the number of passages from one bank to the other which will be necessary. Then it has been shown that if $n = 3$, $y = 11$; if $n = 4$, $y = 9$; and if $n > 4$, $y = 7$.

The following analogous problem is due to E. Lucas.* To find the smallest number x of persons that a boat must be able to carry in order that n married couples may by its aid cross a river in such a manner that no woman shall remain in the company of any man unless her husband is present; it being assumed that the boat can be rowed by one person only. Also to find the least number of passages, say y, from one bank to the other which will be required. M. Delannoy has shown that if $n = 2$, then $x = 2$, and $y = 5$. If $n = 3$, then $x = 2$, and $y = 11$. If $n = 4$, then $x = 3$, and $y = 9$. If $n = 5$, then $x = 3$, and $y = 11$. And finally if $n > 5$, then $x = 4$, and $y = 2n - 1$.

M. De Fonteney has remarked that, if there was an island in the middle of the river, the passage might be always effected by the aid of a boat which could carry only two persons. If there are only two or only three couples, the island is unnecessary, and the case is covered by the preceding method. His solution, involving $8n - 8$ passages, is as follows. The first nine passages will be the same, no matter how many couples there may be : the result is to transfer one couple to the island and one couple to the second bank. The result of the next eight passages is to transfer one couple from the first bank to the second bank; this series of eight operations must be repeated as often as necessary until there is left only one couple on the first bank, only one couple on the island, and all the rest on the second bank. The result of the last seven passages is to transfer all the couples to the second bank. It would, however, seem that if n is greater than 3, we need not require more than $6n - 7$ passages from land to land.†

M. G. Tarry has suggested an extension of the problem,

* *Récréations Mathématiques*, Paris, 1883, vol. I, pp. 15—18, 237—238; hereafter I shall refer to this work by the name of the author.

† See H. E. Dudeney, *Amusements in Mathematics*, London, 1917, p. 237.

which still further complicates its solution. He supposes that each husband travels with a harem of m wives or concubines; moreover, as Mohammedan women are brought up in seclusion, it is reasonable to suppose that they would be unable to row a boat by themselves without the aid of a man. But perhaps the difficulties attendant on the travels of one wife may be deemed sufficient for Christians, and I content myself with merely mentioning the increased anxieties experienced by Mohammedans in similar circumstances.

Geodesics. Geometrical problems connected with finding the shortest routes from one point to another on a curved surface are often difficult, but geodesics on a flat surface or flat surfaces are in general readily determinable.

I append one instance,* though I should have hesitated to do so had not experience shown that some readers do not readily see the solution. It is as follows. A room is 30 feet long, 12 feet wide, and 12 feet high. On the middle line of one of the smaller side walls and 1 foot from the ceiling is a wasp. On the middle line of the opposite wall and 11 feet from the ceiling is a fly. The wasp catches the fly by crawling all the way to it: the fly, paralysed by fear, remaining still. The problem is to find the shortest route that the wasp can follow.

To obtain a solution we observe that we can cut a sheet of paper so that, when folded properly, it will make a model to scale of the room. This can be done in several ways. If, when the paper is again spread out flat, we can join the points representing the wasp and the fly by a straight line lying wholly on the paper, we shall obtain a geodesic route between them. Thus the problem is reduced to finding the way of cutting out the paper which gives the shortest route of the kind.

Here is the diagram corresponding to a solution of the above question, where A represents the floor, B and D the longer side-walls, C the ceiling, and W and F the positions on

* This is due to Mr. H. E. Dudeney. I heard a similar question propounded at Cambridge in 1903, but I first saw it in print in the *Daily Mail*, London, February 1, 1905.

the two smaller side-walls occupied initially by the wasp and fly. In the diagram the square of the distance between W and F is $(32)^2 + (24)^2$; hence the distance is 40 feet.

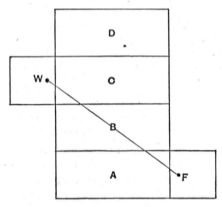

Problems with Counters placed in a Row. Numerous dynamical problems and puzzles may be illustrated with a box of counters, especially if there are counters of two colours. Of course, coins or pawns or cards will serve equally well. I proceed to enumerate a few of these played with counters placed in a row.

First Problem with Counters. The following problem must be familiar to many of my readers. Ten counters (or coins) are placed in a row. Any counter may be moved over two of those adjacent to it on the counter next beyond them. It is required to move the counters according to the above rule so that they shall be arranged in five equidistant couples.

If we denote the counters in their initial positions by the numbers 1, 2, 3, 4, 5, 6, 7, 8, 9, 10, we proceed as follows. Put 7 on 10, then 5 on 2, then 3 on 8, then 1 on 4, and lastly 9 on 6. Thus they are arranged in pairs on the places originally occupied by the counters 2, 4, 6, 8, 10.

Similarly by putting 4 on 1, then 6 on 9, then 8 on 3, then 10 on 7, and lastly 2 on 5, they are arranged in pairs on the places originally occupied by the counters 1, 3, 5, 7, 9.

If two superposed counters are reckoned as only one, solutions analogous to those given above will be obtained by putting 7 on 10, then 5 on 2, then 3 on 8, then 1 on 6, and lastly 9 on 4; or by putting 4 on 1, then 6 on 9, then 8 on 3, then 10 on 5, and lastly 2 on 7.*

There is a somewhat similar game played with eight counters, but in this case the four couples finally formed are not equidistant. Here the transformation will be effected if we move 5 on 2, then 3 on 7, then 4 on 1, and lastly 6 on 8. This form of the game is applicable equally to $(8 + 2n)$ counters, for if we move 4 on 1, we have left on one side of this couple a row of $(8 + 2n - 2)$ counters. This again can be reduced to one of $(8 + 2n - 4)$ counters, and in this way finally we have left eight counters which can be moved in the way explained above.

A more complete generalization would be the case of n counters, where each counter might be moved over the m counters adjacent to it on to the one beyond them. For instance, we may place twelve counters in a row and allow the moving a counter over three adjacent counters. By such movements we can obtain four piles, each pile containing three counters. Thus, if the counters be numbered consecutively, one solution can be obtained by moving 7 on 3, then 5 on 10, then 9 on 7, then 12 on 8, then 4 on 5, then 11 on 12, then 2 on 6, and then 1 on 2. Or again we may place sixteen counters in a row and allow the moving a counter over four adjacent counters on to the next counter available. By such movements we can get four piles, each pile containing four counters. Thus, if the counters be numbered consecutively, one solution can be obtained by moving 8 on 3, then 9 on 14, then 1 on 5, then 16 on 12, then 7 on 8, then 10 on 7, then 6 on 9, then 15 on 16, then 13 on 1, then 4 on 15, then 2 on 13, and then 11 on 6.

Second Problem with Counters. Another problem,† of a

---

* Note by J. Fitzpatrick to a French translation of the third edition of this work, Paris, 1898.

† *Bibliotheca Mathematica*, 1896, series 3, vol. VI, p. 323; P. G. Tait, *Philosophical Magazine*, London, January, 1884, series 5, vol. XVII, p. 39; or *Collected Scientific Papers*, Cambridge, vol. II, 1890, p. 93.

somewhat similar kind, is of Japanese origin. Place four
florins (or white counters) and four halfpence (or black counters) alternately in a line in contact with one another. It is
required in four moves, each of a pair of two contiguous
pieces, without altering the relative position of the pair, to
form a continuous line of four halfpence followed by four
florins.

This can be solved as follows. Let a florin be denoted by a
and a halfpenny by b, and let x x denote two contiguous blank
spaces. Then the successive positions of the pieces may be
represented thus :

Initially	x x $a\,b\,a\,b\,a\,b\,a\,b$.
After the first move . . .	$b\,a\,a\,b\,a\,b\,a$ x x x b.
After the second move . .	$b\,a\,a\,b$ x x $a\,a\,b\,b$.
After the third move. . .	b x x $b\,a\,a\,a\,b\,b$.
After the fourth move . .	$b\,b\,b\,b\,a\,a\,a\,a$ x x.

The operation is conducted according to the following rule.
Suppose the pieces to be arranged originally in circular order,
with two contiguous blank spaces, then we always move to the
blank space for the time being that pair of coins which occupies
the places next but one and next but two to the blank space on
one assigned side of it.

A similar problem with $2n$ counters—n of them being white
and n black—will at once suggest itself, and, if n is greater
than 4, it can be solved in n moves. I have, however, failed to
find a simple rule which covers all cases alike, but solutions, due
to M. Delannoy, have been given * for the four cases where n is
of the form $4m$, $4m + 2$, $4m + 1$, or $4m + 3$; in the first two
cases the first $\frac{1}{2}n$ moves are of pairs of dissimilar counters and
the last $\frac{1}{2}n$ moves are of pairs of similar counters ; in the last
two cases the first move is similar to that given above—namely,
of the penultimate and antepenultimate counters to the beginning of the row—the next $\frac{1}{2}(n - 1)$ moves are of pairs of
dissimilar counters, and the final $\frac{1}{2}(n - 1)$ moves are of similar
counters.

* *La Nature*, June, 1887, p. 10.

The problem is also capable of solution if we substitute the restriction that at each move the pair of counters taken up must be moved to one of the two ends of the row instead of the condition that the final arrangement is to be continuous.

Tait suggested a variation of the problem by making it a condition that the two coins to be moved shall also be made to interchange places; in this form it would seem that five moves are required; or, in the general case, $n + 1$ moves are required.

Problems on a Chess-board with Counters or Pawns. The following three problems require the use of a chess-board as well as of counters or pieces of two colours. It is more convenient to move a pawn than a counter, and if therefore I describe them as played with pawns, it is only as a matter of convenience, and not that they have any connection with chess. The first is characterized by the fact that in every position not more than two moves are permitted; in the second and third problems not more than four moves are permitted in any position. With these limitations, analysis is possible. I shall not discuss the similar problems in which more moves are permitted.

First Problem with Pawns.* On a row of seven squares on a chess-board 3 white pawns (or counters), denoted in the diagram by " a "s, are placed on the 3 squares at one end, and 3 black pawns (or counters), denoted by " b "s, are placed on the 3 squares at the other end—the middle square being left vacant. Each piece can move only in one direction; the " a " pieces can move from left to right, and the " b " pieces from right to left. If the square next to a piece is unoccupied, it can move on

a	a	a		b	b	b

to that; or if the square next to it is occupied by a piece of the opposite colour and the square beyond that is unoccupied, then it can, like a queen in draughts, leap over that piece on to the unoccupied square beyond it. The object is to get all the

* Lucas, vol. II, part 5, pp. 141—143.

white pawns in the places occupied initially by the black pawns and *vice versa*.

The solution requires 15 moves. It may be effected by moving first a white pawn, then successively two black pawns, then three white pawns, then three black pawns, then three white pawns, then two black pawns, and then one white pawn. We can express this solution by saying that if we number the cells (a term used to describe each of the small squares on a chess-board) consecutively, then initially the vacant space occupies the cell 4, and in the successive moves it will occupy the cells 3, 5, 6, 4, 2, 1, 3, 5, 7, 6, 4, 2, 3, 5, 4. Of these moves, six are simple and nine are leaps.

More generally, if we have m white pawns at one end of a row of $m + n + 1$ cells, and n black pawns at the other end, the arrangement can be reversed in $mn + m + n$ moves, of which $m + n$ are simple and mn are leaps.

*Second Problem with Pawns.** A similar game may be played on a rectangular or square board. The case of a square board containing 49 cells, or small squares, will illustrate this sufficiently : in this case the initial position is shown in the annexed diagram where the " a "s denote the pawns or pieces

a	a	a	a	b	b	b
a	a	a	a	b	b	b
a	a	a	a	b	b	b
a	a	a		b	b	b
a	a	a	b	b	b	b
a	a	a	b	b	b	b
a	a	a	b	b	b	b

of one colour, and the " b "s those of the other colour. The " a " pieces can move horizontally from left to right or vertically down, and the " b " pieces can move horizontally from right to left or vertically up, according to the same rules as before.

* Lucas, vol. II, part 5, p. 144.

The solution reduces to the preceding case. The pieces in the middle column can be interchanged in 15 moves. In the course of these moves every one of the seven cells in that column is at some time or other vacant, and whenever that is the case, the pieces in the row containing the vacant cell can be interchanged. To interchange the pieces in each of the seven rows will require 15 moves. Hence to interchange all the pieces will require $15 + (7 \times 15)$ moves—that is, 120 moves.

If we place $2n(n + 1)$ white pawns and $2n(n + 1)$ black pawns in a similar way on a square board of $(2n + 1)^2$ cells, we can transpose them in $2n(n + 1)(n + 2)$ moves: of these $4n(n + 1)$ are simple and $2n^2(n + 1)$ are leaps.

Third Problem with Pawns. The following analogous problem is somewhat more complicated. On a square board of 25 cells, place eight white pawns or counters on the cells

denoted by small letters in the annexed diagram, and eight black pawns or counters on the cells denoted by capital letters, the cell marked with an asterisk (*) being left blank. Each pawn can move according to the laws already explained—the white pawns being able to move only horizontally from left to right or vertically downwards, and the black pawns being able to move only horizontally from right to left or vertically upwards. The object is to get all the white pawns in the places initially occupied by the black pawns and *vice versa*. No moves outside the dark line are permitted.

Since there is only one cell on the board which is unoccupied, and since no diagonal moves and no backward moves are permitted, it follows that at each move not more than two pieces of either colour are capable of moving. There are, however, a very large number of empirical solutions. The following, due to Mr. H. E. Dudeney, is effected in 46 moves :

H h g* F f c* C B H h* G D F f e h b a g* G A B H E F f d g* H h b c* C F f* G H h*

the letters indicating the cells from which the pieces are successively moved. It will be noticed that the first twenty-three moves lead to a symmetrical position, and that the next twenty-two moves can be at once obtained by writing the first twenty-two moves in reverse order and interchanging small and capital letters. Similar problems with boards of various shapes can be easily constructed.

Probably, were it worth the trouble, the mathematical theory of games such as that just described might be worked out by the use of Vandermonde's notation, described later in Chapter VI, or by the analogous method employed in the theory of the game of solitaire.*

Problems on a Chess-board with Chess-pieces. There are several mathematical recreations with chess-pieces, other than pawns. Some of these are given later in Chapter VI.

Paradromic Rings. The difficulty of mentally realizing the effect of geometrical alterations in certain simple figures is illustrated by the familiar experiment of making *paradromic rings* by cutting a paper ring prepared in the following manner.

Take a strip of paper or piece of tape, say, for convenience, an inch or two wide, and at least 9 or 10 inches long, rule a line in the middle down the length AB of the strip, gum one end over the other end B, and we get a ring like a section of a cylinder. If this ring is cut by a pair of scissors along the ruled line, we obtain two rings exactly like the first, except that they are only half the width. Next suppose that the end A is twisted through two right angles before it is gummed to B (the result of which is that the back of the strip at A is gummed

* On the theory of the solitaire, see Reiss, ' Beiträge zur Theorie des Solitär-Spiels,' *Crelle's Journal*, Berlin, 1858, vol. LIV, pp. 344—379; and Lucas, vol. I, part V, pp. 89—141.

over the front of the strip at B), then a cut along the line will produce only one ring. Next suppose that the end A is twisted once completely round (*i.e.* through four right angles) before it is gummed to B, then a similar cut produces two interlaced rings. If any of my readers think that these results could be predicted off-hand, it may be interesting to them to see if they can predict correctly the effect of again cutting the rings formed in the second and third experiments down their middle lines in a manner similar to that above described.

The theory is due to J. B. Listing,* who discussed the case when the end A receives m half-twists—that is, is twisted through $m\pi$—before it is gummed to B.

If m is even, we obtain a surface which has two sides and two edges. If the ring is cut along a line midway between the edges, we obtain two rings, each of which has m half-twists, and which are linked together $\frac{1}{2}m$ times.

If m is odd, we obtain a surface having only one side and one edge. If this ring is cut along its mid-line, we obtain only one ring, but it has $2m + 2$ half-twists, and if m is greater than unity it is knotted. If the ring, instead of being bisected, is trisected,† we obtain two interlocked rings: one like the original ring (coming from the middle third), and one like the bisected ring. The manner in which these two rings are interlocked is illustrated by the following diagrams (of the cases $m = 3$ and $m = 5$).

m=3   m=5

* *Vorstudien zur Topologie, Die Studien,* Göttingen, 1847, part x.
† This remark is due to J. M. Andreas.

ADDENDUM

Note. Page 106. One method of arranging 16 counters in 15 lines, as stated in the text, is as follows. Draw a regular re-entrant pentagon, vertices A_1, A_2, A_3, A_4, A_5, and centre O. The sides intersect in five points B_1, ... B_5. These latter points may be joined so as to form a smaller regular re-entrant pentagon whose sides intersect in five points C_1, ... C_5. The 16 points indicated are arranged as desired (*The Canterbury Puzzles*, 1907, p. 140).

An arrangement of 18 counters in 9 rows, each containing 5 counters, can be obtained thus. From one angle, A, of an equilateral triangle $AA'A''$, draw lines AD, AE inside the triangle making any angles with AA'. Draw from A' and A'' lines similarly placed in regard to $A'A''$ and $A''A$. Let $A'D'$ cut $A''E''$ in F, and $A'E'$ cut $A''D''$ in G. Then AFG is a straight line. The 3 vertices of the triangle and the 15 points of intersection of AD, AE, AF, with the similar pencils of lines drawn from A', A'', will give an arrangement as required.

An arrangement of 19 counters in 10 rows, each containing 5 counters, can be obtained by placing counters at the 19 points of intersection of the 10 lines $x = \pm a$, $x = \pm b$, $y = \pm a$, $y = \pm b$, $y = \pm x$: of these points two are at infinity.

As a further example, consider the problem of arranging 28 counters in 36 rows, each containing 4 counters. Such an arrangement can be obtained by joining certain vertices of a regular enneagon $A_1A_2 \ldots A_9$. We determine two other enneagons, $B_1B_2 \ldots B_9$, $C_1C_2 \ldots C_9$, concentric with the first. B_1 is the point of intersection of A_3A_6 with A_5A_8, while C_1 is the point of intersection of A_2A_6 with A_5A_9. The line B_4B_7 contains C_5 and C_6. The twenty-eighth point is the centre, which lies on nine lines such as $A_1B_1C_1$.

Note. Page 114. The Great Northern Shunting Problem is effected thus. (i) R pushes P into A. (ii) R returns, pushes Q up to P in A, couples Q to P, draws them both out to F, and then pushes them to E. (iii) P is now uncoupled, R takes Q back to A, and leaves it there. (iv) R returns to P, takes P back to C, and leaves it there. (v) R running successively through F, D, B comes to A, draws Q out, and leaves it at B.

Note. Page 115. One solution of the Chifu-Chemulpo Puzzle is as follows. Move successively wagons 2, 3, 4 up, *i.e.*, on to the loop line. [Then push 1 along the straight track close to 5; this is not a " move."] Next, move 4 down, *i.e.* on to the straight track and push it along to 1. Next, move 8 up, 3 down to the end of the track and keep it there temporarily, 6 up, 2 down, e down, 3 up, 7 up. [Then push 5 to the end of the track and keep it there temporarily.] Next, move 7 down, 6 down, 2 up, 4 up. [Then push e along to 1.] Next, move 4 down to the end of the track and keep it there temporarily, 2 down, 5 up, 3 down, 6 up, 7 up, 8 down to the end of the track, e up, 5 down, 6 down, 7 down. In this solution we moved e down to the track at one end, then shifted it along the track, and finally moved it up to the loop from the other end of the track. We might equally well move e down to the track at one end, and finally move it back to the loop from the same end. In this solution the pieces successively moved are 2, 3, 4, 4, e, 8, 7, 3, 2, 6, 5, 5, 6, 3, 2, 7, 2, 5, 6, 3, 7, e, 8, 5, 6, 7

CHAPTER V

POLYHEDRA

" Although a Discourse of Solid Bodies be an uncommon and neglected Part of Geometry, yet that it is no inconsiderable or unprofitable Improvement of the Science will (no doubt) be readily granted by such, whose Genius tends as well to the Practical as Speculative Parts of it, for whom this is chiefly intended." *

A POLYHEDRON is a solid figure † with plane faces and straight edges, so arranged that every edge is both the join of two vertices and a common side of two faces. Familiar instances are the pyramids and prisms. (A pentagonal pyramid has six vertices, ten edges, and six faces; a pentagonal prism has ten, fifteen, and seven. See figure 7 on Plate I.) I would mention also the *antiprism*,‡ whose two bases, though parallel, are not similarly situated, but each vertex of either corresponds to a side of the other, so that the lateral edges form a zig-zag. (Thus a pentagonal antiprism has ten vertices, twenty edges, and twelve faces. See figure 9 on Plate I.)

The tessellations described on page 107 may be regarded as infinite polyhedra.

SYMMETRY AND SYMMETRIES

It is convenient to say that a figure is *reflexible* § if it is superposable with its image in a plane mirror (*i.e.* if it is, in

* Abraham Sharp, *Geometry Improv'd*, London, 1717, p. 65.

† More precisely, it is the *surface* of such a solid figure.

‡ Or " prismoid." See the *Encyclopaedia Britannica* (XIVth Edition), article " Solids."

§ Or " self-reflexible."

K

the most elementary sense, " symmetrical "). A figure which is not reflexible forms, with its mirror-image, an *enantio-morphous* pair. (The obvious example is a pair of shoes.) A reflexible figure has at least one *plane of symmetry*; the operation of reflecting in such a plane leaves the figure unchanged as a whole. A figure may also be symmetrical by rotation about an *axis of symmetry*. The vague statement that a figure has a certain amount of " symmetry " can be made precise by saying that the figure has a certain number of *symmetries*, a symmetry * being defined as any combination of motions and reflections which leaves the figure unchanged as a whole.

For a regular polygon $ABC \ldots X$, there is a symmetry (in fact, a rotation) which changes A into B, B into C, and so on.

The Five Platonic Solids

Let $ABC \ldots X$ and $CBE \ldots Y$ be two adjacent faces of a polyhedron. The polyhedron is said to be *regular* if it admits two particular symmetries : one which changes A into B, and B into C, and one which changes A into C, and C into E. It follows that all the faces are regular and equal, all the edges are equal, and all the vertices are surrounded alike. If each vertex is surrounded by m n-gons, we may denote the polyhedron by the symbol n^m (as on page 107).

If the polyhedron is finite, the faces at one vertex form a solid angle. The internal angle of each face being $(n-2)\pi/n$, we now have $m(n-2)\pi/n < 2\pi$. Therefore $(m-2)(n-2) < 4$. This inequality has to be solved in integers greater than 2, and then in each case the polyhedron can be built up, face by face. Letting V, E, F denote the number of vertices, edges, faces, the results are as follows. (See Plate I, figures 1, 3, 2, 5, 4).

---

* Or "symmetry operation." (Any rotation or translation may be regarded as a combination of two reflections.)

PLATE I

n^m	V	E	F	Name
3^3	4	6	4	Regular Tetrahedron
3^4	6	12	8	Octahedron
4^3	8	12	6	Cube
3^5	12	30	20	Icosahedron
5^3	20	30	12	Dodecahedron

Clearly, $mV = 2E = nF$. A less obvious relation is $E = 2mn/\{4 - (m - 2)(n - 2)\}$. This is a consequence of Euler's Theorem, $V - E + F = 2$, which will be proved in Chapter VIII, on page 233.

In four ways the tetrahedron can be regarded as a triangular pyramid, and the octahedron as a triangular antiprism. In three ways the octahedron can be regarded as a square double-pyramid, and the cube as a square prism. In six ways the icosahedron can be regarded as a pentagonal antiprism with two pentagonal pyramids stuck on to its bases. The faces of the dodecahedron consist of two opposite pentagons (in parallel planes), each surrounded by five other pentagons.

An icosahedron can be inscribed in an octahedron, so that each vertex of the icosahedron divides an edge of the octahedron according to the " golden section." * A cube can be inscribed in a dodecahedron so that each edge of the cube lies in a face of the dodecahedron (and joins two alternate vertices of that face).

These five figures have been known since ancient times. The earliest thorough investigation of them is probably that of Theaetetus.† It has been suggested that Euclid's *Elements* were originally written, not as a general treatise on geometry, but in order to supply the necessary steps for a full apprecia-

* See page 57.

† T. Heath, *A History of Greek Mathematics*, Oxford, 1921, vol. I, p. 162.

tion of the five regular solids. At any rate, Euclid begins by constructing an equilateral triangle, and ends by constructing a dodecahedron.

With each of these polyhedra we may associate three concentric spheres: one (the "circum-sphere") through all the vertices, one touching all the edges, and one (the "insphere") touching all the faces. Consider the second of these spheres. If we replace each edge by a perpendicular line touching this sphere at the same point, the edges at a vertex

(1)   (2)
Icosahedron and Octahedron.   *Cube and Dodecahedron.*

lead to the sides of a polygon. Such polygons are the V faces of another "reciprocal" polyhedron, which has F vertices. The reciprocal of n^m is m^n, and *vice versa*. Thus the cube and octahedron are reciprocal, and so are the dodecahedron and icosahedron. The tetrahedron is self-reciprocal, or rather reciprocal to another tetrahedron. The diagonals of the faces of a cube are the edges of two reciprocal tetrahedra. (See Plate II, figure 27, facing page 134.)

Mystically minded Greeks associated the regular polyhedra with the four Elements and the Universe. Kepler * justified the correspondence as follows. Of the five solids, the tetrahedron has the smallest volume for its surface, the icosahedron

* *Opera Omnia*, Frankfort, 1864, vol. v, p. 121.

the largest; these therefore exhibit the qualities of dryness and wetness, respectively, and correspond to Fire and Water. The cube, standing firmly on its base, corresponds to the stable Earth; but the octahedron, which rotates freely when held by two opposite corners, corresponds to the mobile Air. Finally, the dodecahedron corresponds to the Universe, because the zodiac has twelve signs. He illustrated this correspondence by drawing a bonfire on his tetrahedron, a lobster and fishes on his icosahedron, a tree, a carrot, and gardening tools on his cube, birds and clouds on his octahedron, and the sun, moon, and stars on his dodecahedron.

Kepler also associated these five polyhedra with the spaces between the orbits of the six planets then known.* He imagined a set of six spheres, with the sun for centre, each (approximately) containing the orbit of a planet. Every two consecutive spheres were the in- and circum-spheres of a regular polyhedron. In this sense he put the octahedron between Mercury and Venus, the icosahedron between Venus and the Earth, the dodecahedron between the Earth and Mars, the tetrahedron between Mars and Jupiter, and the cube between Jupiter and Saturn. The approximations are not very close; moreover, this correspondence involves an essential ambiguity. The ratio of circum-radius R to in-radius r is exactly the same for the cube as for the octa-hedron, and for the dodecahedron as for the icosahedron. In fact, if the reciprocating sphere has radius ρ, the reciprocal of a given polyhedron has circum-radius ρ^2/r and in-radius ρ^2/R. Thus the relative size of two reciprocal polyhedra may be adjusted so as to make them have the same circum-sphere and the same in-sphere. (In general, their corresponding edges will no longer intersect.)

If two reciprocal regular solids of the same in-radius (and therefore the same circum-radius) stand side by side on a horizontal plane (such as a table top), the distribution of vertices in horizontal planes is the same for both—*i.e.* the

* *Op. cit.*, p. 276.

planes are the same, and the numbers of vertices in each plane are proportional.   This fact was noticed by Pappus,* but has only recently been adequately explained, although its various extensions indicated that it was no mere accident.   One of these extensions is to the Kepler-Poinsot polyhedra, which will be described later.   Another is to tessellations of a plane. Consider the tessellation 6^3 (*i.e.* hexagons, three around each vertex).   By picking out alternate vertices of each hexagon in a consistent manner, we derive the triangular tessellation 3^6 (which, in a different position, is the reciprocal tessellation). We then find that every circle concentric with a face of the 6^3 contains twice as many vertices of the 6^3 as of the 3^6.   (This, however, is obvious, since the omitted vertices of the 6^3 belong to another 3^6, exactly like the first.)

The fact that the vertices of a hexagonal tessellation belong also to two triangular tessellations is analogous to the more familiar fact that the vertices of a cube belong also to two regular tetrahedra.   These two tetrahedra may be said to form a *compound*—Kepler's *stella octangula*; their eight faces lie in the facial planes of an octahedron.   There is also a compound of *five tetrahedra* having the vertices of a dodeca- hedron and the facial planes of an icosahedron; this occurs in two enantiomorphous varieties.   By putting the two varieties together, so as to have the same twenty vertices, we obtain a compound of *ten tetrahedra*, oppositely situated pairs of which can be replaced by *five cubes* (having the twenty vertices of the dodecahedron, each taken twice).   It is quite easy to visualize one such cube in a given dodecahedron (as in the second drawing on page 132); the whole set of five makes a very pretty model.   Finally, by reciprocating the five cubes we obtain a compound of *five octahedra* having the facial planes of an icosahedron, each taken twice.   This icosahedron is inscribed in each one of the octahedra as in the first drawing on page 132 (see Plate II, figures 27, 33, 35, 36, 37).

* T. Heath, *A History of Greek Mathematics*, vol. ii, pp. 368—369.

PLATE II

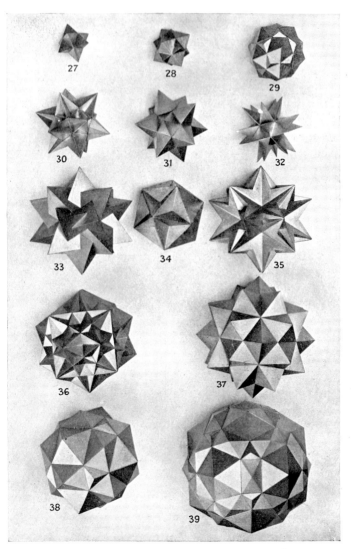

Among the edges of a regular polyhedron, we easily pick out a skew polygon or zig-zag, in which the first and second edges are sides of one face, the second and third are sides of another face, and so on. This zig-zag is known as a *Petrie polygon*, and has many applications. Each finite polyhedron can be orthogonally projected on to a plane in such a way that one Petrie polygon becomes a regular polygon with the rest of the projection inside it. It can be shown in various simple ways that the Petrie polygon of n^m has h sides, where

$$\cos^2 (\pi/h) = \cos^2 (\pi/m) + \cos^2 (\pi/n).$$

The Platonic Solids and their Petrie Polygons.

The h sides of the Petrie polygon of n^m are crossed by h edges of the reciprocal polyhedron m^n; these form a Petrie polygon for m^n.

The regular polyhedra are symmetrical in many different ways. There is an *axis* of symmetry through the centre of every face, through the mid-point of every edge, and through every vertex: $E + 1$ axes altogether. There are also $3h/2$ *planes* of symmetry.

THE ARCHIMEDEAN SOLIDS

A polyhedron is said to be *uniform* if it has regular faces and admits symmetries which will transform a given vertex into every other vertex in turn. The Platonic polyhedra are uniform; so are the right regular prisms and antiprisms, of suitable height—namely, when their lateral faces are squares and equilateral triangles, respectively. Such a polyhedron may be denoted by a symbol giving the numbers of sides of the faces around one vertex (in their proper cyclic order); thus the n-gonal prism and antiprism are $4^2 . n$ and $3^3 . n$. It is quite easy to prove* that, apart from these, there are just thirteen (finite, convex) uniform polyhedra:

$$3 . 6^2, \quad 4 . 6^2, \quad 3 . 8^2, \quad 5 . 6^2, \quad 3 . 10^2, \quad 4 . 6 . 8, \quad 4 . 6 . 10,$$
$$(3 . 4)^2, \quad (3 . 5)^2, \quad 3 . 4^3, \quad 3 . 4 . 5 . 4, \quad 3^4 . 4, \quad 3^4 . 5.$$

These are the *Archimedean solids.*

Let σ denote the sum of the face-angles at a vertex. (This must be less than 2π in order to make a solid angle.) Then the number of vertices is given by the formula † $(2\pi - \sigma)V = 4\pi$. For instance, $3^4 . 5$ has 60 vertices, since $\sigma = (\frac{4}{3} + \frac{3}{5})\pi$.

If we regard the *stella octangula* as consisting of two inter-penetrating solid tetrahedra, we may say that their common part is an octahedron. Also, as we have already observed, their edges are diagonals of the faces of a cube. Analogously, the common part of a cube and an octahedron, in the properly reciprocal position (with corresponding edges perpendicularly bisecting each other), is the *cuboctahedron*, $(3 . 4)^2$. Each pair of corresponding edges (of the cube and octahedron) are the diagonals of a rhomb, and the twelve such rhombs are the faces of a "semi-regular" polyhedron known as the *rhombic dodecahedron*. (The latter is not uniform, but "isohedral." See the first drawing on page 150.) After suitable magnification, the edges of the cuboctahedron intersect those of the rhombic dodecahedron (at right angles); in fact, these two polyhedra are reciprocal, just as the octahedron and cube are reciprocal. The icosahedron and dodecahedron lead similarly to the *icosidodecahedron* $(3 . 5)^2$, and to its reciprocal, the *triacontahedron*. (See Plate II, figures 28, 29, and Plate I, figures 12, 10, 20, 18. Cf. the tessellations drawn on page 107.) The compound of five cubes has the 30 facial planes of a tria-contahedron. Reciprocally, the compound of five octahedra has the 30 vertices of an icosidodecahedron.

The faces of the icosidodecahedron consist of 20 triangles

---

* See, for instance, L. Lines, *Solid Geometry*, London, 1935, p. 165.

† E. Steinitz and H. Rademacher, *Vorlesungen über die Theorie der Polyeder*, Berlin, 1934, p. 11.

and 12 pentagons (corresponding to the faces of the two parent regulars). Its 60 edges are perpendicularly bisected by those of the reciprocal triacontahedron (although the latter edges are not bisected by the former : see Plate II, figure 39). The 60 points where these pairs of edges cross one another are the vertices of a polyhedron whose faces consist of 20 triangles, 12 pentagons, and 30 rectangles. By slightly displacing these points (towards the mid-points of the edges of the triacontahedron), the rectangles can be distorted into squares, and we have another Archimedean solid, the *rhombicosidodecahedron*, 3 . 4 . 5 . 4. (Plate I, figure 23. Cf. the tessellation 3 . 4 . 6 . 4.)

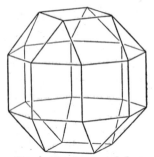

Pseudo-Rhombicuboctahedron.

An analogous construction leads to the *rhombicuboctahedron**
3 . 4³, whose faces consist of 8 triangles and 6 + 12 squares.
(See Plate II, figure 38, and Plate I, figure 13.) In attempting
to make a model of this polyhedron, J. C. P. Miller † accidentally discovered a " pseudo-rhombicuboctahedron," bounded
likewise by 8 triangles and 18 squares, and isogonal in the
loose or " local " sense (each vertex being surrounded by one
triangle and three squares), but not in the strict sense (which
implies that the appearance of the solid as a whole must
remain the same when viewed from the direction of each
vertex in turn).

* *I.e.*, "rhombi-cub-octahedron "; but the other is "rhomb-icosi-
dodecahedron."

† *Philosophical Transactions of the Royal Society*, 1930, series A, vol.
ccxxix, p. 336.

On cutting off the corners of a cube, by planes parallel to the faces of the reciprocal octahedron, we leave small triangles, and reduce the square faces to octagons. For suitable positions of the cutting planes these octagons will be regular, and we have another Archimedean solid, the *truncated cube*, $3 . 8^2$. (Cf. the tessellations $4 . 8^2$ and $3 . 12^2$.) Each of the five Platonic solids has its truncated variety ; * so have the cuboctahedron and the icosidodecahedron, but in these last cases ($4 . 6 . 8$ and $4 . 6 . 10$) a distortion is again required, to convert rectangles into squares.† (Cf. the tessellation $4 . 6 . 12$.)

All the Archimedean solids so far discussed are reflexible (by reflection in the plane that perpendicularly bisects any edge). The remaining two, however, are not reflexible: the *snub cube* $3^4 . 4$, and the *snub dodecahedron* $3^4 . 5$ (Plate I, figures 17 and 21). Let us draw one diagonal in each of the 30 squares of the rhombicosidodecahedron, choosing between the two possible diagonals in such a way that just one of these new lines shall pass through each of the 60 vertices. (The choice in the first square determines that in all the rest.) Each square has now been divided into two right-angled isosceles triangles ; by distorting these into equilateral triangles we obtain the snub dodecahedron.‡ The snub cube is similarly derivable from the rhombicuboctahedron, provided we remember to operate only on the 12 squares that correspond to the edges of the cube (and not on the 6 squares that correspond to its faces). The tessellation $3^4 . 6$ may be regarded as a " snub 6^3," and $3^2 . 4 . 3 . 4$ as a " snub 4^4." Moreover, the " snub tetrahedron " is the icosahedron 3^5, as derived from the cuboctahedron (or " rhombi-tetra-tetrahedron ").

---

* The " truncated n^m " is $m . (2n)^2$. See Plate I, figures 11, 16, 15, 22, 25.

† On account of this distortion, the truncated cuboctahedron ($4 . 6 . 8$) is sometimes called the " great rhombicuboctahedron," and then $3 . 4^3$ is called the *small* rhombicuboctahedron ; similarly for the truncated icosidodecahedron and rhombicosidodecahedron.

‡ This name is unfortunate, since the figure is related to the icosahedron just as closely as to the dodecahedron. " Snub icosidodecahedron " would be far better.

The snub cube and the snub dodecahedron both occur in two enantiomorphous varieties. Their metrical properties involve the solution of cubic equations, whereas those of the reflexible Archimedeans (and of the regulars) involve nothing worse than square roots; in other words, the reflexibles are capable of Euclidean construction, but the two proper snubs are not.

Mrs. Stott's Construction

The above description of the Archimedean solids is essentially Kepler's. A far more elegant construction for the reflexible

(1) *Tetrahedron and Truncated Tetrahedron.*

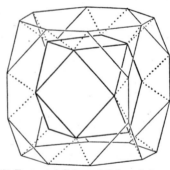

(2) *Cube and Rhombicuboctahedron.*   (3) *Truncated Cube and Cuboctahedron.*

figures has been devised by Alicia Boole Stott.* Her method is free from any employment of distortion, and the final edge-length is the same as that of the regular solid

* *Verhandelingen der Koninklijke Akademie van Wetenschappen*, Amsterdam, 1910, vol. xi, No. 1.

from which we start. In the process called *expansion*, certain
sets of elements (viz., edges or faces) are moved directly away
from the centre, retaining their size and orientation, until
the consequent interstices can be filled with new regular faces.
The reverse process is called *contraction*. By expanding any
regular solid according to its edges, we derive the " truncated "
variety. By expanding the cube (or the octahedron) according
to its faces, we derive the rhombicuboctahedron, $3 . 4^3$. By
expanding this according to its 12 squares which correspond
to the edges of the cube, or by expanding the truncated cube
according to its octagons, we derive the truncated cuboctahedron, $4 . 6 . 8$. By contracting the truncated cube according
to its triangles, we derive the cuboctahedron. And so on.
Mrs. Stott has represented these processes by a compact
symbolism, and extended them to space of more than three
dimensions, where they are extraordinarily fruitful.

Equilateral Zonohedra

The solids that I am about to describe were first investigated
by E. von Fedorow.* Their interest has lately been enhanced
by P. S. Donchian's observation that they may be regarded as
three-dimensional projections of n-dimensional *hyper-cubes*
(or *measure-polytopes*, or *regular orthotopes* †). Their edges are
all equal, and their faces are generally rhombs, but sometimes
higher " parallel-sided $2m$-gons "—*i.e.* equilateral $2m$-gons
whose opposite sides are parallel. The subject begins with
the following theorem on polygonal dissection.

Every parallel-sided $2m$-gon (and, in particular, every

* *Zeitschrift für Krystallographie und Mineralogie*, 1893, vol. xxi, p. 689;
Russisch-kaiserliche Mineralogische Gesellschaft Verhandlungen, 1885,
vol. xxi, Abschnitt iv. (The latter periodical is to be found, under the
title " Mineralogicheskoe obshchestvo, Leningrad," in the American Museum
of Natural History, New York.)

† L. Schläfli, *Quarterly Journal of Mathematics*, 1860, vol. iii, p. 66:
" (4, 3, 3, . . ., 3)." C. H. Hinton, *The Fourth Dimension*, London, 1906;
P. H. Schoute, *Mehrdimensionale Geometrie*, Leipzig, 1905, vol. ii, pp. 243—
246; D. M. Y. Sommerville, *An Introduction to the Geometry of* n *Dimensions*,
London, 1929, pp. 49, 171, 182, 190.

regular $2m$-gon) can be dissected * into $\frac{1}{2}m(m - 1)$ rhombs of the same length of side. This is easily proved by induction, since every parallel-sided $2(m + 1)$-gon can be derived from a parallel-sided $2m$-gon by adding a " ribbon " of m rhombs. In fact, the pairs of parallel sides of such a $2m$-gon can take any m different directions, and there is a component rhomb for every pair of these directions ; hence the number $\frac{1}{2}m(m - 1)$. For two perpendicular directions, the rhomb is a square.

Consider now any sheaf of n lines through one point of space,† and suppose first that no three of the lines are coplanar. Then there is a polyhedron whose faces consist of $n(n - 1)$

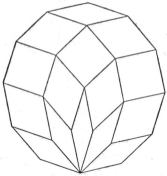

Fifteen Rhombs in a Dodecagon.

rhombs, and whose edges, in sets of $2(n - 1)$, are parallel to the n given lines. In fact, for every pair of the n lines, there is a pair of opposite faces whose sides lie in those directions. To construct this *equilateral zonohedron*, imagine a plane through any one of the n lines, gradually rotating through a complete turn. Each time that this plane passes through one of the other $n - 1$ lines, take a rhomb whose edges are parallel to the two lines, and juxtapose it to the rhomb previously found (without changing its orientation). This process leads eventually to a closed ribbon of $2(n - 1)$ rhombs. By fixing our attention on another of the n lines, we obtain another

* In how many ways ?   † This construction is due to P. S. Donchian.

such ribbon, having two parallel faces in common with the first. When a sufficient number of these ribbons (or *zones*) have been added, the polyhedron is complete.

If m of the n lines are coplanar, we have a pair of opposite parallel-sided $2m$-gons, to replace $\frac{1}{2}m(m-1)$ pairs of opposite rhombs. If these m lines are symmetrically disposed, the $2m$-gons will be regular.

In this manner, three perpendicular lines lead to a cube, and three lines of general direction to a *rhombohedron* * (or rhombic prism). More generally, m coplanar lines and one other line lead to a parallel-sided $2m$-gonal prism (a *right* prism if the " other " line is perpendicular to the plane of the first m).

The four " diameters " of the cube (joining pairs of opposite vertices) lead to the rhombic dodecahedron, the six diameters of the icosahedron lead to the triacontahedron, and the ten diameters of the (pentagonal) dodecahedron lead to an *enneacontahedron* † whose faces are 30 rhombs of one kind and 60 of another. The six diameters of the cuboctahedron lead to the truncated octahedron, whose faces are 6 squares and 8 hexagons (the equivalent of 8×3 rhombs), and the fifteen diameters of the icosidodecahedron lead to the truncated icosidodecahedron, whose faces are 30 squares, 20 hexagons ($= 20 \times 3$ rhombs) and 12 decagons ($= 12 \times 10$ rhombs). As a final example, the nine diameters of the octahedron and cuboctahedron (taken together in corresponding positions) ‡ lead to the truncated cuboctahedron, whose faces are 12 squares, 8 hexagons ($= 24$ rhombs) and 6 octagons ($= 36$ rhombs). (See Plate I, figures 10, 18, 24, 16, 26, 19.)

As in these examples, so in general, the solid has the same type of symmetry as the given sheaf of lines. A rhombic

---

* In using this term, I do not mean to imply that the six rhombic faces are all alike.

† This somewhat resembles a figure described by A. Sharp, *Geometry Improv'd*, p. 87.

‡ *I.e.*, perpendiculars to the nine planes of symmetry of the cube (or of the octahedron).

$n(n-1)$-hedron having the symmetry of a right regular prism occurs for every value of n, being given by a sheaf of n lines symmetrically disposed around a cone.* The faces are all alike when n is 3 ; they can be all alike when n is 4 or 5, if the lines are suitably chosen, viz., if the angle between alternate lines is supplementary to the angle between consecutive lines. Then $n = 4$ gives the rhombic dodecahedron; $n = 5$ gives a *rhombic icosahedron* † (Plate I, figure 14) which can be derived from the triacontahedron by removing any one of the zones and bringing together the two pieces into which the remainder of the surface is thereby divided.

Fedorow's general zonohedron can be derived from the equilateral zonohedron by lengthening or shortening all the edges that lie in each particular direction. Thus rhombic faces become parallelograms, and " parallel-sided $2m$-gons " cease to be equilateral. When each higher face is replaced by its proper number of parallelograms,‡ we have $F = n(n-1)$, $E = 2F$, and $V = F + 2$. The following theorem is irresistibly suggested, although a proof is still lacking. *If all the faces of a convex polyhedron are parallelograms, their number is of the form $n(n-1)$.*

One final remark on this subject : there is a three-dimensional analogue for the theorem that a parallel-sided $2m$-gon can be dissected into $\frac{1}{2}m(m-1)$ parallelograms. The zonohedron can be dissected into $\frac{1}{6}n(n-1)(n-2)$ parallelepipeds (viz., one for every three of the n directions).

The Kepler–Poinsot Polyhedra

By producing the sides of a regular pentagon till they meet again, we derive the star-pentagon or pentacle or *pentagram*, which has long been used as a mystic symbol. We may regard the pentagram as a generalized polygon, having five sides

---

* This family of polyhedra has been investigated by C. H. H. Franklin, *Mathematical Gazette*, 1937, vol. XXI, p. 363.

† Fedorow, *loc. cit.* (" Isozonoëder ").

‡ Fedorow, *loc. cit.* (Satz 27).

which enclose the centre twice. Each side subtends an angle $\frac{4}{5}\pi$ at the centre, whereas each side of an ordinary n-gon subtends an angle $2\pi/n$. Thus the pentagram behaves as if it were an n-gon with $n = \frac{5}{2}$. Analogously, any rational number n (> 2) leads to a polygon, the numerator giving the number of sides, and the denominator the " density " (or " species ").

This process of " stellation " may also be applied in space. The stellated faces of the regular dodecahedron meet by fives at twelve new vertices, forming the *small stellated dodecahedron* $(\frac{5}{2})^5$. These new vertices belong also to an icosahedron. By inserting the edges of this icosahedron, but keeping the original twelve facial planes, we obtain a polyhedron whose faces are twelve ordinary pentagons, while the section near a vertex is a

$$n = \tfrac{7}{2} \qquad\qquad n = \tfrac{7}{3} \qquad\qquad n = \tfrac{8}{3} \qquad\qquad n = \tfrac{9}{4}$$

pentagram; this is the *great dodecahedron*,* $5^{5/2}$. It is reciprocal to $(\frac{5}{2})^5$, as its symbol implies. By stellating the faces of $5^{5/2}$, we derive the *great stellated dodecahedron*, $(\frac{5}{2})^3$, which has the twenty vertices of an ordinary dodecahedron. Its reciprocal, the *great icosahedron* † $3^{5/2}$, has twenty triangular faces, and its vertices are those of an ordinary icosahedron. (See Plate II, figures 31, 34, 32, 30.)

Thus we increase the number of finite regular polyhedra from five to nine. The easiest way to see that these exhaust all the possibilities ‡ is by observing that the " Petrie polygon " of n^m is still characterized by the number h, where

$$\cos^2 (\pi/h) = \cos^2 (\pi/m) + \cos^2 (\pi/n),$$

* The *Encyclopaedia Britannica* (XIVth edition, article " Solids ") unhappily calls this the " small stellated dodecahedron," and *vice versa*. (Cf. the XIth edition, article " Polyhedron.")

† Good drawings of these figures are given by Lucas (in his *Récréations Mathématiques*), vol. II, pp. 206—208, 224.

‡ This was first proved (another way) by Cauchy, *Journal de l'École Polytechnique*, 1813, vol. IX, pp. 68—86.

even when m and n are not integers.   Writing this equation in the symmetrical form

$$\cos^2 (\pi/m) + \cos^2 (\pi/n) + \cos^2 (\pi/k) = 1$$

(where $1/k + 1/h = \frac{1}{2}$), we find its rational solutions to be the three permutations of 3, 3, 4, and the six permutations of 3, 5, $\frac{5}{2}$, making nine in all, as required.

The polyhedra $(\frac{5}{2})^5$ and $5^{5/2}$ fail to satisfy Euler's Theorem, $V - E + F = 2$, which holds for all ordinary polyhedra. The reason for this failure (which apparently induced Schläfli *) to deny the existence of these two figures) will appear in Chapter VIII.   However, all the nine finite regular polyhedra satisfy the following extended theorem, due to Cayley :

$$d_V V - E + d_F F = 2D,$$

where d_F is the " density " of a face (viz., 1 for an ordinary polygon, 2 for a pentagram), d_V is the density of a vertex (or rather, of the section near a vertex), and D is the density of the whole polyhedron (i.e. the number of times the faces enclose the centre).

n^m	V	E	F	D	Name	Discoverer
$(\frac{5}{2})^5$	12	30	12	3	Small stellated dodecahedron	Kepler (1619)
$(\frac{5}{2})^3$	20	30	12	7	Great stellated dodecahedron	,,
$5^{5/2}$	12	30	12	3	Great dodecahedron	Poinsot (1809)
$3^{5/2}$	12	30	20	7	Great icosahedron	,,

" Archimedean " star polyhedra have been investigated,† but are beyond the scope of this book.

The 59 Icosahedra

Imagine a large block of wood with a small tetrahedron or cube (somehow) drawn in the middle.   If we make saw-cuts

---

* *Quarterly Journal of Mathematics*, 1860, vol. III, pp. 66, 67. He defined " $(\frac{5}{2}, 3), (3, \frac{5}{2})$," but not " $(\frac{5}{2}, 5), (5, \frac{5}{2})$."

† Badoureau, *Journal de l'École Polytechnique*, 1881, vol. XXX, pp. 47—172.

L

along all the facial planes of the small solid, and throw away all the pieces that extend to the surface of the block, nothing remains but the small solid itself. But if, instead of a tetrahedron or cube, we start with an octahedron, we shall be left with nine pieces : the octahedron itself, and a tetrahedron on each face, converting it into a *stella octangula* which has the appearance of two interpenetrating tetrahedra (the regular compound mentioned above). Similarly, a dodecahedron leads to $1 + 12 + 30 + 20$ pieces : the dodecahedron itself, twelve pentagonal pyramids which convert this into the small stellated dodecahedron, thirty wedge-shaped tetrahedra which convert the latter into the great dodecahedron, and twenty triangular double-pyramids which convert this last into the great stellated dodecahedron.

Finally, the icosahedron * leads to $1 + 20 + 30 + 60 + 20 + 60 + 120 + 12 + 30 + 60 + 60$ pieces, which can be put together to form 32 different reflexible solids, all having the full icosahedral symmetry, and 27 pairs of enantiomorphous solids, having only the symmetry of rotation. The former set of solids includes the original icosahedron, the compound of five octahedra (made of the first $1 + 20 + 30$ pieces), the compound of ten tetrahedra (made of the first $1 + 20 + 30 + 60 + 20 + 60 + 120$ pieces), and the great icosahedron (made of all save the last 60 pieces). The latter set includes the compound of five tetrahedra, and a number of more complicated figures having the same attractively "twisted" appearance.†

SOLID TESSELLATIONS

Just as there are many symmetrical ways of filling a plane with regular polygons, so there are many symmetrical ways of

---

* A. H. Wheeler, *Proceedings of the International Mathematical Congress, Toronto*, 1924, vol. I, pp. 701—708. M. Brückner, *Vielecke und Vielflache*, Leipzig, 1900 (Plate VIII, Nos. 2, 26; Plate IX, Nos. 3, 6, 11, 17, 20; Plate X, No. 3; Plate XI, Nos. 14, 24).

† For J. F. Petrie's exquisite drawings of all these figures, see "The 59 Icosahedra," *University of Toronto Studies* (Mathematical Series), No. 6, 1938.

filling space with regular and Archimedean solids. For the sake of brevity, let us limit our discussion to those ways in which all the edges (as well as all the vertices) are surrounded alike. Of such "solid tessellations" there are just five,* an edge being surrounded by (i) four cubes, or (ii) two tetrahedra and two octahedra, arranged alternately, or (iii) a tetrahedron and three truncated tetrahedra, or (iv) three truncated octahedra, or (v) an octahedron and two cuboctahedra. Let

The Solid Tessellation [3⁴].

us denote these by the symbols [4⁴], [3⁴], [3² . 6²], [4 . 6²], [3² . 4], which indicate the polygons (interfaces) that meet at an edge.

The "regular" space-filling [4⁴] is familiar. It is "self-reciprocal" in the sense that the centres of all the cubes are the vertices of an identical space-filling. Its alternate vertices give the space-filling [3⁴], one tetrahedron being inscribed in

* A. Andreini, *Memorie della Società italiana delle Scienze*, 1905, series 2, vol. xiv, pp. 75—129, figs. 12, 15, 14, 18, 33.

each cube, and one octahedron surrounding each omitted vertex. This has a particularly high degree of regularity (although its solids are of two kinds, unlike those of [4⁴]); for, not merely the vertices and edges, but also the triangular interfaces, are all surrounded alike; in fact, each triangle belongs to one solid of either kind. If we join the centres of adjacent solids, by lines perpendicular to the interfaces, and by planes perpendicular to the edges, we obtain the " reciprocal " space-filling, say $[3^4]'$; this consists of rhombic dodecahedra, of which four surround some vertices (originally centres of tetrahedra), while six surround others (originally centres of octahedra).

The space-filling $[3^2 . 6^2]$ can be derived from $[3^4]$ by making each of a certain set of tetrahedra of the latter adhere to its four adjacent octahedra and to six other tetrahedra which connect these in pairs, so as to form a truncated tetrahedron.* Thus $[3^2 . 6^2]$ has half the vertices of $[3^4]$, which in turn has half the vertices of $[4^4]$.

The space-filling of truncated octahedra, $[4 . 6^2]$, is reciprocal to a space-filling of " isosceles " tetrahedra (or tetragonal bisphenoids) whose vertices belong to two reciprocal $[4^4]$'s (the " body-centred cubic lattice " of crystallography). The vertices of $[3^2 . 4]$ are the mid-points of the edges (or the centres of the squares) of $[4^4]$.

BALL-PILING OR CLOSE-PACKING

A large box can be filled with a number of small equal spheres arranged in horizontal layers, one on top of another, in various ways, of which I will describe three. It might be filled so that each sphere rests on the top of the sphere immediately below it in the next layer, touches each of four adjacent spheres in the same layer, and touches one sphere in the layer above it; thus each sphere is in contact with six others. Or we might slightly

* Analogously, any of the plane tessellations 6^3, $(3 . 6)^2$, $3^4 . 6$ may be derived from 3^6 by making certain sets of six triangles coalesce to form hexagons.

spread out the spheres of each layer, so as to be not quite in
contact, and let each sphere rest on four in the layer below and
help to support four in the layer above, the " spreading out "
being adjusted so that the points of contact are at the vertices
of a cube. We might also fill the box with spheres arranged so
that each of them is in contact with four spheres in the next
lower layer, with four in the same layer, and with four in the
next higher layer. This last arrangement is known as *normal
piling* or *spherical close-packing*; it gives the greatest number
of spheres with which the box can be filled. (Although it is
impossible for one sphere to touch more than twelve others of
the same size, we shall see later that there are many different
ways of packing equal spheres so that each touches exactly
twelve others.)

These three arrangements may be described as follows. In
the first, the centres of the spheres are at the vertices of the
space-filling $[4^4]$, and the spheres themselves are inscribed in
the cubes of the reciprocal $[4^4]$. In the second, the spheres are
inscribed in the truncated octahedra of $[4 . 6^2]$ (touching the
hexagons, but just missing the squares). In the third, the
spheres are inscribed in the rhombic dodecahedra of $[3^4]'$, and
their centres are at the vertices of $[3^4]$.

Now, the vertices of $[3^4]$ form triangular tessellations 3^6 in a
series of parallel planes.

	A		A		A		A
		B		B		B	
	C		C		C		C
		A		A		A	
	B		B		B		B
		C		C		C	
	A		A		A		A
		B		B		B	
	C		C		C		C

Our figure shows a " plan " of this arrangement of points, projected orthogonally on one of the planes, which we take to be horizontal. The points A are projected from one plane, the points B from the next, C from the next, A again from the next, and so on, in cyclic order. Now imagine solid spheres centred at all these points. The points A give a layer of close-packed spheres, each touching six others. The points B represent another such layer, resting on the first; each sphere of either layer touches three of the other. The points C represent a third layer, resting on the second; but an equally " economical " piling of spheres is obtained if the centres of the third layer lie above the points A again, instead of lying above the points C. And so, at every stage, the new layer may or may not lie vertically above the last but one.

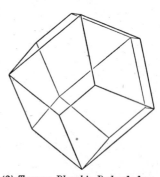

(1) *Rhombic Dodecahedron.*   (2) *Trapezo-Rhombic Dodecahedron.*

The arrangement $A B C A B C \ldots$ represents spherical close-packing; on the other hand, the arrangement $A B A B A B \ldots$ is known as *hexagonal* close-packing. If a large number of plastic spheres, made of bread or putty, are shaken and then squeezed together, those near the middle tend to form rhombic dodecahedra, showing that they were shaken into spherical close-packing. If we deliberately arrange them in hexagonal close-packing before squeezing, the form of each will be an irregular solid bounded by six rhombs and six trapezia.*

* Cf. Steinhaus, *Mathematical Snapshots*, New York, 1938, p. 88.

We also find an approximation to normal piling in a mass of soap-bubbles; the size being uniform, each bubble takes the form of a rhombic dodecahedron.

The two aspects of normal piling are well illustrated by the geometrical interpretation of tetrahedral and pyramidal numbers (see page 59). We know that $\frac{1}{6}n(n+1)(n+2)$ cannon-balls can be piled in the form of a tetrahedron, and that $\frac{1}{6}n(n+1)(2n+1)$ can be piled in the form of a square pyramid; in *both* cases the piling is " normal."

If you stand on wet sand, near the sea-shore, it is very noticeable that the sand gets comparatively dry around your feet, whereas the footprints that you leave contain free water. The following explanation is due, I believe, to Osborne Reynolds. The grains of sand, rolled into approximately spherical shape by the motion of the sea, have been deposited in something like normal piling. The pressure of your feet disturbs this piling, increasing the interstices between the grains. Water is sucked in from round about, to fill up these enlarged interstices. When you remove your feet, the normal piling is partially restored, and the water is left above.

REGULAR SPONGES

The definition of regularity on page 130 depends on two symmetries, which, in every case so far discussed, are *rotations*. By allowing the number of vertices, edges and faces to be infinite, this definition includes the plane tessellations 3^6, 6^3, 4^4. It would be absurd to allow each face to have infinitely many sides, or to allow infinitely many faces to surround one vertex; therefore the special symmetries must be periodic. However, they need not be rotations; they may be rotary reflections. (A rotary reflection is the combination of a rotation and a reflection, which may always be chosen so that the axis of the rotation is perpendicular to the reflecting plane.) Such an operation interchanges the " inside " and " outside " of the polyhedron; consequently the inside and outside are identical, and the polyhedron (dividing space into two equal parts) must be infinite. The dihedral angles

at the edges of a given face are alternately positive and negative, and the edges at a vertex lie alternately on the two sides
of a certain plane. This allows the sum of the face-angles
at a vertex to exceed 2π.

It can be proved that the polyhedra n^m of this type are given
by the integral solutions of the equation

$$2 \sin (\pi/m) \sin (\pi/n) = \cos (\pi/k),$$

namely 6^6 ($k = 3$), 6^4 and 4^6 ($k = 4$), 6^3 and 3^6 ($k = 6$), and
4^4 ($k = \infty$). The three plane tessellations occur because a
plane rotation may be regarded indifferently as a rotation in
space or as a rotary reflection. The three new figures are
" sponges " with k-gonal holes.*

The faces of 6^6 are the hexagons of the solid tessellation
$[3^2 . 6^2]$; those of 6^4 are the hexagons of $[4 . 6^2]$; and those of
4^6 are half the squares of $[4^4]$. The remaining interfaces of
the solid tessellations appear as holes. The sponges 6^4 and
4^6 (discovered by J. F. Petrie in 1926) are *reciprocal*, in the
sense that the vertices of each are the centres of the faces of
the other ; † 6^6 is self-reciprocal, or rather, reciprocal to another
equal 6^6.

* For photographs of models, see Coxeter, *Proceedings of the London
Mathematical Society*, 1937, series 2, vol. XLIII, p. 34, where the three sponges
are denoted by {6,6 | 3}, {6,4 | 4}, {4,6 | 4}.

† Plane tessellations can be reciprocal in this sense, but finite polyhedra
cannot. The centres of the faces of an octahedron are the vertices of a
cube, while the vertices of the octahedron are the centres of the faces of
another (larger) cube.

To make a model of 6^6, cut out sets of four hexagons (of thin cardboard), stick each set together in the form of the hexagonal faces of a truncated tetrahedron ($3 . 6^2$), and then stick the sets together, hexagon on hexagon, taking care that no edge shall belong to more than two faces. (In the finished model, the faces are double, which makes for greater strength besides facilitating the construction.) Similarly, to make 6^4, use sets of eight hexagons, forming the hexagonal faces of truncated octahedra ($4 . 6^2$). Finally, to make 4^6, use rings of four squares. This last model, however, is not rigid; it can gradually collapse, the square holes becoming rhombic. (In fact, I once received, by post, an extensive model, flat in an envelope).

ROTATING RINGS OF TETRAHEDRA

J. M. Andreas and R. M. Stalker have independently discovered a family of non-rigid finite polyhedra having $2n$ vertices, $6n$ edges (of which $2n$ coincide in pairs) and $4n$

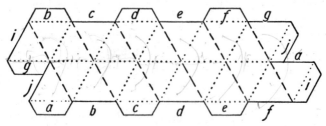

triangular faces, for $n = 6$ or 8 or any greater integer. The faces are those of n tetrahedra, joined together in cyclic order at a certain pair of opposite edges of each, so as to form a kind of ring. When $n = 6$, the range of mobility is quite small, but when $n = 8$, the ring can turn round indefinitely, like a smoke-ring. When n is even, the figure tends to take up a symmetrical position; it is particularly pretty when $n = 10$.*

* One of the "Stephanoids" described by M. Brückner in his *Vielecke und Vielflache*, p. 216 (and Plate VIII, No. 4) consists of a ring of ten irregular tetrahedra.

When n is odd, the entire lack of symmetry seems to make the motion still more fascinating. When $n \geqslant 22$, the ring can occur in a knotted form.

A model of any such ring may be made from a single sheet of paper. For the case when $n = 6$, copy the above diagram, cut it out, bend the paper along the inner lines, upwards or downwards according as these lines are broken or dotted, and stick the flaps in the manner indicated by the lettering. The ends have to be joined somewhat differently when n is a multiple of 4 (see figure xxxiv, page 216). When n is odd, either method of joining can be used at will.

Since there are two types of edge, such a polyhedron is not regular, and no symmetry is lost by making the triangles isosceles instead of equilateral. If the doubled edges are suffici- ently short compared to the others, the ring with $n = 6$ * can be made to turn completely, like the rings with $n \geqslant 8$.

The Kaleidoscope †

The ordinary kaleidoscope consists essentially of two plane mirrors, inclined at $\pi/3$ or $\pi/4$, and an object (or set of objects) placed in the angle between them so as to be reflected in both. The result is that the object is seen 6 or 8 times (according to the angle), in an attractively symmetrical arrangement. By making a hinge to connect two (unframed) mirrors, the angle between them can be varied at will, and it is clear that an angle π/n gives $2n$ images (including the object itself). As a limiting case, we have two parallel mirrors and a theoretically infinite number of images (restricted in practice only by the brightness of the illumination and the quality of the mirrors). If the object is a point on the bisector of the angle between the mirrors, the images are the vertices of a regular $2n$-gon.

---

* Such a ring (of six tetragonal bisphenoids) has been on sale in the United States as a child's toy, with letters of the alphabet on its 24 faces. (Patent No. 1,997,022, issued in 1935.) Michael Goldberg has remarked that a ring of such elongated tetrahedra is also possible with $n = 7$.

† E. Hess, *Neues Jahrbuch für Mineralogie, Geologie und Palaeontologie*, 1889, vol. I, pp. 54—65.

If the object is a point on one of the mirrors, the images coincide
in pairs at the vertices of a regular n-gon. The point may be
represented in practice by a candle, or by a little ball of plastic
clay or putty.

Regarding the two mirrors as being vertical, let us introduce
a third vertical mirror in such a way that each pair of the
three mirrors makes an angle of the form π/n. In other
words, any horizontal section is to be a triangle of angles
π/l, π/m, π/n, where l, m, n are integers. The solutions of
the consequent equation

$$\frac{1}{l} + \frac{1}{m} + \frac{1}{n} = 1$$

are $3, 3, 3$; $2, 3, 6$; $2, 4, 4$. In each case the number of images
is infinite. By varying the position of a point-object in the
triangle, we obtain the vertices of certain isogonal tessellations.*
In particular, if the point is taken at a vertex of the triangle,
or where an angle-bisector meets the opposite side, or at the
in-centre (where all three angle-bisectors concur), then the
tiles of the tessellation are regular polygons. In the notation
of page 107, the results of putting the point in these various
positions are as indicated in the following diagrams.

The network of triangles, which the mirrors appear to
create, may be coloured alternately white and black. By
taking a suitable point within every triangle of one colour

* Placing a lighted candle between three (unframed) mirrors, the reader
will see an extraordinarily pretty effect.

(but ignoring the corresponding point within every triangle of the other colour), we obtain the vertices of 3^6 (again), $3^4 \cdot 6$, and $3^2 \cdot 4 \cdot 3 \cdot 4$, respectively. (The remaining uniform tessellation, $3^3 \cdot 4^2$, is not derivable by any such method.) The above diagrams reveal many relationships between the various tessellations : that the vertices of 3^6 occur among the vertices of 6^3, that the vertices of 6^3 trisect the edges of (another) 3^6, that the vertices of one 4^4 bisect the edges of another, and so on.

If the third mirror is placed horizontally instead of vertically —*i.e.* if the two hinged mirrors stand upon it—the number of images is no longer infinite ; in fact, it is $4n$, where π/n is the angle between the two vertical mirrors. For a point on one of the vertical mirrors, the images coincide in pairs at the vertices of an n-gonal prism. Two of the three dihedral angles between pairs of the three mirrors are now right angles. A natural generalization is the case where these three angles are π/l, π/m, π/n.

Since, for any reflection in a plane mirror, object and image are equidistant from the plane, we easily see that all the images of a point in this generalized kaleidoscope lie on a sphere, whose centre is the point of intersection of the planes of the three mirrors. On the sphere, these planes cut out a spherical triangle, of angles π/l, π/m, π/n. The resulting image-planes divide the whole sphere into a network (or " map ") of such triangles, each containing one image of any object placed within the first triangle. The number of images is therefore equal to the number of such triangles that will suffice to fill the whole spherical surface. Taking the radius as unity, the area of the whole sphere is 4π, while that of each triangle is $(\pi/l) + (\pi/m) + (\pi/n) - \pi$. Hence the required number is

$$4 / \left(\frac{1}{l} + \frac{1}{m} + \frac{1}{n} - 1 \right).$$

Since this must be positive, the numbers l, m, n have to be chosen so as to satisfy

(1)

(2)

(3)

$$\frac{1}{l} + \frac{1}{m} + \frac{1}{n} > 1.$$

This inequality has the solutions 2, 2, n; 2, 3, 3; 2, 3, 4; 2, 3, 5. The first case has already been mentioned; the rest are depicted on page 157 (by J. F. Petrie).

For a practical demonstration, the mirrors should in each case be cut as circular sectors (of the same fairly large radius), whose angles * are equal to the sides of a spherical triangle of angles π/l, π/m, π/n.

By varying the position of a point-object in the spherical triangle (or in the solid angle between the three mirrors) we obtain the vertices of certain isogonal polyhedra. In particular, if the point is on one of the edges where two mirrors meet, or on one of the mirrors and equidistant from the other two, or at the centre of a sphere which touches all three, then the faces of the polyhedra are regular polygons. The manner in which the various uniform polyhedra arise † is indicated in the following diagrams, analogous to those given for tessellations on page 155.

By taking a suitable point within each white (or black) triangle,‡ we obtain the vertices of $3^3 . n$, 3^5, $3^4 . 4$, or $3^4 . 5$, respectively. It has already been remarked that the snub

* In the three cases, these angles are respectively: 54° 44′, 54° 44′, 70° 32′; 35° 16′, 45°, 54° 44′; 20° 54′, 31° 43′, 37° 23′.

† See Möbius, *Gesammelte Werke*, 1861, vol. II, p. 656, figs. 47, 51, 54; W. A. Wythoff, *Proceedings of the Royal Academy of Sciences, Amsterdam*, 1918, vol. XX, pp 966—970; G. de B. Robinson, *Journal of the London Mathematical Society*, 1931, vol. VI, pp. 70—75; H. S. M. Coxeter, *Proceedings of the London Mathematical Society*, 1935, series 2, vol. XXXVIII, pp. 327—339.

‡ Möbius, *loc. cit.*, figs. 46, 49, 53.

cube $3^4 . 4$ exists in two enantiomorphous forms; the vertices of one form lie in the white triangles, those of the other in the black. The same thing happens in the case of the snub dodecahedron, $3^4 . 5$.

By introducing a fourth mirror, we obtain solid tessellations. Tetrahedra of three different shapes can be formed by four planes inclined at angles that are submultiples of π. These three shapes can conveniently be cut out from a rectangular block of dimensions $1 \times \sqrt{2} \times \sqrt{2}$. Suppose $ABCD$ to be a horizontal square of side $\sqrt{2}$, at height 1 above an equal square $A'B'C'D'$. After cutting off the alternate corners A', B, C', D, by planes through sets of three other vertices, we are left with the tetragonal bisphenoid $AB'CD'$, which is

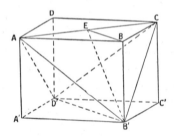

one of the required shapes. Another is any one of the corner pieces that were cut off, such as $ABCB'$. (Two such pieces can be fitted together to make a shape just like $AB'CD'$.) The third is obtained by cutting $ABCB'$ in half along its plane of symmetry, which is the plane $BB'E$, where E is the mid-point of AC. One half is $AEBB'$. Note that the edges AE, EB, BB' are three equal lines in three perpendicular directions.

A point-object in such a tetrahedron will give rise to the vertices of a solid tessellation in various ways,* some of which are indicated in the following diagrams (which show $AB'CD'$, $ABCB'$, $AEBB'$, in the same orientation as before).

Five mirrors can be arranged in the form of certain triangular

* Andreini, *loc. cit.* (p. 147 above), figs. 17—24 bis.

prisms; these lead to solid tessellations of prisms. Six can be arranged rectangularly in three pairs of parallels, as when we have a mirror in the ceiling and floor as well as all four

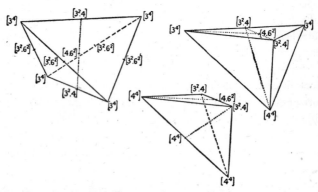

walls of an ordinary room; these give a solid tessellation of rectangular blocks. G. Pólya has proved * that a kaleido-scope cannot have more than six mirrors.

* *Annals of Mathematics*, 1934, vol. xxxv, p. 594.

CHAPTER VI

CHESS-BOARD RECREATIONS

A CHESS-BOARD and chess-men lend themselves to recreations, many of which are geometrical. The problems are, however, of a distinct type, and sufficiently numerous to deserve a chapter to themselves. A few problems which might be included in this chapter have been already considered in Chapter IV.

The ordinary chess-board consists of 64 small squares, known as cells, arranged as shown below in 8 rows and 8 columns. Usually the cells are coloured alternately white and black, or white and red. The cells may be defined by the numbers 11, 12, etc., where the first digit denotes the number of the column,

18	28	38	48	58	68	78	88
17	27	37	47	57	67	77	87
16	26	36	46	56	66	76	86
15	25	35	45	55	65	75	85
14	24	34	44	54	64	74	84
13	23	33	43	53	63	73	83
12	22	32	42	52	62	72	82
11	21	31	41	51	61	71	81

and the second digit the number of the row—the two digits representing respectively the abscissa and ordinate of the mid-points of the cells. I use this notation in the following pages. A generalized board consists of n^2 cells arranged in n rows and n columns. Most of the problems which I shall describe can be extended to meet the case of a board of n^2 cells.

M

The usual chess-pieces are Kings, Queens, Bishops, Knights, and Rooks or Castles ; there are also Pawns. I assume that the moves of these pieces are known to the reader.

With the game itself and with chess problems of the usual type I do not concern myself. Particular positions of the pieces may be subject to mathematical analysis, but in general the moves open to a player are so numerous as to make it impossible to see far ahead. Probably this is obvious, but it may emphasize how impossible it is to discuss the theory of the game effectively if I add that it has been shown that there may be as many as 197299 ways of playing the first four moves, and 71782 different positions at the end of the first four moves (two on each side), of which 16556 arise when the players move pawns only.*

Relative Value of Pieces

The first question to which I will address myself is the determination of the relative values of the different chess-pieces.†

If a piece is placed on a cell, the number of cells it commands depends in general on its position. We may estimate the value of the piece by the average number of cells which it commands when placed in succession on every cell of the board. This is equivalent to saying that the value of a piece may be estimated by the chance that if it and a king are put at random on the board, the king will be in check : if no other restriction is imposed, this is called a simple check. On whatever cell the piece is originally placed there will remain 63 other cells on which the king may be placed. It is equally probable that it may be put on any one of them. Hence the chance that it will be in check is 1/63 of the average number of cells commanded by the piece.

* *L'Intermédiaire des Mathématiciens*, Paris, December, 1903, vol. x, pp. 305—308 : also *Royal Engineers Journal*, London, August—November, 1889; or *British Association Transactions*, 1890, p. 745.

† H. M. Taylor, *Philosophical Magazine*, March, 1876, series 5, vol. i, pp. 221—229.

A rook put on any cell commands 14 other cells. Wherever the rook is placed there will remain 63 cells on which the king may be placed, and on which it is equally likely that it will be placed. Hence the chance of a simple check is 14/63, that is, 2/9. Similarly, on a board of n^2 cells the chance is $2(n-1)/(n^2-1)$—that is, $2/(n+1)$.

A knight, when placed on any of the 4 corner cells like 11, commands 2 cells. When placed on any of the 8 cells like 12 and 21, it commands 3 cells. When placed on any of the 4 cells like 22 or any of the 16 boundary cells like 13, 14, 15, 16, it commands 4 cells. When placed on any of the 16 cells like 23, 24, 25, 26, it commands 6 cells. And when placed on any of the remaining 16 middle cells, it commands 8 cells. Hence the average number of cells commanded by a knight put on a chess-board is $(4\times2+8\times3+20\times4+16\times6+16\times8)/64$— that is, 336/64. Accordingly, if a king and a knight are put on the board, the chance that the king will be in simple check is $336/(64\times63)$—that is, 1/12. Similarly, on a board of n^2 cells the chance is $8(n-2)/n^2(n+1)$.

A bishop when placed on any of the ring of 28 boundary cells commands 7 cells. When placed on any ring of the 20 cells next to the boundary cells, it commands 9 cells. When placed on any of the 12 cells forming the next ring, it commands 11 cells. When placed on the 4 middle cells, it commands 13 cells. Hence, if a king and a bishop are put on the board, the chance that the king will be in simple check is $(28\times7+20\times9+12\times11+4\times13)/(64\times63)$—that is, 5/36. Similarly, on a board of n^2 cells, when n is even, the chance is $2(2n-1)/3n(n+1)$. When n is odd, the analysis is longer, owing to the fact that in this case the number of white cells on the board differs from the number of black cells. I do not give the work, which presents no special difficulty.

A queen when placed on any cell of a board commands all the cells which a bishop and a rook when placed on that cell would do. Hence, if a king and a queen are put on the board, the chance that the king will be in simple check is $2/9+5/36$—

that is, 13/36.   Similarly, on a board of n^2 cells, when n is even, the chance is $2(5n - 1)/3n(n + 1)$.

On the above assumptions the relative values of the rook, knight, bishop, and queen are 8, 3, 5, 13.   According to Staunton's *Chess-Player's Handbook*, the actual values, estimated empirically, are in the ratio of 548, 305, 350, 994; according to Von Bilguer, the ratios are 540, 350, 360, 1000—the value of a pawn being taken as 100.

There is considerable discrepancy between the above results as given by theory and practice.   It has been, however, suggested that a better test of the value of a piece would be the chance that when it and a king were put at random on the board, it would check the king without giving the king the opportunity of taking it.   This is called a safe check, as distinguished from a simple check.

Applying the same method as above, the chances of a safe check work out as follows.   For a rook the chance of a safe check is $(4 \times 12 + 24 \times 11 + 36 \times 10)/(64 \times 63)$—that is, 1/6—or on a board of n^2 cells is $2(n - 2)/n(n + 1)$.   For a knight all checks are safe, and therefore the chance of a safe check is 1/12; or on a board of n^2 cells is $8(n - 2)/n^2(n + 1)$.   For a bishop the chance of a safe check is $364/(64 \times 63)$—that is, 13/144—or on a board of n^2 cells, when n is even, is $2(n-2)(2n-3)/3n^2(n+1)$. For a queen the chance of a safe check is $1036/(64 \times 63)$—that is, 37/144—or on a board of n^2 cells, is $2(n-2)(5n-3)/3n^2(n+1)$, when n is even.

On this view the relative values of the rook, knight, bishop, and queen are 24, 12, 13, 37;   while, according to Staunton, experience shows that they are approximately 22, 12, 14, 40, and according to Von Bilguer, 18, 12, 12, 33.

The same method can be applied to compare the values of combinations of pieces.   For instance, the value of two bishops (one restricted to white cells and the other to black cells) and two rooks, estimated by the chance of a simple check, are respectively 35/124 and 37/93.   Hence on this view a queen in general should be more valuable than two bishops, but less valuable than two rooks.   This agrees with experience.

An analogous problem consists in finding the chance that two kings, put at random on the board, will not occupy adjoining cells—that is, that neither would (were such a move possible) check the other. The chance is 43/48, and therefore the chance that they will occupy adjoining cells is 5/48. If three kings are put on the board, the chance that no two of them occupy adjoining cells is 1061/1488. The corresponding chances* for a board of n^2 cells are $(n-1)(n-2)(n^2+3n-2)/n^2(n^2-1)$ and $(n-1)(n-2)(n^4+3n^3-20n^2-30n+132)/n^2(n^2-1)(n^2-2)$.

The Eight Queens Problem †

One of the classical problems connected with a chess-board is the determination of the number of ways in which eight queens can be placed on a chess-board—or, more generally, in which n queens can be placed on a board of n^2 cells—so that no queen can take any other. This was proposed originally by Franz Nauck in 1850.

In 1874 Dr. S. Günther ‡ suggested a method of solution by means of determinants. For, if each symbol represents the corresponding cell of the board, the possible solutions for a board of n^2 cells are given by those terms, if any, of the determinant

$$
\begin{vmatrix}
a_1 & b_2 & c_3 & d_4 & \cdots \\
\beta_2 & a_3 & b_4 & c_5 & \cdots \\
\gamma_3 & \beta_4 & a_5 & b_6 & \cdots \\
\delta_4 & \gamma_5 & \beta_6 & a_7 & \cdots \\
\cdots & & & & \\
\cdots & & & a_{2n-3} & b_{2n-2} \\
\cdots & & & \beta_{2n-2} & a_{2n-1}
\end{vmatrix}
$$

in which no letter and no suffix appears more than once.

---

* *L'Intermédiaire des Mathématiciens*, Paris, 1897, vol. IV, p. 6, and 1901, vol. VIII, p. 140.

† On the history of this problem see W. Ahrens, *Mathematische Unterhaltungen und Spiele*, Leipzig, 1901, chap. IX. For later developments, see Kraïtchik, *La Mathématique des Jeux*, Brussels, 1930, pp. 300—356.

‡ Grunert's *Archiv der Mathematik und Physik*, 1874, vol. LVI, pp. 281—292.

The reason is obvious. Every term in a determinant contains one, and only one, element out of every row and out of every column : hence any term will indicate a position on the board in which the queens cannot take one another by moves rook-wise. Again, in the above determinant the letters and suffixes are so arranged that all the same letters and all the same suffixes lie along bishop's paths : hence, if we retain only those terms in each of which all the letters and all the suffixes are different, they will denote positions in which the queens cannot take one another by moves bishop-wise. It is clear that the signs of the terms are immaterial.

In the case of an ordinary chess-board the determinant is of the 8th order, and therefore contains 8!—that is, 40320 terms—so that it would be out of the question to use this method for the usual chess-board of 64 cells or for a board of larger size unless some way of picking out the required terms could be discovered.

A way of effecting this was suggested by Dr. J. W. L. Glaisher * in 1874, and so far as I am aware the theory remains as he left it. He showed that if all the solutions of n queens on a board of n^2 cells were known, then all the solutions of a certain type for $n + 1$ queens on a board of $(n + 1)^2$ cells could be deduced, and that all the other solutions of $n + 1$ queens on a board of $(n + 1)^2$ cells could be obtained without difficulty. The method will be sufficiently illustrated by one instance of its application.

It is easily seen that there are no solutions when $n = 2$ or $n = 3$. If $n = 4$ there are two terms in the determinant which give solutions—namely, $b_2 c_5 \gamma_3 \beta_6$ and $c_3 \beta_2 b_6 \gamma_5$. To find the solutions when $n = 5$, Glaisher proceeded thus. In this case, Günther's determinant is

$$\begin{vmatrix} a_1 & b_2 & c_3 & d_4 & e_5 \\ \beta_2 & a_3 & b_4 & c_5 & d_6 \\ \gamma_3 & \beta_4 & a_5 & b_6 & c_7 \\ \delta_4 & \gamma_5 & \beta_6 & a_7 & b_8 \\ \epsilon_5 & \delta_6 & \gamma_7 & \beta_8 & a_9 \end{vmatrix}$$

* *Philosophical Magazine*, London, December, 1874, series 4, vol. XLVII, pp. 457—467.

To obtain those solutions (if any) which involve a_9, it is sufficient to append a_9 to such of the solutions for a board of 16 cells as do not involve a. As neither of those given above involves an a, we thus get two solutions—namely, $b_2 c_5 \gamma_3 \beta_6 a_9$ and $c_3 \beta_2 b_6 \gamma_5 a_9$. The solutions which involve a_1, e_5 and ϵ_5 can be written down by symmetry. The eight solutions thus obtained are all distinct; we may call them of the first type.

The above are the only solutions which can involve elements in the corner squares of the determinant. Hence the remaining solutions are obtainable from the determinant

$$\begin{vmatrix} 0 & b_2 & c_3 & d_4 & 0 \\ \beta_2 & a_3 & b_4 & c_5 & d_6 \\ \gamma_3 & \beta_4 & a_5 & b_6 & c_7 \\ \delta_4 & \gamma_5 & \beta_6 & a_7 & b_8 \\ 0 & \delta_6 & \gamma_7 & \beta_8 & 0 \end{vmatrix}$$

If, in this, we take the minor of b_2 and in it replace by zero every term involving the letter b or the suffix 2, we shall get all solutions involving b_2. But in this case the minor at once reduces to $d_6 a_5 \delta_4 \beta_8$. We thus get one solution—namely, $b_2 d_6 a_5 \delta_4 \beta_8$. The solutions which involve β_2, δ_4, δ_6, β_8, b_8, d_6, and d_4 can be obtained by symmetry. Of these eight solutions it is easily seen that only two are distinct: these may be called solutions of the second type.

Similarly, the remaining solutions must be obtained from the determinant

$$\begin{vmatrix} 0 & 0 & c_3 & 0 & 0 \\ 0 & a_3 & b_4 & c_5 & 0 \\ \gamma_3 & \beta_4 & a_5 & b_6 & c_7 \\ 0 & \gamma_5 & \beta_6 & a_7 & 0 \\ 0 & 0 & \gamma_7 & 0 & 0 \end{vmatrix}$$

If, in this, we take the minor of c_3, and in it replace by zero every term involving the letter c or the suffix 3, we shall get all the solutions which involve c_3. But in this case the minor vanishes. Hence there is no solution involving c_3, and therefore by symmetry no solutions which involve γ_3, γ_7, or c_7. Had there been any solutions involving the third element in the first or last row or column of the determinant, we should have described them as of the third type.

Thus in all there are ten, and only ten, solutions—namely, eight of the first type, two of the second type, and none of the third type.

Similarly, if $n = 6$, we obtain no solutions of the first type, four solutions of the second type, and no solutions of the third type—that is, four solutions in all. If $n = 7$, we obtain sixteen solutions of the first type, twenty-four solutions of the second type, no solutions of the third type, and no solutions of the fourth type—that is, forty solutions in all. If $n = 8$, we obtain sixteen solutions of the first type, fifty-six solutions of the second type, and twenty solutions of the third type—that is, ninety-two solutions in all.

It will be noticed that all the solutions of one type are not always distinct. In general, from any solution seven others can be obtained at once. Of these eight solutions, four consist of the initial or fundamental solution and the three similar ones obtained by turning the board through one, two, or three right angles; the other four are the reflections of these in a mirror: but in any particular case it may happen that the reflections reproduce the originals, or that a rotation through one or two right angles makes no difference. Thus on boards of 4^2, 5^2, 6^2, 7^2, 8^2, 9^2, 10^2, 11^2, 12^2 cells there are respectively 1, 2, 1, 6, 12, 46, 92, 341, 1784 fundamental solutions; while altogether there are respectively 2, 10, 4, 40, 92, 352, 724, 2680, 14200 solutions.

The following collection of fundamental solutions may interest the reader. Each position on the board of the queens is indicated by a number, but as necessarily one queen is on each column, I can use a simpler notation than that explained on page 161. In this case the first digit represents the number of the cell occupied by the queen in the first column reckoned from one end of the column, the second digit the number in the second column, and so on. Thus on a board of 4^2 cells the solution 3142 means that one queen is on the 3rd square of the first column, one on the 1st square of the second column, one on the 4th square of the third column, and one on the 2nd square of the fourth column. If a fundamental solution gives rise to only four solutions, the number which indicates it is placed in curved brackets, ( ); if it gives rise to only two solutions, the number which indicates it is placed in square brackets, [ ]; the other fundamental solutions give rise to eight solutions each.

On a board of 4^2 cells there is 1 fundamental solution— namely, [3142].

On a board of 5^2 cells there are 2 fundamental solutions— namely, 14253, [25314]. It may be noted that the cyclic solutions 14253, 25314, 31425, 42531, 53142 give five superposable arrangements by which five white queens, five black queens, five red queens, five yellow queens, and five blue queens can be put simultaneously on the board so that no queen can be taken by any other queen of the same colour.

On a board of 6^2 cells there is 1 fundamental solution— namely, (246135). The four solutions are superposable. The puzzle for this case was sold in the streets of London for a penny, a small wooden board being ruled in the manner shown in the diagram and having holes drilled in it at the points marked by dots. The object is to put six pins into the holes so that no two are connected by a straight line.

On a board of 7^2 cells there are 6 fundamental solutions: namely, 1357246, 3572461, (5724613), 4613572, 3162574, (2574136). It may be noted that the solution 1357246 gives by cyclic permutations seven superposable arrangements.

On a board of 8^2 cells, the fourth cell from some corner is always occupied. There are 12 fundamental solutions: namely, 41582736, 41586372, 42586137, 42736815, 42736851, 42751863, 42857136, 42861357, 46152837, (46827135), 47526138, 48157263. The arrangement in this order is due to J. M. Andreas. The 7th solution is the only one in which no three queens are in a straight line. It is impossible * to find eight superposable solutions; but we can in five typical ways pick out six solutions which can be superposed, and to some of these it is possible to add 2 sets of 7 queens, thus filling 62 out of the 64 cells with 6 sets of 8 queens and 2 sets of 7 queens, no one of which can take another of the same set. Here is such a solution: 16837425, 27368514, 35714286, 41586372, 52473861, 68241753, 73625140, 04152637. Similar superposition problems can be framed for boards of other sizes.

For any reader who wishes to go further, I may add that it has been shown that on a board of n^2 cells, there are 46 fundamental solutions when $n = 9$, there are 92 when $n = 10$, there are 341 when $n = 11$, there are 1766 when $n = 12$, and there are 1346 when $n = 13$.

On any board empirical solutions may be found with but little difficulty, and Mr. Derrington has constructed the following table of solutions:

2.4.1.3	for a board of 4^2 cells
2.4.1.3.5	,, ,, 5^2 ,,
2.4.6.1.3.5	,, ,, 6^2 ,,
2.4.6.1.3.5.7	,, ,, 7^2 ,,
2.4.6.8.3.1.7.5	,, ,, 8^2 ,,
2.4.1.7.9.6.3.5.8	,, ,, 9^2 ,,
2.4.6.8.10.1.3.5.7.9	,, ,, 10^2 ,,
2.4.6.8.10.1.3.5.7.9.11	,, ,, 11^2 ,,
2.4.6.8.10.12.1.3.5.7.9.11	,, ,, 12^2 ,,
2.4.6.8.10.12.1.3.5.7.9.11.13	,, ,, 13^2 ,,
9.7.5.3.1.13.11.6.4.2.14.12.10.8	,, ,, 14^2 ,,
15.9.7.5.3.1.13.11.6.4.2.14.12.10.8	,, ,, 15^2 ,,
2.4.6.8.10.12.14.16.1.3.5.7.9.11.13.15	,, ,, 16^2 ,,
2.4.6.8.10.12.14.16.1.3.5.7.9.11.13.15.17	,, ,, 17^2 ,,
2.4.6.8.10.12.14.16.18.1.3.5.7.9.11.13.15.17	,, ,, 18^2 ,,
2.4.6.8.10.12.14.16.18.1.3.5.7.9.11.13.15.17.19	,, ,, 19^2 ,,
12.10.8.6.4.2.20.18.16.14.9.7.5.3.1.19.17.15.13.11	,, ,, 20^2 ,,
21.12.10.8.6.4.2.20.18.16.14.9.7.5.3.1.19.17.15.13.11	,, ,, 21^2 ,,

* See Thorold Gosset, *The Messenger of Mathematics*, Cambridge, July, 1914, vol. XLIV, p. 48.

and so on. The rule is obvious except when n is of the form
$6m + 2$ or $6m + 3$.

MAXIMUM PIECES PROBLEM

The Eight Queens Problem suggests the somewhat analogous question of finding the maximum number of kings—
or more generally of pieces of one type—which can be put
on a board so that no one can take any other, and the number
of solutions possible in each case.

In the case of kings the number is 16; for instance, one
solution is when they are put on the cells 11, 13, 15, 17, 31, 33,
35, 37, 51, 53, 55, 57, 71, 73, 75, 77. For queens, it is obvious
that the problem is covered by the analysis already given, and
the number is 8. For bishops the number is 14, the pieces
being put on the boundary cells; for instance, one solution is
when they are put on the cells 11, 12, 13, 14, 15, 16, 17, 81, 82,
83, 84, 85, 86, 87; there are 256 solutions. For knights the
number is 32; for instance, they can be put on all the white
or on all the black cells, and there are 2 fundamental solutions.
For rooks it is obvious that the number is 8, and there are in
all 8! solutions.

MINIMUM PIECES PROBLEM

Another problem of a somewhat similar character is the
determination of the minimum number of kings—or more
generally of pieces of one type—which can be put on a board
so as to command or occupy all the cells.

For kings the number is 9; for instance, they can be put on
the cells 11, 14, 17, 41, 44, 47, 71, 74, 77. For queens the number
is 5; for instance, they can be put on the cells 18, 35, 41,
76, 82. For bishops the number is 8; for instance, they can
be put on the cells 41, 42, 43, 44, 45, 46, 47, 48. For knights
the number is 12; for instance, they can be put on the cells
26, 32, 33, 35, 36, 43, 56, 63, 64, 66, 67, and 73—constituting
four triplets arranged symmetrically. For rooks the number
is 8, and the solutions are obvious.

For queens the problem has been also discussed for a board of n^2 cells where n has various values.* One queen can be placed so as to command all the cells when $n = 2$ or 3, and there is only 1 fundamental solution. Two queens are required when $n = 4$; and there are 3 fundamental solutions—namely, when they are placed on the cells 11 and 33, or on the cells 12 and 42, or on the cells 22, 23 : these give 12 solutions in all. Three queens are required when $n = 5$; and there are 37 fundamental solutions, giving 186 solutions in all. Three queens are also required when $n = 6$, but there is only 1 fundamental solution—namely, when they are put on the cells 11, 35, and 53, giving 4 solutions in all. Four queens are required when $n = 7$; one solution is when they are put on the cells 12, 26, 41, 55.

Jaenisch proposed also the problem of the determination of the minimum number of queens which can be placed on a board of n^2 cells so as to command all the unoccupied cells, subject to the restriction that no queen shall attack the cell occupied by any other queen. In this case three queens are required when $n = 4$—for instance, they can be put on the cells 11, 23, 42; and there are 2 fundamental solutions, giving 16 solutions in all. Three queens are required when $n = 5$—for instance, they can be put on the cells 11, 24, 43, or on the cells 11, 34, 53; and there are 2 fundamental solutions in all. Four queens are required when $n = 6$—for instance, when they are put on the cells 13, 36, 41, 64; and there are 17 fundamental solutions. Four queens are required when $n = 7$, and there is only 1 fundamental solution—namely, that already mentioned, when they are put on the cells 12, 26, 41, 55, which gives 8 solutions in all. Five queens are required when $n = 8$, and there are no less than 91 fundamental solutions—for instance, one is when they are put on the cells 11, 23, 37, 62, 76.

I leave to any of my readers who may be interested in such

* C. F. de Jaenisch, *Applications de l'Analyse Mathématique au Jeu des Échecs*, Petrograd, 1862, Appendix, pp. 244 *et seq.*; see also *L'Intermédiaire des Mathématiciens*, Paris, 1901, vol. VIII, p. 88.

questions the discussion of the corresponding problems for the other pieces,* and of the number of possible solutions in each case.

A problem of the same nature would be the determination of the minimum number of queens (or other pieces) which can be placed on a board so as to protect one another and command all the unoccupied cells. For queens the number is 5; for instance, they can be put on the cells 24, 34, 44, 54 and 84. For bishops the number is 10; for instance, they can be put on the cells 24, 25, 34, 35, 44, 45, 64, 65, 74, and 75. For knights the number is 14; for instance, they can be put on the cells 32, 33, 36, 37, 43, 44, 45, 46, 63, 64, 65, 66, 73, and 76 : the solution is semi-symmetrical. For rooks the number is 8, and a solution is obvious. I leave to any who are interested in the subject the determination of the number of solutions in each case.

In connection with this class of problems, I may mention two other questions, to which Captain Turton first called my attention, of a somewhat analogous character.

The first of these is to place eight queens on a chess-board so as to command the fewest possible squares. Thus, if queens are placed on cells 21, 22, 62, 71, 73, 77, 82, 87, eleven cells on the board will not be in check; the same number can be obtained by other arrangements. Is it possible to place the eight queens so as to leave more than eleven cells out of check ? I have never succeeded in doing so, nor in showing that it is impossible to do it.

The other problem is to place m queens (m being less than 5) on a chess-board so as to command as many cells as possible. For instance, four queens can be placed in several ways on the board so as to command 58 cells besides those on which the queens stand, thus leaving only 2 cells which are not com-

* The problem for knights was discussed in *L'Intermédiaire des Mathématiciens*, Paris, 1896, vol. III, p. 58; 1897, vol. IV, pp. 15—17, 254; 1898, vol. V, pp. 87, 230—231.

manded; for instance, queens may be placed on the cells 35, 41, 76, and 82. Analogous problems with other pieces will suggest themselves.

There are endless similar questions in which combinations of pieces are involved. For instance, if queens are put on the cells 35, 41, 76, and 82, they command or occupy all but two cells, and these two cells may be commanded or occupied by a queen, a king, a rook, a bishop, or a pawn. If queens are put on the cells 22, 35, 43, and 54, they command or occupy all but three cells, and two of these three cells may be commanded by a knight which occupies the third of them.

RE-ENTRANT PATHS ON A CHESS-BOARD

Another problem connected with the chess-board consists in moving a piece in such a manner that it shall move successively on to every possible cell once, and only once.

Knight's Re-entrant Path. I begin by discussing the classical problem of a knight's tour. The literature * on this subject is so extensive that I make no attempt to give a full account of the various methods for solving the problem, and I shall content myself by putting together a few notes on some of the solutions I have come across, particularly on those due to De Moivre, Euler, Vandermonde, Warnsdorff, and Roget.

On a board containing an even number of cells the path may or may not be re-entrant, but on a board containing an odd number of cells it cannot be re-entrant. For, if a knight begins on a white cell, its first move must take it to a black cell, the next to a white cell, and so on. Hence, if its path passes through all the cells, then on a board of an odd number

---

* For a bibliography see A. van der Linde, *Geschichte und Literatur des Schachspiels*, Berlin, 1874, vol. II, pp. 101—111. On the problem and its history see a memoir by P. Volpicelli in *Atti della Reale Accademia de Lincei*, Rome, 1872, vol. XXV, pp. 87—162: also *Applications de l'Analyse Mathématique au Jeu des Échecs*, by C. F. de Jaenisch, 3 vols., Petrograd 1862-3; and General Parmentier, *Association Française pour l'Avancement des Sciences*, 1891, 1892, 1894.

of cells the last move must leave it on a cell of the same colour as that on which it started, and therefore these cells cannot be connected by one move.

The earliest solutions of which I have any knowledge are those given at the beginning of the eighteenth century by De Montmort and De Moivre.* They apply to the ordinary chess-board of 64 cells, and depend on dividing (mentally) the board into an inner square containing sixteen cells surrounded by an outer ring of cells two deep. If initially the knight is placed on a cell in the outer ring, it moves round that ring always in the same direction so as to fill it up completely—going into

34	49	22	11	36	39	24	1
21	10	35	50	23	12	37	40
48	33	62	57	38	25	2	13
9	20	51	54	63	60	41	26
32	47	58	61	56	53	14	3
19	8	55	52	59	64	27	42
46	31	6	17	44	29	4	15
7	18	45	30	5	16	43	28

30	21	6	15	28	19
7	16	29	20	5	14
22	31	8	35	18	27
9	36	17	26	13	4
32	23	2	11	34	25
1	10	33	24	3	12

De Moivre's Solution.   *Euler's Thirty-six Cell Solution.*

the inner square only when absolutely necessary. When the outer ring is filled up, the order of the moves required for filling the remaining cells presents but little difficulty. If initially the knight is placed on the inner square, the process must be reversed. The method can be applied to square and rectangular boards of all sizes. It is illustrated sufficiently by De Moivre's solution, which is given above, where the numbers indicate the order in which the cells are occupied successively. I place by its side a somewhat similar re-entrant solution, due to Euler, for a board of 36 cells. If a chess-board is used it

* They were sent by their authors to Brook Taylor who seems to have previously suggested the problem. I do not know where they were first published; they were quoted by Ozanam and Montucla, see Ozanam, 1803 edition, vol. I, p. 178; 1840 edition, p. 80.

is convenient to place a counter on each cell as the knight leaves it.

The earliest serious attempt to deal with the subject by mathematical analysis was made by Euler * in 1759 : it was due to a suggestion made by L. Bertrand of Geneva, who subsequently (in 1778) issued an account of it. This method is applicable to boards of any shape and size, but in general the solutions to which it leads are not symmetrical, and their mutual connection is not apparent.

Euler commenced by moving the knight at random over the board until it has no move open to it. With care this will leave only a few cells not traversed : denote them by $a, b, \ldots$. His method consists in establishing certain rules by which these vacant cells can be interpolated into various parts of the circuit, and by which the circuit can be made re-entrant.

The following example, mentioned by Legendre as one of exceptional difficulty, illustrates the method. Suppose that

55	58	29	40	27	44	19	22
60	39	56	43	30	21	26	45
57	54	59	28	41	18	23	20
38	51	42	31	8	25	46	17
53	32	37	a	47	16	9	24
50	3	52	33	36	7	12	15
1	34	5	48	b	14	c	10
4	49	2	35	6	11	d	13

22	25	50	39	52	35	60	57
27	40	23	36	49	58	53	34
24	21	26	51	38	61	56	59
41	28	37	48	3	54	33	62
20	47	42	13	32	63	4	55
29	16	19	46	43	2	7	10
18	45	14	31	12	9	64	5
15	30	17	44	1	6	11	8

Figure i.   *Figure* ii.
Example of Euler's Method.

we have formed the route given in figure i above—namely, 1, 2, 3, . . . , 59, 60 ; and that there are four cells left untraversed namely, a, b, c, d.

We begin by making the path 1 to 60 re-entrant. The

* *Mémoires de Berlin* for 1759, Berlin, 1766, pp. 310—337; or *Commentationes Arithmeticae Collectae*, Petrograd, 1849, vol. I, pp. 337—355.

cell 1 commands a cell p, where p is 32, 52, or 2. The cell 60 commands a cell q, where q is 29, 59, or 51. Then, if any of these values of p and q differ by unity, we can make the route re-entrant. This is the case here if $p = 52$, $q = 51$. Thus the cells 1, 2, 3, ..., 51; 60, 59, ..., 52 form a re-entrant route of 60 moves. Hence, if we replace the numbers 60, 59, ..., 52 by 52, 53, ..., 60, the steps will be numbered consecutively. I recommend the reader who wishes to follow the subsequent details of Euler's argument to construct this square on a piece of paper before proceeding further.

Next, we proceed to add the cells a, b, d to this route. In the new diagram of 60 cells formed as above the cell a commands the cells there numbered 51, 53, 41, 25, 7, 5, and 3. It is in-different which of these we select: suppose we take 51. Then we must make 51 the last cell of the route of 60 cells, so that we can continue with a, b, d. Hence, if the reader will add 9 to every number on the diagram he has constructed, and then replace 61, 62, ..., 69 by 1, 2, ..., 9, he will have a route which starts from the cell occupied originally by 60, the 60th move is on to the cell occupied originally by 51, and the 61st, 62nd, 63rd moves will be on the cells a, b, d respectively.

It remains to introduce the cell c. Since c commands the cell now numbered 25, and 63 commands the cell now num-bered 24, this can be effected in the same way as the first route was made re-entrant. In fact, the cells numbered 1, 2, ..., 24; 63, 62, ..., 25, c form a knight's path. Hence we must replace 63, 62, ..., 25 by the numbers 25, 26, ..., 63, and then we can fill up c with 64. We have now a route which covers the whole board.

Lastly, it remains to make this route re-entrant. First, we must get the cells 1 and 64 near one another. This can be effected thus. Take one of the cells commanded by 1, such as 28, then 28 commands 1 and 27. Hence the cells 64, 63, ..., 28; 1, 2, ..., 27 form a route; and this will be represented in the diagram if we replace the cells numbered 1, 2, ..., 27 by 27, 26, ..., 1.

N

The cell now occupied by 1 commands the cells 26, 38, 54, 12, 2, 14, 16, 28; and the cell occupied by 64 commands the cells 13, 43, 63, 55. The cells 13 and 14 are consecutive, and therefore the cells 64, 63, . . . , 14; 1, 2, . . . , 13 form a route. Hence we must replace the numbers 1, 2, . . . , 13 by 13, 12, . . . , 1, and we obtain a re-entrant route covering the whole board, which is represented in the second of the diagrams given on page 176. Euler showed how seven other re-entrant routes can be deduced from any given re-entrant route.

It is not difficult to apply the method so as to form a route which begins on one given cell and ends on any other given cell.

58	43	60	37	52	41	62	35
49	46	57	42	61	36	53	40
44	59	48	51	38	55	34	63
47	50	45	56	33	64	39	54
22	7	32	1	24	13	18	15
31	2	23	6	19	16	27	12
8	21	4	29	10	25	14	17
3	30	9	20	5	28	11	26

50	45	62	41	60	39	54	35
63	42	51	48	53	36	57	38
46	49	44	61	40	59	34	55
43	64	47	52	33	56	37	58
26	5	24	1	20	15	32	11
23	2	27	8	29	12	17	14
6	25	4	21	16	1ð	10	31
3	22	7	28	9	30	13	18

Euler's Half-board Solution.   *Roget's Half-board Solution.*

Euler next investigated how his method could be modified so as to allow of the imposition of additional restrictions.

An interesting example of this kind is where the first 32 moves are confined to one-half of the board. One solution of this is delineated above. The order of the first 32 moves can be determined by Euler's method. It is obvious that, if to the number of each such move we add 32, we shall have a corresponding set of moves from 33 to 64 which would cover the other half of the board; but in general the cell numbered 33 will not be a knight's move from that numbered 32, nor will 64 be a knight's move from 1.

Euler, however, proceeded to show how the first 32 moves

might be determined so that, if the half of the board containing the corresponding moves from 33 to 64 was twisted through two right angles, the two routes would become united and re-entrant. If x and y are the numbers of a cell reckoned from two consecutive sides of the board, we may call the cell whose distances are respectively x and y from the opposite sides a complementary cell. Thus the cells (x, y) and $(9 - x, 9 - y)$ are complementary, where x and y denote respectively the column and row occupied by the cell. Then in Euler's solution the numbers in complementary cells differ by 32: for instance, the cell $(3, 7)$ is complementary to the cell $(6, 2)$, the one is occupied by 57, the other by 25.

Roget's method, which is described later, can be also applied to give half-board solutions. The result is indicated above. The close of Euler's memoir is devoted to showing how the method could be applied to crosses and other rectangular figures. I may note in particular his elegant re-entrant symmetrical solution for a square of 100 cells.

The next attempt of any special interest is due to Vandermonde,* who reduced the problem to arithmetic. His idea was to cover the board by two or more independent routes taken at random, and then to connect the routes. He defined the position of a cell by a fraction x/y, whose numerator x is the number of the cell from one side of the board, and whose denominator y is its number from the adjacent side of the board; this is equivalent to saying that x and y are the co-ordinates of a cell. In a series of fractions denoting a knight's path, the differences between the numerators of two consecutive fractions can be only one or two, while the corresponding differences between their denominators must be two or one respectively. Also x and y cannot be less than 1 or greater than 8. The notation is convenient, but Vandermonde applied it merely to obtain a particular solution of the problem for a board of 64 cells : the method by which he effected this is analogous to that established by Euler,

* *L'Histoire de l'Académie des Sciences* for 1771, Paris, 1774, pp. 566—574.

but it is applicable only to squares of an even order. The route that he arrives at is defined in his notation by the following fractions : 5/5, 4/3, 2/4, 4/5, 5/3, 7/4, 8/2, 6/1, 7/3, 8/1, 6/2, 8/3, 7/1, 5/2, 6/4, 8/5, 7/7, 5/8, 6/6, 5/4, 4/6, 2/5, 1/7, 3/8, 2/6, 1/8, 3/7, 1/6, 2/8, 4/7, 3/5, 1/4, 2/2, 4/1, 3/3, 1/2, 3/1, 2/3, 1/1, 3/2, 1/3, 2/1, 4/2, 3/4, 1/5, 2/7, 4/8, 3/6, 4/4, 5/6, 7/5, 8/7, 6/8, 7/6, 8/8, 6/7, 8/6, 7/8, 5/7, 6/5, 8/4, 7/2, 5/1, 6/3.

The path is re-entrant, but unsymmetrical. Had he transferred the first three fractions to the end of this series, he would have obtained two symmetrical circuits of thirty-two moves joined unsymmetrically and might have been enabled to advance further in the problem. Vandermonde also considered the case of a route in a cube.

In 1773 Collini * proposed the exclusive use of symmetrical routes arranged without reference to the initial cell, but connected in such a manner as to permit of our starting from it. This is the foundation of the modern manner of attacking the problem. The method was re-invented in 1825 by Pratt,† and in 1840 by Roget, and has been subsequently employed by various writers. Neither Collini nor Pratt showed skill in using this method. The rule given by Roget is described later.

One of the most ingenious of the solutions of the knight's path is that given in 1823 by Warnsdorff.‡ His rule is that the knight must be always moved to one of the cells from which it will command the fewest squares not already traversed. The solution is not symmetrical and not re-entrant ; moreover, it is difficult to trace practically. The rule has not been proved to be true, but no exception to it is known : apparently it applies also to all rectangular boards which can be covered completely by a knight. It is somewhat curious that in most

* Solution du Problème du Cavalier au Jeu des Échecs, Mannheim, 1773.

† Studies of Chess, sixth edition, London, 1825.

‡ H. C. Warnsdorff, Des Rösselsprunges einfachste und allgemeinste Lösung, Schmalkalden, 1823 : see also Jaenisch, vol. II, pp. 56—61, 273 — 289.

cases a single false step, except in the last three or four moves, will not affect the result.

Warnsdorff added that when, by the rule, two or more cells are open to the knight, it may be moved to either or any of them indifferently. This is not so, and with great ingenuity two or three cases of failure have been constructed, but it would require exceptionally bad luck to happen accidentally on such a route.

The above methods have been applied to boards of various shapes, especially to boards in the form of rectangles, crosses, and circles.*

All the more recent investigations impose additional restrictions : such as to require that the route shall be re-entrant, or more generally that it shall begin and terminate on given cells.

The simplest solution with which I am acquainted is due to De Lavernède, but is more generally associated with the name of Roget, whose paper in 1840 attracted general notice to it.† It divides the whole route into four circuits, which can be combined so as to enable us to begin on any cell and terminate on any other cell of a different colour. Hence, if we like to select this last cell at a knight's move from the initial cell, we obtain a re-entrant route. On the other hand, the rule is applicable only to square boards containing $(4n)^2$ cells : for example, it could not be used on the board of the French *jeu des dames*, which contains 100 cells.

Roget began by dividing the board of 64 cells into four quarters. Each quarter contains 16 cells, and these 16 cells can be arranged in 4 groups, each group consisting of 4 cells which form a closed knight's path. All the cells in each such path are denoted by the same letter *l*, *e*, *a*, or *p*, as the case

* See, *e.g.*, T. Ciccolini's work *Del Cavallo degli Scacchi*, Paris, 1836.

† J. E. T. de Lavernède, *Mémoires de l'Académie Royale du Gard*, Nimes, 1839, pp. 151—179. P. M. Roget, *Philosophical Magazine*, April, 1840, series 3, vol. XVI, pp. 305—309; see also the *Quarterly Journal of Mathematics* for 1877, vol. XIV, pp. 354—359; and the *Leisure Hour*, Sept. 13, 1873, pp. 587—590, and Dec. 20, 1873, pp. 813—815.

may be. The path of 4 cells indicated by the consonants *l* and the path indicated by the consonants *p* are diamond-shaped : the paths indicated respectively by the vowels *e* and *a* are square-shaped, as may be seen by looking at one of the four quarters in figure i below.

Now, all the 16 cells on a complete chess-board which are marked with the same letter can be combined into one circuit, and wherever the circuit begins we can make it end on any other cell in the circuit, provided it is of a different colour from the initial cell. If it is indifferent on what cell the circuit terminates, we may make the circuit re-entrant, and

l	*e*	*a*	*p*	*l*	*e*	*a*	*p*
a	*p*	*l*	*e*	*a*	*p*	*l*	*e*
e	*l*	*p*	*a*	*e*	*l*	*p*	*a*
p	*a*	*e*	*l*	*p*	*a*	*e*	*l*
l	*e*	*a*	*p*	*l*	*e*	*a*	*p*
a	*p*	*l*	*e*	*a*	*p*	*l*	*e*
e	*l*	*p*	*a*	*e*	*l*	*p*	*a*
p	*a*	*e*	*l*	*p*	*a*	*e*	*l*

Roget's Solution (i).

34	51	32	15	38	53	18	3
31	14	35	52	17	2	39	54
50	33	16	29	56	37	4	19
13	30	49	36	1	20	55	40
48	63	28	9	44	57	22	5
27	12	45	64	21	8	41	58
62	47	10	25	60	43	6	23
11	26	61	46	7	24	59	42

Roget's Solution (ii).

in this case we can make the direction of motion round each group (of 4 cells) the same. For example, all the cells marked *p* can be arranged in the circuit indicated by the successive numbers 1 to 16 in figure ii above. Similarly all the cells marked *a* can be combined into the circuit indicated by the numbers 17 to 32; all the *l* cells into the circuit 33 to 48; and all the *e* cells into the circuit 49 to 64. Each of the circuits indicated above is symmetrical and re-entrant. The consonant and the vowel circuits are said to be of opposite kinds.

The general problem will be solved if we can combine the four circuits into a route which will start from any given cell, and terminate on the 64th move on any other given cell of a different colour. To effect this Roget gave the two following rules.

First. If the initial cell and the final cell are denoted the one by a consonant and the other by a vowel, take alternately circuits indicated by consonants and vowels, beginning with the circuit of 16 cells indicated by the letter of the initial cell and concluding with the circuit indicated by the letter of the final cell.

Second. If the initial cell and the final cell are denoted both by consonants or both by vowels, first select a cell, Y, in the same circuit as the final cell, Z, and one move from it; next select a cell, X, belonging to one of the opposite circuits and one move from Y. This is always possible. Then, leaving out the cells Z and Y, it always will be possible, by the rule already given, to travel from the initial cell to the cell X in 62 moves, and thence to move to the final cell on the 64th move.

In both cases, however, it must be noticed that the cells in each of the first three circuits will have to be taken in such an order that the circuit does not terminate on a corner, and it may be desirable also that it should not terminate on any of the border cells. This will necessitate some caution. As far as is consistent with these restrictions, it is convenient to make these circuits re-entrant, and to take them and every group in them in the same direction of rotation.

As an example, suppose that we are to begin on the cell numbered 1 in figure ii above, which is one of those in a p circuit, and to terminate on the cell numbered 64, which is one of those in an e circuit. This falls under the first rule: hence first we take the 16 cells marked p, next the 16 cells marked a, then the 16 cells marked l, and lastly the 16 cells marked e. One way of effecting this is shown in the diagram. Since the cell 64 is a knight's move from the initial cell, the route is re-entrant. Also each of the four circuits in the diagram is symmetrical, re-entrant, and taken in the same direction, and the only point where there is any apparent breach in the uniformity of the movement is in the passage from the cell numbered 32 to that numbered 33.

A rule for re-entrant routes, similar to that of Roget, has been given by various subsequent writers, especially by De Polignac * and by Laquière,† who have stated it at much greater length. Neither of these authors seems to have been aware of Roget's theorems. De Polignac, like Roget, illustrates the rule by assigning letters to the various squares in the way explained above, and asserts that a similar rule is applicable to all even squares.

Roget's method can be also applied to two half-boards, as indicated in the figure given above on page 178.

The method which Jaenisch gives as the most fundamental is not very different from that of Roget. It leads to eight forms, similar to that in the diagram printed below, in which the sum of the numbers in every column and every row is 260; but, although symmetrical, it is not, in my opinion, so easy to reproduce as that given by Roget. Other solutions, notably those by Moon and by Wenzelides, were given in former editions of this work. The two re-entrant routes printed below,

63	22	15	40	1	42	59	18
14	39	64	21	60	17	2	43
37	62	23	16	41	4	19	58
24	13	38	61	20	57	44	3
11	36	25	52	29	46	5	56
26	51	12	33	8	55	30	45
35	10	49	28	53	32	47	6
50	27	34	9	48	7	54	31

Jaenisch's Solution.

15	20	17	36	13	64	61	34
18	37	14	21	60	35	12	63
25	16	19	44	5	62	33	56
38	45	26	59	22	55	4	11
27	24	39	6	43	10	57	54
40	49	46	23	58	3	32	9
47	28	51	42	7	30	53	2
50	41	48	29	52	1	8	31

Two Half-board Solutions.

* *Comptes Rendus*, April, 1861; and *Bulletin de la Société Mathématique de France*, 1881, vol. IX, pp. 17—24.

† *Bulletin de la Société Mathématique de France*, 1880, vol. VIII, pp. 82—102, 132—158.

each covering 32 cells, and together covering the board, are remarkable as constituting a magic square.*

It is as yet impossible to say how many solutions of the problem exist. Legendre † mentioned the question, but Minding ‡ was the earliest writer to attempt to answer it. More recent investigations have shown that on the one hand the number of possible routes is less § than the number of combinations of 168 things taken 63 at a time, and on the other hand is greater than 122,802512—since this latter number is the number of re-entrant paths of a particular type.‖

Analogous Problems. Similar problems can be constructed in which it is required to determine routes by which a piece moving according to certain laws (*e.g.* a chess-piece such as a king, etc.) can travel from a given cell over a board so as to occupy successively all the cells, or certain specified cells, once, and only once, and terminate its route in a given cell. Euler's method can be applied to find routes of this kind : for instance, he applied it to find a re-entrant route by which a piece that moved two cells forward like a castle and then one cell like a bishop would occupy in succession all the black cells on the board.

King's Re-entrant Path.¶ As one example here is a re-entrant tour of a king which moves successively to every cell of the board. I give it because the numbers indicating the cells successively occupied form a magic square. Of course, this also gives a solution of a re-entrant route of a queen covering the board.

* See A. Rilly, *Le Problème du Cavalier des Échecs*, Troyes, 1905.

† *Théorie des Nombres*, Paris, 2nd edition, 1830, vol. II, p. 165.

‡ *Cambridge and Dublin Mathematical Journal*, 1852, vol. VII, pp. 147—156; and *Crelle's Journal*, 1853, vol. XLIV, pp. 73—82.

§ Jaenisch, vol. II, p. 268.

‖ Kraïtchik, pp. 360, 402.

¶ Cf. I. Ghersi, *Matematica dilettevole e curiosa*, Milan, 1921, p. 320 (fig. 261).

61	62	63	64	1	2	3	4
60	11	58	57	8	7	54	5
12	59	10	9	56	55	6	53
13	14	15	16	49	50	51	52
20	19	18	17	48	47	46	45
21	38	23	24	41	42	27	44
37	22	39	40	25	26	43	28
36	35	34	33	32	31	30	29

King's Magic Tour on a Chess-board.

Rook's Re-entrant Path. There is no difficulty in constructing re-entrant tours for a rook which moves successively
to every cell of the board. For instance, if the rook starts
from the cell 11, it can move successively to the cells 18, 88, 81,
71, 77, 67, 61, 51, 57, 47, 41, 31, 37, 27, 21, and so back to 11 :
this is a symmetrical route. Of course, this also gives a solution
of a re-entrant route for a king or a queen covering the board.
If we start from any of the cells mentioned above, the rook
takes sixteen moves. If we start from any cell in the middle
of one of these moves, it will take seventeen moves to cover
this route, but I believe that in most cases wherever the initial
cell be chosen, sixteen moves will suffice, though in general the
route will not be symmetrical. On a board of n^2 cells it is
possible to find a route by which a rook can move successively
from its initial cell to every other cell once, and only once.
Moreover,* starting on any cell, its path can be made to terminate, if n be even, on any other cell of a different colour, and
if n be odd, on any other cell of the same colour.

Bishop's Re-entrant Path. As yet another instance, a bishop
can traverse all the cells of one colour on the board in seventeen moves if the initial cell is properly chosen ; † for instance,

---

* *L'Intermédiaire des Mathématiciens*, Paris, 1901, vol. VIII, pp. 153—154.
† H. E. Dudeney, *The Tribune*, Dec. 3, 1906.

starting from the cell 11, it may move successively to the cells
55, 82, 71, 17, 28, 46, 13, 31, 86, 68, 57, 48, 15, 51, 84, 66, 88.
One more move will bring it back to the initial cell. From
the nature of the case, it must traverse some cells more than
once.

MISCELLANEOUS PROBLEMS

We may construct numerous such problems concerning
the determination of routes which cover the whole or part of
the board subject to certain conditions. I append a few others
which may tax the ingenuity of those not accustomed to such
problems.

Routes on a Chess-board. One of the simplest is the
determination of the path taken by a rook, placed in the cell
11, which moves, one cell at a time, to the cell 88, so that in
the course of its path it enters every cell once, and only once.
This can be done, though I have seen good mathematicians
puzzled to effect it. A hasty reader is apt to misunderstand
the conditions of the problem.

Another simple problem of this kind is to move a queen from
the cell 33 to the cell 66 in fifteen moves, entering every cell once
and only once, and never crossing its own track or entering a
cell more than once.*

A somewhat similar, but more difficult, question is the
determination of the greatest distance which can be travelled
by a queen starting from its own square in five consecutive
moves, subject to the condition that it never crosses its own
track or enters a cell more than once.† In calculating the
distance, it may be assumed that the paths go through the
centres of the cells. If the length of the side of a cell is 1
inch, the distance exceeds 33·97 inches.

Another familiar problem can be enunciated as follows.
Construct a rectangular board of mn cells by ruling $m + 1$
vertical lines and $n + 1$ horizontal lines. It is required to
know how many routes can be taken from the top left-hand

* H. E. Dudeney, *The Tribune*, Oct. 3, 1906.   † *Ibid.*, Oct. 2, 1906.

corner to the bottom right-hand corner, the motion being along the ruled lines and its direction being always either vertically downwards or horizontally from left to right. The answer is the number of permutations of $m + n$ things, of which m are alike of one kind and n are alike of another kind : this is equal to $(m + n)!/m!n!$. Thus on a square board containing 16 cells (*i.e.* one-quarter of a chess-board), where $m = n = 4$, there are 70 such routes ; while on a common chess-board, where $m = n = 8$, there are no less than 12870 such routes. A rook, moving according to the same law, can travel from the top left-hand cell to the bottom right-hand cell in $(m + n - 2)!/(m - 1)!(n - 1)!$ ways. Similar theorems can be enunciated for a parallelepiped.

Another question of this kind is the determination of the number of closed routes through mn points arranged in m rows and n columns, following the lines of the quadrilateral network, and passing once and only once through each point.[*]

Guarini's Problem. One of the oldest European problems connected with the chess-board is the following, which was propounded in 1512. It was quoted by Lucas in 1894, but I believe has not been published otherwise than in his works and the earlier editions of this book. On a board of nine cells, such as that drawn below, the two white knights are placed on the

a	C	d
D		B
b	A	c

two top corner cells (a, d), and the two black knights on the two bottom corner cells (b, c) : the other cells are left vacant. It is required to move the knights so that the white knights shall occupy the cells b and c, while the black shall occupy the cells a and d. The solution is obvious.

---

[*] See C. F. Sainte-Marie in *L'Intermédiaire des Mathématiciens*, Paris, vol. XI, March, 1904, pp. 86—88.

Queens' Problem. Another problem consists in placing sixteen queens on a board so that no three are in a straight line.* One solution is to place them on the cells 15, 16, 25, 26, 31, 32, 41, 42, 57, 58, 67, 68, 73, 74, 83, 84. It is, of course, assumed that each queen is placed on the middle of its cell.

LATIN SQUARES

Another problem of the chess-board type is the determination of the number x_n of Latin squares of any assigned order n : a Latin square of the nth order being defined as a square of n^2 cells (in n rows and n columns) in which n^2 letters consisting

2	0	1
1	2	0
0	1	2

$(1, 1)_3$

2	1	0
1	0	2
0	2	1

$(2, 1)_3$

1	2	3	0
2	3	0	1
3	0	1	2
0	1	2	3

$(1, 3)_4$

4	1	3	0	2
3	0	2	4	1
2	4	1	3	0
1	3	0	2	4
0	2	4	1	3

$(2, 1)_5$

of n " a's," n " b's," ..., are arranged in the cells so that the n letters in each row and each column are different. The general theory is difficult,† but it may amuse my readers to verify that $x_n = n! \ (n-1)! \ R_n$, where R_n is an integer, the first few values being $R_2 = R_3 = 1$, $R_4 = 4$, $R_5 = 56$, $R_6 = 9408$. H. W. Norton has conjectured that $R_7 = 16,927968$.

Latin squares of a special type may be constructed as *tables*

* H. E. Dudeney, *The Tribune*, November 7, 1906.

† See Fisher and Yates, *Proceedings of the Cambridge Philosophical Society*, 1934, vol. xxx, pp. 492–507; Norton, *Annals of Eugenics*, 1939, vol. ix, pp. 269–307.

of addition in the finite arithmetic modulo n (cf. page 109). The bottom row contains the numbers $0, \alpha, 2\alpha, \ldots, (n-1)\alpha$, and the left-hand column contains $0, \beta, 2\beta, \ldots, (n-1)\beta$. In every other cell we place the sum of the numbers which thus define its column and row. The resulting square may be denoted by $(\alpha, \beta)_n$.

Clearly α and β must be prime to n. If also $\alpha + \beta$ and $\alpha - \beta$ are prime to n (as in the last of the above examples), we have a " diagonal " Latin square : the n numbers in each diagonal (as well as those in each row and column) are all different.

Magic Card Square.* By superposing two properly related Latin squares of the fourth order, we can solve the familiar problem of placing the sixteen court cards (taken out of a pack) in the form of a square so that no row, no column, and neither of the diagonals shall contain more than one card of each suit and one card of each rank. There are 72 fundamental solutions, each of which by reflections and reversals produces 7 others.

Euler's Officers Problem.† A similar problem, proposed by Euler in 1779, consists in arranging, if it be possible, thirty-six officers taken from six regiments—the officers being in six groups, each consisting of six officers of equal rank, one drawn from each regiment; say officers of rank, a, b, c, d, e, f, drawn from the 1st, 2nd, 3rd, 4th, 5th, and 6th regiments—in a solid square formation of six by six, so that each row and each file shall contain one and only one officer of each rank and one and only one officer from each regiment. The problem is insoluble.

Eulerian Squares. This suggests the general problem of superposing two Latin squares of the nth order in such a way

---

* Ozanam, 1723 edition, vol. IV, p. 434.

† Euler's *Commentationes Arithmeticae*, Petrograd, 1849, vol. II, pp. 302—361. See also a paper by G. Tarry in the *Comptes rendus* of the French Association for the Advancement of Science, Paris, 1900, vol. II, pp. 170—203; and various notes in *L'Intermédiaire des Mathématiciens*, Paris, vol. III, 1896, pp. 17, 90; vol. V, 1898, pp. 83, 176, 252; vol. VI, 1899, p. 251; vol. VII, 1900, pp. 14, 311.

that the n^2 "marks," each consisting of two digits, shall be all different.   Such arrangements are termed Eulerian Squares. So far as I know, the problem is insoluble when n is singly-even. But it is easily solved in every other case.

22	01	10
11	20	02
00	12	21

34	41	03	10	22
13	20	32	44	01
42	04	11	23	30
21	33	40	02	14
00	12	24	31	43

12	03	30	21
31	20	13	02
23	32	01	10
00	11	22	33

The two Latin squares $(\alpha, \beta)_n$ and $(\alpha', \beta')_n$ can be superposed to form an Eulerian square, say * $(\alpha'\alpha, \beta'\beta)_n$, whenever the determinant $\alpha\beta' - \alpha'\beta$ is prime to n.   Since also α, β, α', β' must be prime to n, this method applies only when n is odd. The Eulerian square $(\alpha'\alpha, \beta'\beta)_n$, is "diagonal" if $\alpha \pm \beta$ and $\alpha' \pm \beta'$ are prime to n.   The squares $(12, 11)_3$ and $(12, 21)_5$ are drawn above, along with a diagonal Eulerian square of order 4, which solves the problem of the Magic Card Square.†
There is an Eulerian square $(12, 11)_n$ for every odd value of n; and a diagonal Eulerian square $(12, 21)_n$ for every odd value not divisible by 3.   There is no diagonal Eulerian square of

---

* This square may be regarded as a table of addition in a Galois arithmetic (page 73), the bottom row containing the multiples of $a'a$, and the left-hand column the multiples of $\beta'\beta$.   See E. Cazalas, *Sphinx*, 1936, pp. 134, 135.

† If the two Latin squares of which this Eulerian square is composed are written out in the binary scale, they are formally identical with tables of addition in the Galois arithmetic with moduli 2 and 111.   In both cases the bottom row contains the four marks of the arithmetic in their "natural" order: 0, 1, 10, 11.   The left-hand column contains these same marks in a different order, derivable from the "natural" order by multiplying throughout by the mark 10 or 11, respectively.   Extending the $(a, \beta)_n$ notation, we might call these Latin squares $(1, 10)_{2^2}$ and $(1, 11)_{2^2}$.   Such a construction leads to a Latin square $(a, \beta)_{p^m}$, whenever p is prime and $a\beta \neq 0$.   This is a *diagonal* square if also $(a - \beta)(a + \beta) \neq 0$.   Finally, two Latin squares $(a, \beta)_{p^m}$, $(a', \beta')_{p^m}$ make an Eulerian square whenever $a\beta' - a'\beta \neq 0$.

order **3** ; for one of order 9 see figure xxix of the next chapter (page 213) ; it is also possible to construct one of order 27.*

Given Eulerian squares of orders m and n, we can easily construct one of order mn. Since Eulerian squares of every odd order are known, and also one of order 4 and one of order 8 (see figure xxviii of the next chapter), it follows that such squares can be constructed for every doubly-even order. Moreover, since the special squares of orders 4, 8, 9, and 27 are diagonal, diagonal Eulerian squares can be constructed for every odd or doubly-even order, except, possibly, when the order is divisible by 3, but not by 9.

Generalized Eulerian Squares. These notions may be generalized in two different directions. First, we may superpose more than two Latin squares, so as to obtain a square of n^2 "marks" each consisting of $k \; (> 2)$ digits. For instance, the Latin squares $(\alpha, \beta)_n, (\alpha', \beta')_n, (\alpha'', \beta'')_n$ lead to a three-digit Eulerian square $(\alpha''\alpha'\alpha, \beta''\beta'\beta)_n$ whenever one (at least) of the determinants $\alpha\beta' - \alpha'\beta, \alpha\beta'' - \alpha''\beta, \alpha'\beta'' - \alpha''\beta'$ is prime to n.

Secondly, we may use Latin cubes instead of Latin squares, a Latin cube of the nth order being defined as a cube of n^3 cells (in n rows, n columns, and n files) in which n^3 letters (or numbers) consisting of n^2 a's, n^2 b's, ..., are arranged in the cells so that the n letters in each row, each column, and each file, are different. In particular, a three-dimensional table of addition (mod n) provides a Latin cube $(\alpha, \beta, \gamma)_n$. Three such cubes can be superposed so as to form the Eulerian Cube $(\alpha''\alpha'\alpha, \beta''\beta'\beta, \gamma''\gamma'\gamma)_n$ provided the determinant

$$\begin{vmatrix} \alpha & \beta & \gamma \\ \alpha' & \beta' & \gamma' \\ \alpha'' & \beta'' & \gamma'' \end{vmatrix}$$

is prime to n. (It is necessary to superpose at least three Latin cubes, in order to make the n^3 "marks" all different.)

* In the notation of the preceding footnote, a diagonal Eulerian square of order 27 can be derived from the Latin squares $(1, 10)_{3^3}, (1, 11)_{3^3}$, which are constructed as tables of addition in the Galois arithmetic with moduli **3** and 1021.

CHAPTER VII

MAGIC SQUARES

A *Magic Square* consists of a number of integers arranged in the form of a square, so that the sum of the numbers in every row, in every column, and in each diagonal is the same. If the integers are the consecutive numbers from 1 to n^2, the square is said to be of the nth order, and it is easily seen that in this case the sum of the numbers in every row, column, and diagonal is equal to $\frac{1}{2}n(n^2 + 1)$. Unless otherwise stated, I confine my account to such magic squares—that is, to squares formed with consecutive integers from 1 upwards. The same rules cover similar problems with n^2 numbers in arithmetical progression.

Thus the first 16 integers, arranged in either of the forms in figures i and ii below, represent magic squares of the fourth

16	3	2	13
5	10	11	8
9	6	7	12
4	15	14	1

15	10	3	6
4	5	16	9
14	11	2	7
1	8	13	12

Figure i. $n = 4.$ *Figure* ii. $n = 4.$

order, the sum of the numbers in each row, column, and diagonal being 34. Similarly, figure iii on page 195 and figure xvi on page 206 represent magic squares of the fifth order; figure vi on page 197 represents a magic square of the sixth order; figure xiv on page 201 and figure xvii on page 206 represent magic squares of the seventh order; figures xiii, xx, xxviii, xxxix represent magic squares of the eighth order;

o

figures xxii, xxix represent magic squares of the ninth order ; and figure ix represents a magic square of the tenth order.

The formation of these squares is an old amusement, and in times when mystical ideas were associated with particular numbers it was natural that such arrangements should be studied. Magic squares were constructed in China before the Christian era : their introduction into Europe appears to have been due to Moschopulus, who lived at Constantinople in the early part of the fifteenth century. The famous Cornelius Agrippa (1486—1535) constructed magic squares of the orders 3, 4, 5, 6, 7, 8, 9, which were associated by him with the seven astrological " planets " : namely, Saturn, Jupiter, Mars, the Sun, Venus, Mercury, and the Moon. A magic square engraved on a silver plate was sometimes prescribed as a charm against the plague, and one—namely, that represented in figure i on the previous page—is drawn in the picture of Melancholy, painted in 1514 by Albert Dürer, the numbers in the middle cells of the bottom row giving the date of the work. The mathematical theory of the construction of these squares was taken up in France in the seventeenth century, and later has been a favourite subject with writers in many countries.*

It is convenient to use the following terms. The spaces or small squares occupied by the numbers are called *cells*. It is customary to call the rows first, second, etc., reckoning from the top, and the columns first, second, etc., reckoning from the left. The hth and $(n + 1 - h)$th rows (or columns) are said to be *complementary*. The kth cell in the hth row is said to be *skewly related* to the $(n + 1 - k)$th cell in the $(n + 1 - h)$th row. Skewly related cells are situated symmetrically to the centre of the square.

Magic squares of any order higher than two can be constructed at sight. The rule to be used varies according as the

* For a sketch of the history of the subject and its bibliography see S. Günther's *Geschichte der mathematischen Wissenschaften*, Leipzig, 1876, chapter IV; W. Ahrens, *Mathematische Unterhaltungen und Spiele*, Leipzig, 1901, chapter XII; and W. S. Andrews, *Magic Squares and Cubes*, Chicago, 1917.

order n is odd—that is, of the form $2m + 1$; or singly-even—
that is, of the form $2(2m + 1)$; or doubly-even—that is, of the
form $4m$. In each case, I now give the simplest rule with
which I am acquainted.

MAGIC SQUARES OF AN ODD ORDER

A magic square of the nth order, where $n = 2m + 1$, can
be constructed by the following rule due to De la Loubère.*
First, the number 1 is placed in the middle cell of the top row.
The successive numbers are then placed in their natural order
in a diagonal line which slopes upwards to the right, except
that (i) when the top row is reached, the next number is
written in the bottom row as if it came immediately above the
top row; (ii) when the right-hand column is reached, the next

17	24	1	8	15
23	5	7	14	16
4	6	13	20	22
10	12	19	21	3
11	18	25	2	9

31	43	00	12	24
42	04	11	23	30
03	10	22	34	41
14	21	33	40	02
20	32	44	01	13

Figure iii. $n = 5$.   *Figure* iv. $n = 5$.

number is written in the left-hand column, as if it immediately
succeeded the right-hand column; and (iii) when a cell which
has been filled up already or when the top right-hand square
is reached, the path of the series drops to the row vertically
below it and then continues to mount again. Probably a
glance at the diagram in figure iii, showing the construction by
this rule of a square of the fifth order, will make the rule clear.

The reason why such a square is magic can be best explained
by taking a particular case, for instance $n = 5$, and expressing
all the numbers in the scale of notation whose radix is 5 (or n,

* S. De la Loubère, *Du Royaume de Siam* (Eng. Trans.), London, 1693,
vol. II, pp. 227—247. De la Loubère was the envoy of Louis XIV to Siam
in 1687—1688, and there learnt this method.

if the magic square is of order n). To simplify the discussion, let us at the same time diminish each number by unity; this clearly makes no difference to the magic properties. The resulting square (figure iv) may be regarded as an Eulerian square.* Since every row and every column contains one of each of the 5 possible unit digits and one of each of the radix digits, the magic property of the rows and columns is automatically assured; so is that of the leading diagonal. The other diagonal suffers from a repetition of the radix digit 2 (in general, m), but it still has the correct sum. Moreover, every number from 0 to $n^2 - 1$ occurs once and only once.

The reader can easily apply this rule to construct a magic square of the third order. Such a square, called the *lo-shu*,† is attributed to the Chinese Emperor Yu, about 2200 B.C., and is still used as a charm by various Oriental peoples. Even in the West it is generally to be seen on the deck of any large passenger ship, for scoring in such games as " shuffleboard."

Magic Squares of a Singly-Even Order

A magic square of the nth order, where $n = 2(2m + 1)$, can be constructed by the following rule due to Ralph Strachey.‡ Divide the square into four equal quarters A, B, C, D. Construct in A, by De la Loubère's method, a magic square with

A	C
D	B

the numbers 1 to u^2 where $u = n/2$. Construct by the same rule, in B, C, D, similar magic squares with the numbers

* See page 191. The Eulerian square that underlies De la Loubère's rule is derivable from $(12, 11)_n$ by reversing the order of the rows, and cyclically permuting the columns.

† D. E. Smith, *History of Mathematics*, Boston, 1925, vol. II, p. 591.

‡ Communicated to me in a letter, August 1918.

$u^2 + 1$ to $2u^2$, $2u^2 + 1$ to $3u^2$, and $3u^2 + 1$ to $4u^2$. Clearly the resulting composite square is magic in columns. In the middle row of A take the m cells next but one to the left-hand side, in each of the other rows take the m cells nearest to the left-hand side, and interchange the numbers in these cells with the numbers in the corresponding cells in D. Next interchange the numbers in the cells in each of the $m - 1$ columns

8	1	6	26	19	24
3	5	7	21	23	25
4	9	2	22	27	20
35	28	33	17	10	15
30	32	34	12	14	16
31	36	29	13	18	11

Figure v. Initial Quarter-Squares.

35	1	6	26	19	24
3	32	7	21	23	25
31	9	2	22	27	20
8	28	33	17	10	15
30	5	34	12	14	16
4	36	29	13	18	11

Figure vi. Final Square, $n = 6$.

27+8	0+1	0+6	18+8	18+1	18+6
0+3	27+5	0+7	18+3	18+5	18+7
27+4	0+9	0+2	18+4	18+9	18+2
0+8	27+1	27+6	9+8	9+1	9+6
27+3	0+5	27+7	9+3	9+5	9+7
0+4	27+9	27+2	9+4	9+9	9+2

Figure vii. Final Square, $n = 6$.

next to the right-hand side of C with the numbers in the corresponding cells in B. Of course, the resulting square remains magic in columns. It will also now be magic in rows and diagonals, since the construction is equivalent to writing in each of the quarters A, B, C, D, equal magic squares of the order u made with the numbers 1 to u^2, and then superposing on them a magic square of the nth order made with the four radix numbers 0, u^2, $2u^2$, $3u^2$, each repeated u^2 times. The

component squares being magic, the square resulting from
their superposition must be magic, and they are so formed

17	24	1	8	15	67	74	51	58	65
32	5	7	14	16	73	55	57	64	6
4	6	13	20	22	54	56	63	70	72
0	12	19	21	3	60	62	69	71	53
11	18	25	2	9	61	68	75	52	59
92	99	76	83	90	42	49	26	33	40
98	80	82	89	91	48	30	32	39	41
79	81	88	95	97	29	31	38	45	47
85	87	94	96	78	35	37	44	46	28
86	93	100	77	84	36	43	50	27	34

Figure viii.   *Initial Quarter-Squares, $n = 10$.*

92	99	1	8	15	67	74	51	58	40
98	80	7	14	16	73	55	57	64	41
4	81	88	20	22	54	56	63	70	47
85	87	19	21	3	60	62	69	71	28
86	93	25	2	9	61	68	75	52	34
17	24	76	83	90	42	49	26	33	65
23	5	82	89	91	48	30	32	39	66
79	6	13	95	97	29	31	38	45	72
10	12	94	96	78	35	37	44	46	53
11	18	100	77	84	36	43	50	27	59

Figure ix.   *Final Square, $n = 10$.*

that their superposition ensures that every number from 1 to
n^2 appears once and only once in the resulting square.

Figures v and vi show the application of the rule to the
construction of a magic square of the sixth order. In figure v,

those numbers in the cells in the initial quarter-square A which are to be interchanged vertically with the numbers in the corresponding cells in D are underlined; figure vi represents the final square obtained; and figure vii shows how these interchanges serve to bring the radix numbers to a position which makes the square magic.

Since this construction is novel, I add figures to show the application of the rule to the formation of a square of the tenth order: in figure viii those numbers in the quarter-squares A and C which have to be interchanged vertically with the numbers in the corresponding cells in D and B are underlined, while figure ix represents the final magic square of the tenth order thus obtained.

MAGIC SQUARES OF A DOUBLY-EVEN ORDER

A magic square of the fourth order (figure xi), scarcely different from Dürer's (figure i), can be constructed by writing the numbers from 1 to 16 in their natural order in rows of

	2	3	
5			8
9			12
	14	15	

Figure x.

16	2	3	13
5	11	10	8
9	7	6	12
4	14	15	1

Figure xi. $n = 4$.

	2	3			6	7	
9			12	13			16
17			20	21			24
	26	27			30	31	
	34	35			38	39	
41			44	45			48
49			52	53			56
	58	59			62	63	

Figure xii.

64	2	3	61	60	6	7	57
9	55	54	12	13	51	50	16
17	47	46	20	21	43	42	24
40	26	27	37	36	30	31	33
32	34	35	29	28	38	39	25
41	23	22	44	45	19	18	48
49	15	14	52	53	11	10	56
8	58	59	5	4	62	63	1

Figure xiii. $n = 8$.

four, and then replacing the numbers in the *diagonal* cells by their complements. The same rule* applies to a magic square of any doubly-even order, if we change the numbers in those cells which are crossed by the diagonals of every component block of 4^2 cells. Figures xii and xiii show the case when $n = 8$.

BORDERED SQUARES

One other general method, due to Frénicle, of constructing magic squares of any order should be mentioned. By this method, to form a magic square of the nth order we first construct one of the $(n - 2)$th order, add to every number in it an integer, and then surround it with a border of the remaining numbers in such a way as to make the resulting square magic. In this manner from the magic square of the 3rd order we can build up successively squares of the orders 5, 7, 9, etc.—that is, every odd magic square. Similarly from a magic square of the 4th order we can build up successively all higher even magic squares.

The method of construction will be clear if I explain how the square in figure xiv, where $n = 7$, is built up. First the inner magic square of the $(n - 2)$th order is formed by any rule we like to choose: the sum of the numbers in each line being $(n - 2)\{(n - 2)^2 + 1\}/2$. To every number in it, $2n - 2$ is added: thus the sum of the numbers in each row, column, and diagonal is now $(n - 2)\{n^2 + 1\}/2$. The numbers not used are $1, 2, \ldots, 2n - 2$, and their complements, n^2, $n^2 - 1$, $\ldots$, $n^2 - 2n + 3$. These reserved numbers are placed in the $4(n - 1)$ border cells so that complementary numbers occur at the end of each row, column, and diagonal of the inner square: this makes the sum of the numbers in each of these latter lines equal to $n(n^2 + 1)/2$. It only remains to make the sum of the numbers in each of the border lines also have this value: such an arrangement is easily

* Kraïtchik, p. 176. R. V. Heath has devised a similar rule for constructing a Magic Cube.

made by trial and error. With a little patience a magic square of any order can be thus built up, border upon border, and, of course, it will have the property that, if each border is successively stripped off, the remaining square will still be magic. This is a method of construction much favoured by self-taught mathematicians.

Definite rules for arranging the numbers in the border cells have been indicated,* though usually not in a precise form. Recently, Mr. J. Travers † has proposed a simple rule for constructing an odd square, where $n = 2m + 1$. Rather

46	1	2	3	42	41	40
45	35	13	14	32	31	5
44	34	28	21	26	16	6
7	17	23	25	27	33	43
12	20	24	29	22	30	38
11	19	37	36	18	15	39
10	49	48	47	8	9	4

Figure xiv. *A Bordered Square,*
$n = 7$.

	1	2	3			
		13	14			5
			21		16	6
7	17	23	25			
12	20	24		22		
11	19			18	15	
10				8	9	4

Figure xv.

than describe it in words, I illustrate its application to the above example (which is in fact a multiple bordered square). Figure xv indicates the proper positions for the numbers 1, 2, ..., m; $m + 1$; $m + 2$, ..., $2m$; $2m + 1$; $2m + 2$, ..., $3m$; $3m + 1$, ..., $4m$. The complementary numbers are easily inserted afterwards. It may interest my readers to see if they can evolve a similar simple rule for the formation of bordered even squares.‡

* For instance, see *Japanese Mathematics* by D. E. Smith and Y. Mikami, Chicago, 1914, pp. 116—120 : in this work, in the diagram on p. 120, the numbers 8 and 29 should be interchanged.

† *Education Outlook*, 1936. For another good rule, see R. V. Heath, *Scripta Mathematica*, 1936, vol. IV, p. 67.

‡ A somewhat more complicated rule for even squares has been given by J. Travers, *Engineering Gazette*, Aug. 13, 1938, p. 6.

NUMBER OF SQUARES OF A GIVEN ORDER

One unsolved problem in the theory is the determination of the number of magic squares of the fifth (or any higher) order. There is, in effect, only one magic square of the third order, though by reflections and rotations it can be presented in 8 forms. There are 880 magic squares of the fourth order, but by reflections and rotations these can be presented in 7040 forms. The problem of the number of magic squares of the fifth order is incompletely solved. From the square given in figure iv (page 195) formed by De la Loubère's method, we can get 720 distinct squares; for we can permute the unit digits 0, 1, 2, 3, 4 in 5! ways, and the radix digits 0, 1, 3, 4 in 4! ways. We thus obtain 2880 magic squares of the fifth order, though only 720 of them are distinct. Bachet gave a somewhat similar construction,* in which he began by placing 1 in the cell immediately above the middle cell; his method gives another 720 distinct magic squares of the fifth order. There are, however, numerous other rules for constructing odd magic squares, and De la Hire showed that by methods known in his day, and apart from mere reflections and rotations, there were 57600 magic squares of the fifth order which could be formed by the methods he enumerated, and taking account of other methods, it is now known that the total number of magic squares of the fifth order considerably exceeds thirteen million.

SYMMETRICAL AND PANDIAGONAL SQUARES

With the exception of determining the number of squares of a given order, we may fairly say that the theory of the construction of magic squares, as defined above, has been sufficiently worked out. Accordingly, attention has of late been chiefly directed to the construction of squares which, in addition to being magic, satisfy other conditions. It has been suggested that we might impose on the construction of

* See Kraïtchik, p. 128.

a square of order n the condition that the sum of any two
numbers in cells skewly related to one another shall be
constant and equal to $n^2 + 1$. Such squares are called
Symmetrical (or *Associated*). Dürer's square (figure i) is symmetrical; so are all De la Loubère's squares (such as figure
iii), and all squares of doubly-even order that are constructed
by the rule described above (such as figures xi and xiii).
There are no symmetrical magic squares of singly-even order.*

One of the earliest additional conditions to be suggested
was that the square should be magic along the broken diagonals
as well as along the two ordinary diagonals.† Such squares
are called *Pandiagonal*. They are also known as nasik,
perfect, and diabolic squares.

A magic pandiagonal square of the fourth order ‡ was
inscribed at Khajuraho, India, as long ago as the eleventh or
twelfth century. A slightly different square of the same kind
is represented in figure ii on page 193. In it the sum of the
numbers in each row, column, and in the two diagonals is 34,
as also is the sum of the numbers in the six broken diagonals
formed by the numbers 15, 9, 2, 8, the numbers 10, 4, 7, 13,
the numbers 3, 5, 14, 12, the numbers 6, 4, 11, 13, the numbers
3, 9, 14, 8, and the numbers 10, 16, 7, 1.

It follows from the definition that if a pandiagonal square
be cut into two pieces along a line between any two rows or
any two columns, and the two pieces be interchanged, the new
square so formed will be also pandiagonally magic. Hence it
is obvious that by one vertical and one horizontal transposition

---

* C. Planck, *The Monist*, Chicago, 1919, vol. XXIX, p. 308.

† Squares of this type were mentioned by P. De la Hire, J. Sauveur, and
Euler. Attention was again called to them by A. H. Frost in the *Quarterly
Journal of Mathematics*, London, 1878, vol. XV, pp. 34—49, and subsequently
their properties have been discussed by several writers. Besides Frost's
papers I have made considerable use of a paper by E. McClintock in the
American Journal of Mathematics, vol. XIX, 1897, pp. 99—120.

‡ D. E. Smith, *History of Mathematics*, Boston, 1925, vol. II, p. 594. For
the general theory of such squares, see J. B. Rosser and R. J. Walker,
Bulletin of the American Mathematical Society, 1938, vol. XLIV, pp. 416—
420.

of this kind any number can be made to occupy any specified cell.

I have already remarked that there is essentially only one magic square of the third order; this is not pandiagonal, so the order of a pandiagonal square must exceed three. Moreover, there are no pandiagonal squares of singly-even order.[*] Pandiagonal squares of odd order, not divisible by 3, can be constructed by a rule somewhat analogous to De la Loubère's; and new rules have been devised to cover the cases where the order is divisible by 3 or 4.

Of the 880 magic squares of the fourth order, 48 are pandiagonal. Rosser and Walker have shown that there are exactly 3600 pandiagonal squares of the fifth order, more than 38 million of the seventh order, and more than $6\frac{1}{2}$ billion[†] of the eighth order.

Generalization of De la Loubère's Rule. It is convenient to name the n^2 cells by pairs of co-ordinates in such a way that the cells of the bottom row (from left to right) are $(0, 0)$, $(1, 0)$, ..., $(n - 1, 0)$, while those of the left-hand column (from bottom to top) are $(0, 0)$, $(0, 1)$, ..., $(0, n - 1)$. It follows that the cell (x, y) lies in the $(n - y)$th row and in the $(x + 1)$th column. The conventions (i) and (ii) on page 195 are equivalent to reducing the co-ordinates modulo n, so that the cells $(n + x, y)$ and $(x, n + y)$ are identified with (x, y).

In De la Loubère's method, the step from 1 to 2 increases both co-ordinates by unity—*i.e.* it is made by the " vector " $(1, 1)$. Similarly, the " cross-step " from n to $n + 1$ is made by the vector $(0, - 1)$. This method may evidently be generalized by taking other vectors : say (a, b) for the step from ξ to $\xi + 1$ ($\xi = 1, 2, ..., n - 1$), and $(a + a', b + b')$ for the cross-step from $\xi'n$ to $\xi'n + 1$ ($\xi' = 1, 2, ..., n - 1$). Consequently the step from 1 to $n + 1$ is $(n - 1)(a, b) + (a + a', b + b') \equiv (a', b')$ (mod n); the step from 1 to $\xi'n + 1$ is $(a'\xi', b'\xi')$; and the step from 1 to $\xi'n + \xi + 1$ is $(a\xi + a'\xi', b\xi + b'\xi')$.

* C. Planck, *loc. cit.*   † For American readers, $6\frac{1}{2}$ *trillion*.

Let (i, j) be the cell occupied by the number 1. The position of any other number s can be deduced by expressing $s - 1$ (as $\xi'\xi$) in the scale of n—i.e. by expressing s in the form $\xi'n + \xi + 1$, where ξ' and ξ are integers less than n (and positive or zero).

Applying the vector $(a\xi + a'\xi', b\xi + b'\xi')$, the required position is found to be $(i + a\xi + a'\xi', j + b\xi + b'\xi')$. Any other number—say $s + X'n + X$—must have a different position; therefore the congruences

$$aX + a'X' \equiv 0, \quad bX + b'X' \equiv 0 \pmod{n}$$

must imply $X \equiv X' \equiv 0$. The condition for this is that $ab' - a'b$ shall be prime to n. (In De la Loubère's case $ab' - a'b = -1$.)

If also a, b, a', b' are prime to n (and therefore not zero), the square will be magic as far as rows and columns are concerned. For, the numbers in a column are given by the n solutions of a congruence of the form $a\xi + a'\xi' \equiv c$, and these involve all the possible values, $0, 1, \ldots, n - 1$ for both ξ and ξ' (in some combination); similarly for the numbers in a row. Since a, b, a', b' and $ab' - a'b$ are all prime to n, n must be odd. For, if n were even, a, b, a', b' would have to be odd, and then $ab' - a'b$ would be even. Accordingly we may write $n = 2m + 1$.

Finally, let us choose i and j so as to put the middle number (for which $\xi = \xi' = m$) into the middle cell (m, m). This requires

$$i \equiv (1 - a - a')m, \quad j \equiv (1 - b - b')m.$$

(In De la Loubère's case, $i = m$, $j = 2m$; hence the position of 1 in the middle of the top row.) It now follows that the square is symmetrical—i.e. that the numbers in the skewly related cells (x, y) and $(2m - x, 2m - y)$ are complementary. This ensures the magic property for the diagonals.

It is convenient to denote this magic square by the symbol $\begin{pmatrix} a\ a' \\ b\ b' \end{pmatrix}_n$. Thus De la Loubère's square is $\begin{pmatrix} 1 - 1 \\ 1 - 2 \end{pmatrix}_n$, and

Bachet's is $\begin{pmatrix} 1 & -1 \\ 1 & 1 \end{pmatrix}_n$. What we have proved is that such a square can be constructed whenever a, b, a', b' and $ab' - a'b$ are all prime to n.

If also $a + b$, $a - b$, $a' + b'$, $a' - b'$ are prime to n, the square will be *pandiagonal*. For, the numbers in a generalized diagonal are given by the n solutions of a congruence of the form $(a \pm b)\xi + (a' \pm b')\xi' \equiv c$. It is impossible to satisfy all these conditions when n is a multiple of 3; in such cases, therefore, the method has to be modified.

When the conditions are all satisfied, the values of i and j

(*Pandiagonal Squares.*)

7	20	3	11	24
13	21	9	17	5
19	2	15	23	6
25	8	16	4	12
1	14	22	10	18

Figure xvi. $n = 5$.

26	21	9	4	48	36	31
44	39	34	22	17	12	7
20	8	3	47	42	30	25
38	33	28	16	11	6	43
14	2	46	41	29	24	19
32	27	15	10	5	49	37
1	45	40	35	23	18	13

Figure xvii. $n = 7$.

obtained above render the square symmetrical as well as pandiagonal; but, of course, the square will still be pandiagonal if the position of the number 1 is chosen arbitrarily. For instance, n being prime to 6, the conditions are all satisfied by $\begin{pmatrix} 1 & -1 \\ 2 & -3 \end{pmatrix}_n$. Thus, to form a pandiagonal square of the fifth order (figure xvi) we may put 1 in any cell; proceed by four successive steps, like a knight's move, of one cell to the right, and two cells up, writing consecutively numbers 2, 3, 4, 5 in each cell, until we come to a cell already occupied; then take one step, like a rook's move, one cell down; and so on until the square is filled. Again, in the square $\begin{pmatrix} 1 & 1 \\ 2 & -3 \end{pmatrix}_n$ the successive numbers can be written in with a knight's move at *every* step, as in figure xvii; but, since $ab' - a'b = -5$, this formation is impossible when n is 5 or a multiple of 5.

Arnoux's Method.* If the numbers in figures xvi and xvii are all diminished by 1 and expressed in the scale of $n(=5$ or 7$)$, the results are immediately recognizable as the Eulerian squares $(23, 44)_5$ and $(62, 43)_7$. Conversely, it is obvious that any diagonal Eulerian square, composed of the marks 00, 01, ..., $(n-1)(n-1)$, becomes a magic square when its marks are interpreted as numbers in the scale of n.

Moreover, any Eulerian square of the form $(\alpha'\alpha, \beta'\beta)_n$ (even if not *diagonally* Eulerian) becomes a magic square when its rows and columns are cyclically permuted in such a way as to put the middle number mm into the middle cell (m, m); for, this permutation makes the square symmetrical— *i.e.* it puts complementary numbers into the cells $(m + x, m + y)$ and $(m - x, m - y)$. In fact, the number in the cell $(m + x, m + y)$ has digits congruent to $m + \alpha'x + \beta'y$, $m + \alpha x + \beta y \pmod{n}$. (In order to make the numbers run from 1 to n^2, instead of 0 to $n^2 - 1$, we merely have to add 1 throughout.)

On the other hand, the above generalization of De la Loubère's rule puts the number $(m + \xi')n + (m + \xi) + 1$ into the cell $(m + a\xi + a'\xi', \ m + b\xi + b'\xi')$. The two methods lead to the same square if the congruences

$$x \equiv a\xi + a'\xi', \ y \equiv b\xi + b'\xi', \ \xi \equiv \alpha x + \beta y, \ \xi' \equiv \alpha'x + \beta'y \pmod{n}$$

are consistent—*i.e.* if

$$a\alpha + a'\alpha' \equiv b\beta + b'\beta' \equiv 1 \text{ and } a\beta + a'\beta' \equiv b\alpha + b'\alpha' \equiv 0.$$

Under these circumstances, $\begin{pmatrix} a\ a' \\ b\ b' \end{pmatrix}$ and $\begin{pmatrix} \alpha\ \beta \\ \alpha'\ \beta' \end{pmatrix}$ are called "inverse matrices," since, on multiplying them together by the usual rule for determinants, the result is $\begin{pmatrix} 1\ 0 \\ 0\ 1 \end{pmatrix} \pmod{n}$. In fact, the two methods correspond to the two aspects of a

* G. Arnoux, *Arithmétique graphique. Les espaces arithmétiques hypermagiques*, Paris, 1894, p. 51. Cf. Kraïtchik, pp. 130—146.

transformation of co-ordinates.* Clearly, the statement that
a, b, a', b' and $ab' - a'b$ are prime to n is equivalent to the
statement that α, β, α', β' and $\alpha\beta' - \alpha'\beta$ are prime to n.

When n is prime to 6, we can choose α, β, α', β' so as to
make $\alpha \pm \beta$, $\alpha' \pm \beta'$ (as well as α, β, α', β', $\alpha\beta' - \alpha'\beta$) all
prime to n. Then the square $(\alpha'\alpha, \beta'\beta)_n$ is not merely diagonal,
but *pandiagonal*. (There is no need to permute the rows or
columns, unless the extra quality of symmetry is desired.)
The simplest example, from this point of view, is $(12, 21)_n$.
(See page 191.)

Margossian's Method.† I next describe an extension of
Arnoux's method which enables us to construct a pandiagonal
square whose order is a multiple of 4 or an odd multiple of 3
(but not 3 itself, of course).

23	31	03	11
02	10	22	30
21	33	01	13
00	12	20	32

32	21	02	11
03	10	33	20
31	22	01	12
00	13	30	23

Figure xviii.   *Figure* xix.

Figure xviii shows the square $(12, 21)_4$ (which is not properly
Eulerian, since 2 divides 4). Though not magic as it stands,
this square becomes magic, in fact pandiagonal, when every
digit 2 is replaced by 3, and *vice versa*, as in figure xix. Figure
ii shows the same square in the ordinary notation.

More generally, α being any even ‡ number, the square
$(1\alpha, \alpha1)_{2\alpha}$ becomes pandiagonally magic when the digits
α, $\alpha + 1$, ..., $2\alpha - 1$ are replaced by $2\alpha - 1$, $2\alpha - 2$, ..., α.
The unit digits in a row consist of two particular digits, each

* O. Veblen, " On Magic Squares," *Messenger of Mathematics*, 1908,
vol. xxxvii, pp. 116—118.

† Kraïtchik, pp. 148—152.

‡ This would fail if a were odd, since then the numbers in the square would
not be all distinct. In fact, $a\beta' - a'\beta$ ($= a^2 - 1$) would not be prime to
n ($= 2a$).

repeated α times; Margossian's substitution makes these two digits have the uniform sum $2\alpha - 1$; similarly for the radix digits in a column. A square formed by this rule (with $\alpha = 4$) is shown in figure xx.

74	63	54	43	04	13	24	33
05	12	25	32	75	62	55	42
76	61	56	41	06	11	26	31
07	10	27	30	77	60	57	40
73	64	53	44	03	14	23	34
02	15	22	35	72	65	52	45
71	66	51	46	01	16	21	36
00	17	20	37	70	67	50	47

Figure xx.   *A Pandiagonal Square, $n = 8$ (in the scale of 8).*

35	48	52	65	78	82	05	18	22
04	17	21	34	47	51	64	77	81
63	76	80	03	16	20	33	46	50
32	45	58	62	75	88	02	15	28
01	14	27	31	44	57	61	74	87
60	73	86	00	13	26	30	43	56
38	42	55	68	72	85	08	12	25
07	11	24	37	41	54	67	71	84
66	70	83	06	10	23	36	40	53

Figure xxi.

Similarly, a square of the form $(13, 31)_{3m}$, where m is odd, becomes pandiagonally magic when the digits, $0, 1, \ldots, 3m - 1$ are so permuted that, if they are written in their new order in m rows of three, the sum of the columns is uniform. For this purpose, $\frac{1}{2}(m - 1)$ of the m triads $0, 1, 2; \ 3, 4, 5;$

P

... can be left unchanged if two of the rest are cyclically permuted (opposite ways) and the remaining $\frac{1}{2}(m-3)$ are reversed. Thus, for a square of the fifteenth order, the digits 0, 1, 2, 3, 4, 5 can be left unchanged if the rest are replaced by 7, 8, 6; 11, 9, 10; 14, 13, 12. In the special case when $m = 3$, *i.e.* for a square of the ninth order, we may cyclically permute the rows and columns of $(13, 31)_9$ so as to put 44 into the middle cell (figure xxi) and then replace the digits 0, 1, 2, 3, 4, 5, 6, 7, 8 by 1, 2, 0, 3, 4, 5, 8, 6, 7 ; the resulting square (figure xxii) is not merely pandiagonal * but also symmetrical.

35	47	50	85	67	70	15	27	00
14	26	02	34	46	52	84	66	72
83	68	71	13	28	01	33	48	51
30	45	57	80	65	77	10	25	07
12	24	06	32	44	56	82	64	76
81	63	78	11	23	08	31	43	58
37	40	55	87	60	75	17	20	05
16	22	04	36	42	54	86	62	74
88	61	73	18	21	03	38	41	53

Figure xxii. *A Pandiagonal Symmetrical Square, n* = 9
(*in the scale of* 9).

MAGIC SQUARES OF NON-CONSECUTIVE NUMBERS

Although it is impossible to make a pandiagonal or symmetrical magic square of singly-even order, using *consecutive* numbers, C. Planck † has devised a method for making such squares with numbers that are *almost* consecutive. For a square of singly-even order n, he uses the numbers from 1 to $n^2 + 3$, omitting the " middle number " $\frac{1}{2}n^2 + 2$ and any two other even numbers whose sum is $n^2 + 4$. In particular, he

---

* Arnoux, *loc. cit.*, pp. 152—154.
† *The Monist* (Chicago), 1919, vol. XXIX, pp. 307—316.

might simply omit the multiples of $\frac{1}{4}n^2 + 1$. The sum of the numbers in a row, column or diagonal is $\frac{1}{2}n(n^2 + 4)$. Moreover, for the pandiagonal square, the sum of the numbers in any component square of $(\frac{1}{2}n)^2$ cells is $\frac{1}{8}n^2(n^2 + 4)$.

28	1	26	36	8	21
3	35	7	27	23	25
34	24	22	2	29	9
4	32	19	12	39	14
13	17	15	37	5	33
38	11	31	6	16	18

Figure xxiii.   A Pandiagonal
Square, $n = 6$.

28	1	26	21	8	36
3	35	7	25	23	27
34	24	22	9	29	2
38	11	31	18	16	6
13	17	15	33	5	37
4	32	19	14	39	12

Figure xxiv.   A Symmetrical
Square, $n = 6$.

Figures xxiii and xxiv show the case when $n = 6$, omitting the multiples of 10.

Another problem involving non-consecutive numbers is that of constructing a magic square of *primes*. The first of the following examples is due to H. E. Dudeney, the second (figure xxvi) to E. Bergholt and C. D. Shuldham. Such squares, of orders 5, 6, ..., 12, have been constructed by H. A. Sayles and J. N. Muncey.* Muncey's square of the twelfth order is especially remarkable in that the 144 primes involved are the *first* 144 odd primes—namely 1, 3, 5, 7, 11, ..., 827. (It has been proved that the *first* n^2 odd primes cannot be used when $n < 12$.)

67	1	43
13	37	61
31	73	7

Figure xxv.

3	71	5	23
53	11	37	1
17	13	41	31
29	7	19	47

Figure xxvi.

Figure xxvii shows Bergholt's general form for any magic
* *The Monist*, 1913, vol. XXIII, pp. 623—630.

square of the fourth order * (pandiagonal if $a = b = d - c = \frac{1}{2}(A - B - C + D)$), symmetrical if $a + c = d = b - c$ and $A + C = B + D$; therefore never both pandiagonal and

$A - a$	$C + a + c$	$B + b - c$	$D - b$
$D + a - d$	B	C	$A - a + d$
$C - b + d$	A	D	$B + b - d$
$B + b$	$D - a - c$	$A - b + c$	$C + a$

Figure xxvii.

symmetrical, since then we should have $A - a = B$). Figure xxvi is obtained by taking $A = 13$, $B = 11$, $C = 37$, $D = 41$, $a = 10$, $b = 18$, $c = 24$, $d = -2$.

DOUBLY-MAGIC SQUARES

For certain values of n (not less than 8) it is possible to construct a magic square of the nth order in such a way that if the number in each cell is replaced by its square the resulting square shall also be magic.†

17	50	43	04	32	75	66	21
31	76	65	22	14	53	40	07
00	47	54	13	25	62	71	36
26	61	72	35	03	44	57	10
45	02	11	56	60	27	34	73
63	24	37	70	46	01	12	55
52	15	06	41	77	30	23	64
74	33	20	67	51	16	05	42

Figure xxviii.   A Doubly-Magic Pandiagonal Square, $n = 8$
(in the scale of 8).

---

* *Nature*, 1910, vol. LXXXIII, p. 368. See also J. Chernick, *American Mathematical Monthly*, 1938, vol. XLV, pp. 172—175.

† See M. Coccoz in *L'Illustration*, May 29, 1897. The subject has been studied by Messrs. G. Tarry, B. Portier, M. Coccoz, A. Rilly, E. Barbette and W. S. Andrews. More than 200 such squares have been given by Rilly in his *Études sur les Triangles et les Carrés Magiques aux deux premiers degrés*, Troyes, 1901.

Here are two examples. Figure xxviii represents a pan-diagonal magic square of the eighth order, due to M. H. Schots.* The numbers are expressed in the scale of 8 in order to exhibit the underlying Eulerian square. After adding 1 throughout, the sum of the numbers in each line is equal to 260, and the sum of their squares is equal to 11180. Figure xxix represents R. V. Heath's doubly-magic square of the ninth order, written in the scale of 9.

76	82	64	15	27	00	41	53	38
11	23	08	46	52	34	75	87	60
45	57	30	71	83	68	16	22	04
62	74	86	07	10	25	33	48	51
03	18	21	32	44	56	67	70	85
37	40	55	63	78	81	02	14	26
84	66	72	20	05	17	58	31	43
28	01	13	54	36	42	80	65	77
50	35	47	88	61	73	24	06	12

Figure xxix. *A Doubly-Magic Symmetrical Square, n =9*
(in the scale of 9).

Trebly-Magic Squares. The construction of squares which shall be magic for the original numbers, for their squares, and for their cubes has also been studied. I know of no square of this kind which is of a lower order than 64, and the construction of a square of that order is not a " recreation."

OTHER MAGIC PROBLEMS

Other problems, closely related to magic squares, will suggest themselves; the following will serve as specimens.

Magic Domino Squares. An ordinary set of dominoes, ranging from double zero to double six, contains 28 dominoes.

* *Bulletin de la classe des Sciences de l'Académie Royale de Belgique*, 1931, pp. 339—361. Cf. *Sphinx*, 1931, p. 137. It should be observed that this is *not* a pandiagonal *Eulerian* square, since the broken diagonals contain repeated digits (although they have the proper sum).

Each domino is a rectangle formed by fixing two small square blocks together side by side : of these 56 blocks, eight are blank, on each of eight of them is one pip, on each of another eight of them are two pips, and so on.   It is required to arrange the dominoes so that the 56 blocks form a square of 7 by 7 bordered by one line of 7 blank squares, and so that the sum of the pips in each row, column, and diagonal of the square is equal to 24.   A solution * is given below.

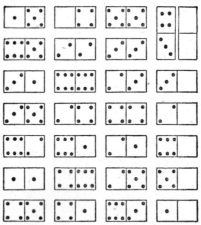

Figure xxx.   *Magic Domino Square.*

Figure xxxi.   *Magic Domino Squares.*

* See *L'Illustration*, July 10, 1897.

If we select certain dominoes out of the set and reject the others we can use them to make various magic puzzles. As instance, I give in figure xxxi two examples of magic squares of this kind due respectively to Escott and Dudeney.

Cubic and Octahedral Dice. The faces of a cube can obviously be numbered from 1 to 6 in such a way that the pairs of opposite faces sum to 7. A cube so marked is called a die. Dice are used in pairs, but no attention seems to have been paid to specifying whether a pair should be identical or enantiomorphous.

Another kind of die might be made by numbering the faces of a polyhedron from 1 to F in such a way that the faces around a vertex give a constant sum. If there are m faces around each vertex, the constant sum must be equal to $\frac{1}{2}m(F+1)$; hence either m is even or F is odd. Every regular polyhedron has an even number of faces, so the only one which could be made into this kind of die is the octahedron (for which $m = 4$ and $F = 8$). The faces of the octahedron can be numbered (so that those around each vertex sum to 18) in three essentially distinct ways, each of which occurs in two enantiomorphous forms. Pairs of opposite faces have a constant difference, 1 or 2 or 4.

Figure xxxii.   *Octahedral Dice.**

Interlocked Hexagons. The problem of numbering the faces of the Rotating Ring of n tetrahedra (page 153), so that the faces around each vertex sum to $3(4n + 1)$, appears to be insoluble. But R. V. Heath has elegantly solved the corre-

* The third of these is due to J. M. Andreas.

sponding problem for the network of $36n$ triangles obtained by dividing each face of the Ring into nine. Such a network of triangles may be regarded as a symmetrical "map" on a torus (page 234), even when $n < 6$. (When $n \geqslant 6$, the map can be drawn on the rotating ring in nine distinct ways.) Figure xxxiii shows the simplest case ($n = 2$), but a similar method * applies in every case. The six triangles around any

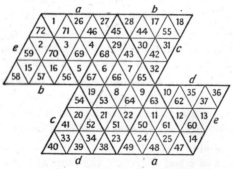

Figure xxxiii.   *Interlocked Hexagons on a Torus.*

Figure xxxiv.   *A Magic Rotating Ring.*

vertex sum to $3(36n + 1)$; so do the six triangles adjacent to these (which form a kind of star). Heath has succeeded in covering many other surfaces with such interlocked hexagons.

Figure xxxiv shows Heath's special arrangement of the numbers from 1 to 32 on the ring of eight tetrahedra, which is

* The method is precisely the same for all singly-even values of n. When n is odd or doubly-even, the ends have to be joined as in figure xxxiv. In the latter case, the regular arrangement of numbers has to be broken after $9n$ and $27n$.

magic in a quite different sense. The four faces of each tetrahedron sum to 66; "corresponding" faces, one from each tetrahedron, sum to 132 (for instance, $9 + 7 + 17 + 31 + 10 + 8 + 18 + 32 = 132$), and so do eight sets of eight faces which wind helically around the ring (for instance, $1 + 12 + 31 + 21 + 2 + 11 + 32 + 22 = 132$).

MAGIC CUBES

A *Magic Cube* of the *n*th order consists of the consecutive numbers from 1 to n^3, arranged in the form of a cube, so that the sum of the numbers in every row, every column, every file, and in each of the four diagonals (or "diameters"), is the same—namely, $\frac{1}{2}n(n^3 + 1)$. This sum occurs in $3n^2 + 4$ ways. I do not know of any rule for constructing magic cubes of singly-even order. But such cubes of any odd or doubly-even order can be constructed by a natural extension of the methods already used for squares.

As in the two-dimensional case (page 204), we proceed from cell to cell by steps, only now the vectors that make the steps are three-dimensional. In fact, we define the step (a, b, c) as taking us *a* cells "east," *b* cells "north," and *c* cells "up." As before, all the movements are taken cyclically, so that the numbers *a*, *b*, *c* may at any stage be reduced modulo *n*. We can make the same step $n - 1$ times before coming to an occupied cell. Then we make one cross-step $(a + a', b + b', c + c')$, follow this by $n - 1$ more steps (a, b, c), and so on. There will be no difficulty until we try to write the number $n^2 + 1$. At that stage the cross-step has to be altered, say to $(a + a' + a'', b + b' + b'', c + c' + c'')$, and this new kind of cross-step has to be used again after each multiple of n^2 has been reached. If a'', b'', c'' are suitably chosen, the whole cube can now be filled up. In fact, the position of the number $\xi'' n^2 + \xi' n + \xi + 1$ is derived from that of the number 1 by applying ξ steps (a, b, c), ξ' steps (a', b', c'), and ξ'' steps (a'', b'', c''). Thus, if 1 is in the cell whose co-ordinates are (i, j, k), then $\xi''n^2 + \xi'n + \xi + 1$ is in that whose co-ordinates are

$$(i + a\xi + a'\xi' + a''\xi'', \ j + b\xi + b'\xi' + b''\xi'',$$
$$k + c\xi + c'\xi' + c''\xi'').$$

In order that different numbers may always occupy different positions, the congruences

$$aX + a'X' + a''X'' \equiv 0, \ bX + b'X' + b''X'' \equiv 0,$$
$$cX + c'X' + c''X'' \equiv 0 \ (\text{mod } n)$$

must imply $X \equiv X' \equiv X'' \equiv 0$. The condition for this is that the determinant

$$\begin{vmatrix} a & a' & a'' \\ b & b' & b'' \\ c & c' & c'' \end{vmatrix}$$

shall be prime to n. The magic property of the rows, columns and files is secured by making all the two-rowed minors of the determinant likewise prime to n. (This is impossible if n is even). The magic property of the diagonals is secured by adjusting i, j, k so as to place the middle number in the middle cell; the cube will then be *symmetrical*.

(Bottom layer)			(Middle layer)			(Top layer)		
4	12	26	20	7	15	18	23	1
11	25	6	9	14	19	22	3	17
27	5	10	13	21	8	2	16	24

Figure xxxv. *A Magic Cube, n = 3.*

It is convenient to denote this magic cube by the symbol

$$\begin{pmatrix} a & a' & a'' \\ b & b' & b'' \\ c & c' & c'' \end{pmatrix}_n$$

What we have proved is that such a cube can be constructed whenever the determinant and all its first minors are prime to n. Clearly, these conditions are satisfied, for any odd value of n, if

$$a = a' = b = b'' = c' = c'' = 1, \ a'' = b' = c = 0,$$

and $i = j = k = \frac{1}{2}(n + 1)$. In practice it is easiest to insert first the numbers 1, $n^2 + 1$, $2n^2 + 1$, ..., proceeding by steps (0, 1, 1), then to insert the rest of the numbers 1, $n + 1$, $2n + 1$, ..., proceeding by steps (1, 0, 1), and finally to fill in the remaining numbers, proceeding by steps (1, 1, 0). Figure xxxv shows the three " horizontal " layers of the magic cube

$$\begin{pmatrix} 1 & 1 & 0 \\ 1 & 0 & 1 \\ 0 & 1 & 1 \end{pmatrix}_3$$

The reader may be interested to try the same rule with $n = 5$. The resulting cube is *pandiagonal*, having the magic property not merely in its four main diagonals, but in all the broken diagonals as well. In such a cube the magic sum occurs $(3 + 4)n^2$ times, instead of only $3n^2 + 4$.

It can be shown that the cube

$$\begin{pmatrix} a & b & 0 \\ b & 0 & a \\ 0 & a & b \end{pmatrix}_n$$

is pandiagonal whenever a, b, $a + b$ and $a^2 \pm ab \pm b^2$ (with all four distributions of sign) are prime to n. Thus $a = b = 1$ gives a solution whenever n is not divisible by 3 (nor by 2); $a = 2$, $b = 1$ gives another solution whenever n is divisible by none of 2, 3, 5, 7.

If a, b, $a \pm b$ and $a^2 + b^2$ are prime to n, the cube, without necessarily being pandiagonal itself, has pandiagonal squares for its n layers in each of the three principal directions, so that the magic sum occurs $(3 + 6)n^2$ times. For instance, $a = 2$, $b = 1$ gives a solution whenever n is prime to 30, and in particular when n is 7 or any larger prime. This cube will

itself be pandiagonal if n is prime to 210, and in particular
when $n = 11$ or any larger prime. The magic sum will then
occur $(3 + 4 + 6)n^2$ times. Rosser and Walker have shown
that a magic cube can be pandiagonal in this stricter sense
when $n = 8$ or any multiple of 8, and when $n = 9$ or any
larger odd number, but in no other cases.

010	102	221	201	020	112	122	211	000
101	220	012	022	111	200	210	002	121
222	011	100	110	202	021	001	120	212

Figure xxxvi.   An Eulerian Cube, $n = 3$.

Figure xxxvi shows the same cube as figure xxxv, but with
every number diminished by 1 and expressed in the scale of 3.
Apart from cyclic permutations of the layers, this is just the
Eulerian cube $(122, 212, 221)_3$; for, the row, column, and file
involving 000 contain the Galois multiples (mod 3) of the
marks 122, 212 and 221, and the whole cube constitutes a
table of Galois addition based on this row, column, and file.*

Since

$$\begin{pmatrix} 1 & 1 & 0 \\ 1 & 0 & 1 \\ 0 & 1 & 1 \end{pmatrix} \quad \text{and} \quad \begin{pmatrix} 2 & 2 & 1 \\ 2 & 1 & 2 \\ 1 & 2 & 2 \end{pmatrix}$$

are inverse matrices (mod 3), the two methods of construction
again correspond to the two aspects of a transformation of
co-ordinates.

232	310	032	110	013	131	213	331	230	312	030	112	011	133	211	333
020	102	220	302	201	323	001	123	022	100	222	300	203	321	003	121
212	330	012	130	033	111	233	311	210	332	010	132	031	113	231	313
000	122	200	322	221	303	021	103	002	120	202	320	223	301	023	101

Figure xxxvii. $n = 4$.

* Arnoux, *loc. cit.*, p. 63.

Figure xxxvii shows the cube $(122, 212, 221)_4$ (which is not properly Eulerian, since 2 divides 4). This becomes magic, in fact pandiagonal, when every digit 2 is replaced by 3, and *vice versa*. The result, in the ordinary notation, is shown in figure xxxviii. In fact, Margossian's substitution (page 208) gives a pandiagonal cube $(1\alpha\alpha, \alpha1\alpha, \alpha\alpha1)_{2a}$ for every even value of α.

60	37	12	21	7	26	55	42	57	40	9	24	6	27	54	43
13	20	61	36	50	47	2.	31	16	17	64	33	51	46	3	30
56	41	8	25	11	22	59	38	53	44	5	28	10	23	58	39
1	32	49	48	62	35	14	19	4	29	52	45	63	34	15	18

Figure xxxviii. *A Pandiagonal Magic Cube, n = 4.*

(*First layer*)   (*Second layer*)

1	8	61	60	48	41	20	21
62	59	2	7	19	22	47	42
52	53	16	9	29	28	33	40
15	10	51	54	34	39	30	27
32	25	36	37	49	56	13	12
35	38	31	26	14	11	50	55
45	44	17	24	4	5	64	57
18	23	46	43	63	58	3	6

(*Fourth layer*)   (*Third layer*)

Figure xxxix. *A Magic Square which is also a Pandiagonal Cube.*

Figure xxxix, by R. V. Heath, is remarkable as being both a magic square of the eighth order and a pandiagonal cube of the fourth order. As a magic square, it has the interesting property that *alternate* numbers in any row or column, or in either diagonal, sum to 130. As a pandiagonal cube, it excels figure xxxviii in that the four horizontal layers (which are the four quarters of the eighth-order square) are themselves magic squares.

CHAPTER VIII

MAP-COLOURING PROBLEMS

THIS chapter and the next are concerned with the branch of
mathematics known as Topology or Analysis Situs, which
differs from Geometry in having no connection with the idea of
straightness, flatness, or measurement. Here every oval is
equivalent to a circle, every spheroid to a sphere; in fact, no
distinction is made between any two figures derivable from
one another by the kind of transformations that are familiar
as crumpling and stretching, without tearing or joining.
(One's thoughts turn naturally to indiarubber.) But topology
does distinguish between a solid sphere and a hollow sphere,
and between either of these and a *torus* or anchor-ring. It
also distinguishes between a simple closed curve and a knotted
curve, provided these are definitely understood to lie in the
same three-dimensional space; in four-dimensional space, any
such knot could be untied without breaking the circuit.

THE FOUR-COLOUR THEOREM

I shall first mention a famous theorem which appears to be
simple, and seems to be true, but has never yet been proved,
although more complicated theorems of a similar type are
fairly easy to prove. The theorem is that *not more than four
colours are necessary in order to colour a map of a country (divided
into districts) in such a way that no two contiguous districts
shall be of the same colour*. By contiguous districts are meant
districts having a common *line* as part of their boundaries—
districts which touch only at points are not contiguous in this
sense. The map is drawn on a simply-connected surface, such
as a plane or a sphere. The number of districts is finite, and no

district consists of two or more disconnected pieces. The map
may or may not fill up the whole surface. (If the map is
plane, and fills up the plane, one district at least must have
an infinite area, since the number is finite.) Of course, some
maps can be coloured with fewer than four colours; thus a
chess-board requires only two, a hexagonal tessellation three.

The problem was mentioned by A. F. Möbius * in his
Lectures in 1840, but it was not until Francis Guthrie † com-

municated it to De Morgan about 1850 that attention was
generally called to it : it is said that the fact had been familiar
to practical map-makers for a long time previously. Through
De Morgan the proposition then became generally known ; and
in 1878 Cayley ‡ recalled attention to it by stating that he could
not obtain a rigorous proof of it.

Probably the following argument, though not a formal
demonstration, will satisfy the reader that the result is true.
Let A, B, C be three contiguous districts, and let X be any

* *Leipzig Transactions* (*Math.-phys. Classe*), 1885, vol. xxxvii, pp. 1—6.

† See *Proceedings of the Royal Society of Edinburgh*, July 19, 1880, vol. x,
p. 728.

‡ *Proceedings of the London Mathematical Society*, 1878, vol. ix, p. 148,
and *Proceedings of the Royal Geographical Society*, London, 1879, N.S.,
vol. i, pp. 259—261, where some of the difficulties are indicated.

other district contiguous with all of them.   Then X must lie either wholly outside the external boundary of the area ABC or wholly inside the internal boundary—that is, it must occupy a position either like X or like X'.   In either case there is no possible way of drawing another area Y which shall be contiguous with A, B, C, and X.   In other words, it is possible to draw on a plane four areas which are contiguous, but it is not possible to draw five such areas.   If A, B, C are not contiguous, each with the other, or if X is not contiguous with A, B, and C, it is not necessary to colour them all differently, and thus the most unfavourable case is that already treated.   Moreover any of the above areas may diminish to a point, and finally disappear without affecting the argument.

That we may require at least four colours is obvious from the above diagram, since in that case the areas A, B, C, and X would have to be coloured differently.

A proof of the proposition involves difficulties of a high order, which as yet have baffled all attempts to surmount them. This is partly due to the fact that if, using only four colours, we build up our map, district by district, and assign definite colours to the districts as we insert them, we can always contrive the addition of two or three fresh districts which cannot be coloured differently from those next to them, and which accordingly upset our scheme of colouring.   But by starting afresh, it would seem that we can always rearrange the colours so as to allow of the addition of such extra districts.

The argument by which the truth of the proposition was formerly supposed to be demonstrated was given by A. B. Kempe * in 1879, but there is a flaw in it.

In 1880, Tait published a solution † depending on the

* He sent his first demonstration across the Atlantic to the *American Journal of Mathematics*, 1879, vol. II, pp. 193—200; but subsequently he communicated it in simplified forms to the London Mathematical Society, *Transactions*, 1879, vol. X, pp. 229—231, and to *Nature*, Feb. 26, 1880, vol. XXI, pp. 399—400.   The flaw in the argument was indicated in articles by P. J. Heawood in the *Quarterly Journal of Mathematics*, London, 1890, vol. XXIV, pp. 332—338; and 1897, vol. XXIX, pp. 270—285.

† *Proceedings of the Royal Society of Edinburgh*, July 19, 1880, vol. X,

theorem that if a closed network of lines joining an even number of points is such that three and only three lines meet at each point, then three colours are sufficient to colour the lines in such a way that no two lines meeting at a point are of the same colour; a closed network being supposed to exclude the case where the lines can be divided into two groups between which there is but one connecting line.

This theorem may be true, if we understand it with the limitation that the network is in one plane and that no line meets any other line except at one of the vertices, which is all

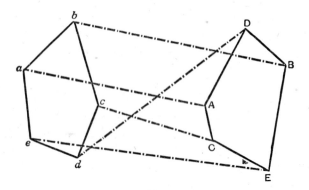

that we require for the map theorem; but it has not been proved. Without this limitation it is not correct. For instance, the accompanying figure, representing a closed network in three dimensions of 15 lines formed by the sides of two pentagons and the lines joining their corresponding angular points, cannot be coloured as described by Tait. If the figure is in three dimensions, the lines intersect only at the ten vertices of the network. If it is regarded as being in two dimensions, only the ten angular points of the pentagons are treated as vertices of the network, and any other point of intersection of the lines is not regarded as such a vertex. Expressed in

p. 729; *Philosophical Magazine*, January, 1884, series 5, vol. xvii, p. 41; and *Collected Scientific Papers*, Cambridge, vol. ii, 1890, p. 93.

Q

simple language the difficulty is this. Petersen * has shown that any network in which just three lines meet at each point can be coloured with two colours, say red and green, in such a way that at each point one red and two green lines meet. The green lines will form certain loops, and Tait assumed that these loops can always be arranged so that each contains an even number of lines. This would enable us to colour the lines of each loop alternately blue and yellow, instead of all green.

Let us suppose that Tait's assumption, as applied to a *plane* network, can in fact be justified. His argument that four colours will suffice for a map is divided into two parts and is as follows.

First, suppose that the boundary lines of contiguous districts form a closed network of lines joining an even number of points such that three and only three lines meet at each point. Then if the number of districts is $n + 1$, the number of boundaries will be $3n$, and there will be $2n$ points of junction; also by Tait's theorem, the boundaries can be marked with three colours β, γ, δ, so that no two like colours meet at a point of junction. Suppose this done. Now take four colours, A, B, C, D, wherewith to colour the map. Paint one district with the colour A; paint the district adjoining A and divided from it by the line β with the colour B; the district adjoining A and divided from it by the line γ with the colour C; the district adjoining A and divided from it by the line δ with the colour D. Proceed in this way so that a line β always separates the colours A and B, or the colours C and D; a line γ always separates A and C, or D and B; and a line δ always separates A and D, or B and C. It is easy to see that, if we come to a district bounded by districts already coloured, the rule for crossing each of its boundaries will give the same colour; this

* See J. Petersen of Copenhagen, *L'Intermédiaire des Mathématiciens*, vol. v, 1898, pp. 225—227; and vol. vi, 1899, pp. 36—38. Also *Acta Mathematica*, Stockholm, vol. xv, 1891, pp. 193—220. The simplest non-plane graph that *can* be given a Tait colouring has six vertices, say P, Q, R, p, q, r, joined as follows: Pp, Qr, Rq; Qq, Rp, Pr; Rr, Pq, Qp.

also follows from the fact that, if we regard β, γ, δ as indicating certain operations, then an operation like δ may be represented as equivalent to the effect of the two other operations β and γ performed in succession in either order. Thus for such a map the problem is solved.

In the second case, suppose that at any point four or more boundaries meet, then at any such point introduce a small district as indicated below : this will reduce the problem to the first case. The small district thus introduced may be

coloured by the previous rule ; but after the rest of the map is coloured this district will have served its purpose, it may be then made to contract without limit to a mere point and will disappear leaving the boundaries as they were at first.

For a further discussion of the problem * it is desirable to develop the notion of reducing the map to a " standard " map, of simpler type than the original, and such that, if the reduced map can be coloured with four colours, so can the original. (*A fortiori*, if the reduced map can be coloured with five or more colours, so can the original.)

We suppose the map drawn on a sphere; if it does not already cover the whole sphere, we regard " the rest of the world " as one more district. Secondly, we reduce to vertices of degree three, not as above (since that method increases the number of districts), but by observing that a higher vertex

must involve a pair of non-contiguous districts, which can be given the same colour; we then open out the vertex, and

* Heawood, *Quarterly Journal of Mathematics*, 1890, vol. XXIV, p. 333. This simplified account of Heawood's paper is due to L. A. Pars.

merge these two into one district. Thirdly, we get rid of
districts having one, two or three sides. (We merely have to

remove one side, and merge the district into an adjacent
district.) Fourthly, we get rid of four-sided districts. (Of the
four districts that surround such a district, at least one pair are
non-contiguous; this pair can be merged with the four-sided
district. If the map so formed can be coloured with four

colours, so can the original; for, when we restore the four-
sided district, only three colours at most surround it, and we
have a colour to spare for it.) Fifthly, we get rid of ring-
shaped districts, so that each district is bounded by a single
continuous line, and no district encloses one or more others.

(A ring-shaped district may be broken by a corridor joining
one district inside to one outside, and these two districts may
be merged with the corridor.)

If we started with a fairly simple sort of map, the chances are
that we have reduced the map away, so that we are left with a
single district covering the sphere, and the theorem is proved
for that particular map. At worst we shall be left with a
" standard " map, in which no district has fewer than five
sides.

Such a map may be regarded as a polyhedron, having F

faces (the districts), E edges (the lines separating pairs of contiguous districts), and V vertices. Since each vertex belongs to three districts, and each edge to two, we have

$$3V = 2E = aF,$$

where a is the average number of sides of a district. By Euler's Theorem (which we shall prove later),

$$F - E + V = 2.$$

Eliminating V and E, we find that $a = 6 - 12/F$. Since $a < 6$, there is at least one pentagon.

We can now prove by induction that a standard map, and therefore any map, can be coloured with *six* colours. Consider a district having five sides, and merge it with one of the contiguous districts by removing one side. If the new map can be coloured with six colours, so can the original; for, when we restore the five-sided district, only five colours are adjacent to it, and we have a colour to spare for it. But we can reduce, step by step, and the six-colour theorem is proved. (The argument is rather subtler than it looks at first sight. For, when we remove the side, the new map will not necessarily be "standard," and we may have to reduce it by one of the above processes before we can apply the same argument again. I shall refer to this later as " the crude induction argument.")

By a subtler argument, likewise due to Heawood,* we can show that *five* colours are always sufficient. Consider a five-sided district, P. Of the districts Q, R, S, T, U which touch it, there must be at least one non-contiguous pair—say Q and S. Merge Q, P, S into a single district P' by deleting two sides of P. If the resulting map can be coloured with five colours, so can the original; for the districts P', R, T, U use up at most four colours, and there is a colour left for P when we return to the original map. Again we reduce, step by step, until the five-colour theorem is proved.

But this is as far as we can go. The gap between the five colours that are always sufficient and the four that are generally

* *Loc. cit.*, p. 337.

necessary has never been bridged, save for small values of F.
Suppose the map has F_n n-sided regions ($n = 5, 6, 7, \ldots$).
Then

$$F - E + V = F - \tfrac{1}{6}aF$$
$$= (F_5 + F_6 + F_7 + \ldots) - \tfrac{1}{6}(5F_5 + 6F_6 + 7F_7 + \ldots)$$
$$= \tfrac{1}{6}(F_5 - F_7 - 2F_8 - \ldots),$$

whence $F_5 - F_7 - 2F_8 - 3F_9 - \ldots = 12$

and $F_5 \geqslant 12$. Thus every standard map contains (at least)
twelve pentagons. The simplest standard map is the dodecahedron. We can colour this with four colours. It follows
that every map having not more than 12 districts can be
coloured with four colours. In other words, any map that
requires five colours must have at least 13 districts, including
at least 12 pentagons.

These numbers have been improved by various investigators.* In 1922, P. Franklin showed that a map requiring
five colours must have at least 26 districts. In 1924, A.
Errera showed that such a map must include at least 13
pentagons. In 1926, C. N. Reynolds increased the number of
districts to 28. In 1936, Franklin increased the number of
districts to 32, and the number of pentagons to 15. Still more
recently, C. E. Winn showed that such a map must contain at
least two districts with more than six sides.

In his second paper † Heawood showed how the problem may
be reduced to purely number-theoretical considerations.
Consider again Tait's network of $3n$ lines joining pairs of $2n$
vertices (page 226). Through each vertex pass three lines,
marked β, γ, δ. We may distribute the vertices into two
classes—say " positive " and " negative "—according as the
incident lines β, γ, δ occur in a counter-clockwise or clockwise
sense. Then every district has a number of positive vertices,
and a number of negative vertices, which differ by a multiple

* *Transactions of the American Mathematical Society*, 1922, vol. XLIV,
pp. 225—236; *Annals of Mathematics*, 1927, series 2, vol. XXVIII, pp. 1—15;
Bulletin of the American Mathematical Society, 1936, vol. XLII, p. 491;
American Journal of Mathematics, 1937, vol. LIX, pp. 515—528.
† *Quarterly Journal of Mathematics*, 1897, vol. XXIX, pp. 277, 278.

of 3.   For, in the succession of sides of a district, taken clockwise, each positive vertex takes us one step onwards, and each
negative vertex one step backwards, in the cyclic order β, γ, δ ;
and when we get round to the starting-point, the difference
between the numbers of onward and backward steps must be a
multiple of 3.   Conversely, given such a distribution of the
vertices into two classes, the lines can be consistently marked

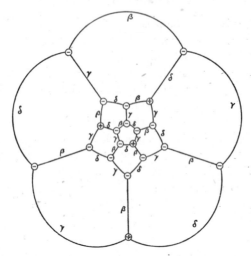

β, γ, δ, and then Tait's argument shows that the given map can
be coloured with four colours.

The description of the vertices as positive or negative is
equivalent to associating with them $2n$ variables x_1, x_2, . . .,
x_{2n}, having the values ± 1.   The colouring problem thus
reduces to the solution of a system of $n + 2 \;(= F)$ congruences
of the form

$$x_a + x_b + \ldots \equiv 0 \;(\text{mod } 3),$$

without any zeros.   Each of the $2n \;(= V)$ variables occurs in
just three of the congruences.   The question now is, whether
every such system is soluble.

Considering " extended " congruences of the form

$$x_a + x_b + \ldots \equiv \rho \;(\text{mod } 3),$$

where ρ may take any of the values 0, 1, 2, Heawood found *
that, as the number n increases, the number of " failures "
(*i.e.* of insoluble systems of congruences) diminishes rapidly.
But in a later paper he showed that failures (for the extended
congruences) always occur.

UNBOUNDED SURFACES

A surface is said to be *orientable* if a positive sense of rotation
can be assigned consistently at all points of it.† A surface in
ordinary space is orientable or unorientable according as it is
two-sided or one-sided. For instance, the " paradromic
rings " described on page 126 are orientable or unorientable
according as m is even or odd.

In order to investigate the topology of an unbounded ‡
surface (such as the surface of a sphere or a torus), we cover it
with a map—*i.e.* we divide it into F polygonal " districts " by
means of E arcs, joining (pairs of) V points. When the
surface is crumpled or stretched, the map is supposed to go
with it, so that the numbers F, E, V are unaltered. I proceed
to prove that the number $F - E + V$ is a property of the
surface itself, and not merely of a particular map—*i.e.* that if
a second map on the same surface has F' districts, E' lines and
V' points, then $F' - E' + V' = F - E + V$. For this
purpose let us superpose the two maps,§ allowing the lines of
each to break up the districts of the other, so as to make a third
map, having (say) f districts, e lines and v points. The v

* *Proceedings of the London Mathematical Society*, 1932, series 2, vol.
XXXIII, pp. 253—286.

† To be more precise, the positive sense of rotation may be defined at
any point by a " directrix," that is, a small circle with an arrow-head
marked on its circumference. A surface is *unorientable* if there can be
found on it a closed path such that the directrix is reversed when moved
around this path.

‡ *I.e.* without any periphery (or " rim," or " edge "). For an interesting
bounded surface, see Steinhaus, *Mathematical Snapshots*, New York, 1938,
p. 117.

§ This method of proof was suggested to me by Professor J. W. Alexander vertices of this third map consist of the $V + V'$ vertices of the other two,* together with the points where their lines cross.

Let us modify the first map by admitting these crossing-points as vertices, and consequently breaking up the lines on which they lie. Since E and V are equally increased, the value of $F - E + V$ is unchanged. The remaining lines and vertices of the third map may now be added in the form of successive " chains," each joining two given vertices and dividing a given district into two parts. Such a chain consists of (say) n new lines meeting consecutively at $n - 1$ new vertices ($n \geqslant 1$). Its insertion therefore increases F by 1, E by n, and V by $n - 1$, leaving $F - E + V$ unchanged. Continuing in this way until the third map is complete, we thus find that $f - e + v = F - E + V$. Similarly, $f - e + v = F' - E' + V'$. Hence $F' - E' + V' = F - E + V$, as required.

This incidentally proves Euler's Theorem (viz., that for a sphere, $F - E + V = 2$), since it shows that every map on a sphere has the same value for $F - E + V$ as a particular map, such as the tetrahedron (for which $F = V = 4$ and $E = 6$). The invariant $F - E + V$ is called the *characteristic* † of any surface. The value for a torus is zero, since two circles crossing at one point make a map for which $F = V = 1$ and $E = 2$. (More convincingly, two systems of r circles on a torus make a map for which $F = V = r^2$ and $E = 2r^2$.)

From any given surface, we can derive a topologically different surface by adding a " handle," which may be thought of as a bent prism connecting two separate n-gons of a map on the given surface. Such a prism has $2n$ vertices, all of which belong to the original map, $3n$ edges, of which all but n belong to the original map, and $n + 2$ faces, of which 2 (the bases) are

---

* There is no loss of generality in supposing these $V + V'$ points to be distinct, since a slight distortion would shift any vertex of either map.

† It " characterizes " the surface in the following sense. Two unbounded surfaces, both orientable or both unorientable, which have the same characteristic, are homeomorphic (or topologically equivalent). Some authors prefer to change the sign—*i.e.* to define the characteristic as $- V + E - F$.

the faces of contact, which are supposed to be removed. Hence the operation of adding the handle leaves V unchanged, increases E by n, and increases F by $n - 2$; altogether, it diminishes the characteristic by 2.

The most general (unbounded) orientable surface may be regarded as a sphere with p handles. The number p is called the *genus* of the surface. Thus the sphere is of genus zero; the torus, of genus one. The above argument shows that the characteristic is equal to $2 - 2p$. Thus every orientable surface has an even characteristic.

The characteristic of an unorientable surface may be either even or odd (but cannot be greater than 1). In ordinary space there is no unbounded unorientable surface that does not cut itself.

Dual Maps

Given any map (covering an unbounded surface), we can define a *dual* map (covering the same surface), each of whose vertices lies within a corresponding district of the first map, while each of its lines crosses a corresponding line of the first map. (For an example, see page 107.) Clearly, the vertices of the first map lie in separate districts of the second, and the relationship between the two maps is symmetrical. The dualizing process replaces the numbers F, E, V by V, E, F, respectively. The dual of a " standard " map has triangular districts throughout. Reciprocal polyhedra may be regarded as a special case of dual maps.

The great dodecahedron, $5^{5/2}$ (page 144), is a map of twelve pentagons on a surface of genus 4, since $F - E + V = 12 - 30 + 12 = 2 - 8$. This map being self-dual (or rather, dual to an identical map), the polyhedra $5^{5/2}$ and $(\frac{5}{2})^5$ are topologically equivalent (or " homeomorphic "). In the same sense, the polyhedra $3^{5/2}$ and $(\frac{5}{2})^3$ are equivalent to the ordinary icosahedron and dodecahedron, respectively.

The rotating ring of tetrahedra (page 153) provides a map of $4n$ triangles on a torus. The genus is 1, since $F - E + V = 4n - 6n + 2n = 0$.

The Seven-Colour Theorem

It is natural to ask how many colours are required for a map on a torus, or on any other orientable surface. Heawood * has discussed this question, with the remarkable conclusion that for these surfaces of higher genus the problem is capable of complete solution.

Consider a map covering a torus, reduced so as to have all vertices of degree three (and no ring-shaped districts). As before, $3V = 2E = aF$, where a is the average number of sides of a district. But now $F - E + V = 0$, whence $a = 6$;

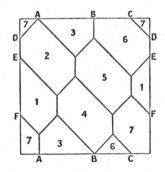

so there is a district having not more than six sides. The crude induction argument, which proves that every map on a sphere can be coloured with six colours, suffices to prove that every map on a torus can be coloured with seven. But, whereas in the spherical case the number six was soon seen to be too large, in the present case the number seven is exactly right; for we can construct a map consisting of seven hexagons each of which touches all the other six. For such a map †
seven colours are clearly necessary; and, as we have just seen,

---

* *Quarterly Journal of Mathematics*, 1890, vol. xxiv, pp. 332—335.

† Drawn in this elegant form by A. E. Ingham. (The rectangle is rolled into a cylinder or "tube" by bringing together the two sides *ABC*. This is bent into a torus by bringing together the two ends *DEF*.) Andreas has pointed out that the seven hexagons can easily be drawn on his Rotating Ring (page 153), whose surface is very accessible to examination. Cf. D. Hilbert and S. Cohn-Vossen, *Anschauliche Geometrie* (Berlin, 1932), p. 296.

seven colours are always sufficient. There is thus no gap waiting to be filled, and the problem is completely solved.

For the general surface of genus $p \ (\geqslant 1)$ the situation is similar. Since $F - E + V = 2 - 2p$, we have

$$a = 6 + 12(p - 1)/F.$$

Let F_0 denote $\frac{1}{2}(7 + \sqrt{48p + 1})$—i.e. the positive root of the equation (for F) $a + 1 = F$. When $F \leqslant F_0$, $[F_0]$* colours are certainly sufficient, since F are sufficient.

When $F > F_0$, $a + 1 < F_0$. Since a is the average number of sides, there is a district having not more than a sides. *A fortiori*, there is a district having not more than $[F_0] - 1$ sides. By merging such a district with one of its neighbours, we see that the given map (of F districts) can be coloured with $[F_0]$ colours *if* a certain map of $F - 1$ districts can be so coloured. If $F - 1 > F_0$, this argument can be repeated, until we reach a map of only $[F_0]$ districts. Hence, finally, $[\frac{1}{2}(7 + \sqrt{48p + 1})]$ colours always suffice.†

This formula gives the correct value (seven) when $p = 1$; and it is interesting to note that it gives the presumably correct value (four) when $p = 0$, although then, of course, the argument which led to it is quite inapplicable.

The fact that so many colours may be *necessary* can hardly be doubted, although it depends on the possibility of constructing certain special maps. If each district of a map touches every other district at least once, we must have $a \geqslant F - 1$, and therefore $F \leqslant F_0$. If such a map exists with $F = [F_0]$, then this number of colours will be necessary for its colouring. Suppose that there are x $(F - 1)$-sided and $F - x$ F-sided districts, where x remains to be determined. Then

$$x(F - 1) + (F - x)F = aF = 6F + 12(p - 1),$$

whence $x = F^2 - 6F - 12(p - 1)$. For instance, when $p = 2$, so that $F = [\frac{1}{2}(7 + \sqrt{97})] = 8$, we have $x = 4$, and the required map consists of four heptagons and four octagons.

---

* $[F_0]$ means the greatest integer not exceeding F_0.

† The *great dodecahedron* $(p = 4)$ does not need its full allowance of 10 colours, but can obviously be done with 6 by colouring opposite faces alike.

(In I. N. Kagno's drawing of this 8-colour map, districts 1, 3, 5, 7 are heptagons, while 2, 4, 6, 8 are octagons. The free edges are to be identified in pairs, according to the lettering.) When $48p + 1$ is a perfect square (*i.e.* when $p = 0, 1, 6, 11, 13, \ldots$), we have $x = F$, and the map consists solely of $(F - 1)$-gons (each touching all the rest).

Although these "standard" maps have not all been drawn, L. Heffter * has established the necessity of the full number of

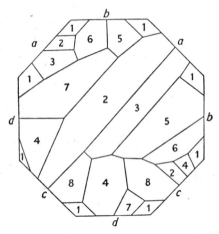

colours for every $p \leqslant 6$ (and for many higher values) by constructing special maps of F $(F - 1)$-sided districts, in which some vertices may belong to more than three districts. (When $1 \leqslant p \leqslant 6$, the full number of colours is given by the simple formula $F = p + 6$.)

The above proof, of the sufficiency of $[\frac{1}{2}(7 + \sqrt{49 - 24K})]$ colours for a surface of characteristic K ($= 2 - 2p$), remains valid when the surface is unorientable. Heffter and Kagno † have established the necessity of the full number of colours in the special cases $K = 1, -1, -2, -4$. But Franklin ‡

* *Mathematische Annalen*, 1891, vol. XXXVIII, pp. 477—508.

† I. N. Kagno, *Journal of Mathematics and Physics*, 1935, vol. XIV, pp. 228—231.

‡ P. Franklin, *ibid.*, 1934, vol. XIII, pp. 363—369. (A particularly interesting paper.)

has obtained the remarkable theorem that *six* colours suffice when $K = 0$ (in the unorientable case). Thus Heawood's formula does not always give the best possible result.

COLOURING THE ICOSAHEDRON

The faces of a tetrahedron can be map-coloured with four given colours in two enantiomorphous ways, and those of a dodecahedron * in four ways, consisting of two enantiomorphous pairs. The faces of an octahedron or of a cube can be coloured with two or three colours, respectively, in just one way. It is therefore interesting to observe that the faces of an icosahedron can be coloured with three given colours in as many as 144 ways. This number seems to have been first obtained by J. M. Andreas.

It is easily found to be impossible to colour the icosahedron in such a way that no face is surrounded by three that are all coloured alike. In fact, there are always just two such faces. Let the three colours be white, black, and grey, and suppose that one black face is surrounded by three white faces. Between each pair of these there occur two further faces, which must be black and grey (since they are contiguous). Beyond these, again, occur two more faces, which may be grey and black, white and black, grey and white, or both white. Let these four possibilities be denoted by a, b, c, d, respectively, with or without a dash ($'$) according as the first-mentioned " black and grey " occur clockwise or counterclockwise when we go round the original black face. The colouring (of $1 + 3 + 6 + 6$ of the twenty faces) may now be represented by a symbol consisting of three of the letters a, b, c, d (repetitions allowed), with a certain distribution of dashes. The colouring is unaltered by cyclic permutation of the three letters, and it is natural to let the same symbol describe any new colouring that may result from permuting the colours. Thus, in the above definitions for a, b, c, d, *black* merely means the colour of the

* See the elegant self-unfolding model at the end of Steinhaus's *Mathematical Snapshots*.

special face, *white* the colour of the three surrounding faces, and *grey* the remaining colour.

Given any colouring, we can derive another by making the special face grey instead of black. This is equivalent to leaving it black, and interchanging black and grey everywhere else, which involves changing b into c, c into b, and adding or removing dashes. (Thus a^2b becomes a'^2c'.)

a^2b ab^2 adc $b'c^2$

ac^2 $a'd'b'$ b^2c' $ac'd'$

$ad'b'$ $ac'd$ adb' $ad'c$

In the twelve cases depicted above, the colouring of the first sixteen faces unequivocally determines that of the remaining four. (The icosahedron has been projected radially on its circum-sphere, and then stereographically on a plane. One vertex has been projected to infinity. In each case, the special black face is the one just above the centre of the drawing.)

I have already remarked that there is always a second face surrounded by three that are all coloured alike. (In the drawings, this face is distinguished by a spot.) After a suitable permutation of the colours, this will be a black face surrounded by white faces, and then an alternative symbol can be assigned, to describe the colouring from this second point of view. This change of aspect leaves a^2b, ab^2, adc and $b'c^2$ unaltered, but interchanges ac^2 and $a'd'b'$, b^2c' and $ac'd'$, $ad'b'$ and $ac'd$, adb' and $ad'c$. Since neither of the two special

$(a^3)^3$ $(a^3)(a'^3)$ $(b^3)(c^3)$

$(a^3d)^3$ $(a^2d)(a''c)$ $(b^3)(b'^3)$

$(a^2d')^3$ $(a'd')(abd')$ $(c^3)(c'^3)$

faces takes precedence over the other, it is desirable to combine the two symbols, and to describe the colouring types as $(a^2b)^2$, $(ab^2)^2$, $(adc)^2$, $(b'c^2)^2$, $(ac^2)(a'd'b')$, $(b^2c')(ac'd')$, $(ad'b')(ac'd)$, $(adb')(ad'c)$.

Each of these eight colouring types gives rise to another by reflection in a mirror. The new symbol is derived by inserting or removing dashes, and reversing the cyclic order of the letters in each triad. Thus $(b^2c')(ac'd')$ leads to the enantiomorph $(b'^2c)(a'dc)$.

In the nine cases given on page 240, the colouring of the first 16 faces does not determine that of the remaining four; but the ambiguity is removed by the use of double symbols.

In order to show that these and their enantiomorphs cover all possibilities, we merely have to make a list of all cyclic triads of letters which do not include any of the following consecutive pairs : aa', $a'a$, ab', ba', $a'c$, $c'a$, bb', $b'b$, cc', $c'c$, bc, $c'b'$, $b'c'$, cb, $b'd$, $d'b$, $b'd'$, db, cd, $d'c'$, cd', dc', d^2, dd', $d'd$, d'^2. For, each of these pairs leads to two adjacent faces having the same colours. For the same reason, the triads acb' and $a'bc'$ must also be ruled out. The remaining triads are just those which have been considered above.

The actual enumeration now proceeds as follows. Each of the 14 colourings $(a^3)^2$, $(a'^3)^2$, $(a^2b)^2$, $(a'^2b')^2$, $(ab^2)^2$, $(a'b'^2)^2$, $(a^2d)^2$, $(a'^2d')^2$, $(adc)^2$, $(a'c'd')^2$, $(a^2d')^2$, $(a'^2d)^2$, $(b'c^2)^2$, $(bc'^2)^2$ is unchanged by transposing a certain pair of colours ; therefore these (by cyclic permutation of the colours) give rise to 42 solutions. In the case of $(b^3)(b'^3)$ or of $(c^3)(c'^3)$, transposition of a pair of colours is equivalent to reflection in a mirror; these give rise to 12 solutions. Finally, the 15 colourings $(a^3)(a'^3)$, $(b^3)(c^3)$, $(b'^3)(c'^3)$, $(a^2d)(a'^2c')$, $(a'^2d')(a^2c)$, $(ac^2)(a'd'b')$, $(a'c'^2)(abd)$, $(a^2d')(abd')$, $(a'^2d)(a'db')$, $(b^2c')(ac'd')$, $(b'^2c)(a'dc)$, $(ad'b')(ac'd)$, $(a'bd)(a'd'c)$, $(adb')(ad'c)$, $(a'bd')(a'c'd)$ admit all six permutations of the colours, and so give rise to 90 solutions, making the grand total $42 + 12 + 90 = 144$.

The six solutions $(a^3)(a'^3)$ are special, in that reflection leaves them entirely unaltered. We may call these six reflexible solutions, and describe the rest as 69 enantiomorphous pairs.

CHAPTER IX

UNICURSAL PROBLEMS

I PROPOSE to consider in this chapter some problems which arise out of the theory of unicursal curves. I shall commence with *Euler's Problem and Theorems*, and shall apply the results briefly to the theories of *Mazes* and *Geometrical Trees*. The reciprocal unicursal problem of the *Hamilton Game* will be discussed in the latter half of the chapter.

EULER'S PROBLEM

Euler's problem has its origin in a memoir* presented by him in 1736 to the St. Petersburg Academy, in which he solved a question then under discussion, as to whether it was possible from any point in the town of Königsberg to take a walk in such a way as to cross every bridge in it once and only once and return to the starting point.

The town is built near the mouth of the river Pregel, which there takes the form indicated below and includes the island of Kneiphof. In the eighteenth century there were seven bridges in the positions shown in the diagram, and it is easily seen that with such an arrangement the problem is insoluble. (Since then, an eighth bridge has been built.) Euler, however, did not confine himself to the case of Königsberg, but discussed the general problem of any number of islands connected in any way by bridges. It is evident that the question will not

* 'Solutio problematis ad Geometriam situs pertinentis,' *Commentarii Academiae Scientiarum Petropolitanae* for 1736, Petrograd, 1741, vol. VIII, pp. 128—140. This has been translated into French by M. Ch. Henry; see Lucas, vol. I, part 2, pp. 21—33.

be affected if we suppose the islands to diminish to points and the bridges to lengthen out.   In this way we ultimately obtain

a geometrical figure or network.   In the Königsberg problem this figure is of the shape indicated below, the areas being represented by the points *A*, *B*, *C*, *D*, and the bridges being represented by the lines *l*, *m*, *n*, *p*, *q*, *r*, *s*.

Euler's problem consists therefore in finding whether a given geometrical figure can be described by a point moving so as to traverse every line in it once and only once.   A more general question is to determine how many strokes are necessary to describe such a figure so that no line is traversed twice : this is covered by the rules hereafter given.   The figure may be either in three or in two dimensions, and it may be represented by lines, straight, curved, or tortuous, joining a number of given points, or a model may be constructed by taking a number of rods or pieces of string furnished at each end with a hook so as to allow of any number of them being connected together at one point.

The theory of such figures is included as a particular case

in the propositions proved by Listing in his *Topologie*.* I shall, however, adopt here the methods of Euler, and I shall begin by giving some definitions, as it will enable me to put the argument in a more concise form.

A *node* (or isle) is a point to or from which lines are drawn. A *branch* (or bridge or path) is a line connecting two consecutive nodes. An *end* (or hook) is the point at each termination of a branch. The *order* of a node is the number of branches which meet at it. A node to which only one branch is drawn is a *free* node or a free end. A node at which an even number of branches meet is an *even* node : evidently the presence of a node of the second order is immaterial. A node at which an odd number of branches meet is an *odd* node. A figure is closed if it has no free end : such a figure is often called a closed network.

A *route* consists of a number of branches taken in consecutive order and so that no branch is traversed twice. A *re-entrant* route terminates at a point from which it started. A figure is described *unicursally* when the whole of it is traversed in one route.

The following are Euler's results. (i) In any network the number of odd nodes is even. (ii) A figure which has no odd node can be described unicursally, in a re-entrant route, by a moving point which starts from any point on it. (iii) A figure which has two and only two odd nodes can be described unicursally by a moving point which starts from one of the odd nodes and finishes at the other. (iv) A figure which has more than two odd nodes cannot be described completely in one route; to which Listing added the corollary that a figure which has $2n$ odd nodes, and no more, can be described completely in n separate routes. I now proceed to prove these theorems.

* *Die Studien*, Göttingen, 1847, part x. See also Tait on 'Listing's *Topologie*,' *Philosophical Magazine*, London, January, 1884, series 5, vol. XVII, pp. 30—46; and *Collected Scientific Papers*, Cambridge, vol II, 1900, pp. 85—98. The problem was discussed by J. C. Wilson in his *Traversing of Geometrical Figures*, Oxford, 1905.

First. *The number of odd nodes in any network is even.*

Suppose the number of branches to be b. Therefore the number of hooks is $2b$. Let k_n be the number of nodes of the nth order. Since a node of the nth order is one at which n branches meet, there are n hooks there.

$$\therefore \quad k_1 + 2k_2 + 3k_3 + 4k_4 + \ldots + nk_n + \ldots = 2b.$$

Hence $\qquad k_1 + 3k_3 + 5k_5 + \ldots \quad$ is even.

$$\therefore \quad k_1 + k_3 + k_5 + \ldots \quad \text{is even.}$$

Second. *A figure which has no odd node can be described unicursally in a re-entrant route.*

Since the route is to be re-entrant, it will make no difference where it commences. Suppose that we start from a node A. Every time our route takes us through a node we use up one hook in entering it and one in leaving it. There are no odd nodes, therefore the number of hooks at every node is even : hence, if we reach any node except A, we shall always find a hook which will take us into a branch previously untraversed. Hence the route will take us finally to the node A from which we started. If there are more than two hooks at A, we can continue the route over one of the branches from A previously untraversed, but in the same way as before we shall finally come back to A.

It remains to show that we can arrange our route so as to make it cover all the branches. Suppose each branch of the network to be represented by a string with a hook at each end, and that at each node all the hooks there are fastened together. The number of hooks at each node is even, and if they are unfastened, they can be re-coupled together in pairs, the arrangement of the pairs being immaterial. The whole network will then form one or more closed curves, since now each node consists merely of two ends hooked together.

If this random coupling gives us one single curve, then the proposition is proved; for, starting at any point, we shall go along every branch and come back to the initial point. But if this random coupling produces anywhere an isolated loop, L, then where it touches some other loop, M, say at the node P, unfasten the four hooks there (viz., two of the loop L and two of the loop M) and re-couple them in any other order : then the loop L will become a part of the loop M. In this way, by altering the couplings, we can transform gradually all the separate loops into parts of only one loop.

For example, take the case of three isles, A, B, C, each connected with both the others by two bridges. The most unfavourable way of re-coupling the ends at A, B, C would be to make ABA, ACA, and BCB separate loops. The loops ABA and ACA are separate and touch at A ; hence we should re-couple the hooks at A so as to combine ABA and ACA into

one loop $ABACA$. Similarly, by re-arranging the couplings of the four hooks at B, we can combine the loop BCB with $ABACA$, and thus make only one loop.

I infer from Euler's language that he had attempted to solve the problem of giving a practical rule which would enable one to describe such a figure unicursally without knowledge of its form, but that in this he was unsuccessful. He, however, added that any geometrical figure can be described completely in a single route provided each part of it is described twice and only twice, for, if we suppose that every branch is duplicated, there will be no odd nodes and the figure is unicursal. In this case any figure can be described completely without knowing its form : rules to effect this are given below.

Third. *A figure which has two and only two odd nodes can be described unicursally by a point which starts from one of the odd nodes and finishes at the other odd node.*

This at once reduces to the second theorem. Let A and Z be the two odd nodes. Consider the new figure derived by adding an extra branch from A to Z. In this new figure, all the nodes are even, including A and Z; hence, by Euler's second proposition, it can be described unicursally, and, if the route begins at Z, it will end at Z. We may suppose ZA to be the first branch of the route. The effect of removing this branch, and so restoring the original figure, is just to make the route begin at A; but it still ends at Z.

Fourth. *A figure having* $2n$ *odd nodes, and no more, can be described completely in* n *separate routes.*

If any route starts at an odd node, and if it is continued until it reaches a node where no fresh path is open to it, this latter node must be an odd one. For every time we enter an even node there is necessarily a way out of it; and similarly every time we go through an odd node we use up one hook in entering and one hook in leaving, but whenever we reach it as the end of our route, we use only one hook. If this route is suppressed there will remain a figure with $2n - 2$ odd nodes. Hence n such routes will leave one or more networks with only even nodes. But each of these must have some node common to one of the routes already taken, and therefore can be described as a part of that route. Hence the complete passage will require n, and not more than n, routes. It follows, as stated by Euler, that, if there are more than two odd nodes, the figure cannot be traversed completely in one route.

The Königsberg bridges lead to a network with four odd nodes; hence, by Euler's fourth proposition, it cannot be described unicursally in a single journey, though it can be traversed completely in two separate routes.

The first and second diagrams figured below contain only even nodes, and therefore each of them can be described unicursally. The first of these is a regular re-entrant pentagon; the second is the so-called sign-manual of Mohammed, said to have been originally traced in the sand by the point of his scimitar without taking it off the ground or retracing any part of the figure—which, as it contains only even nodes, is possible. The third diagram is taken from Tait's article: it contains only two odd nodes, and can therefore be described unicursally if we start from one of them, and finish at the other.

The re-entrant pentagon, figured below, has some interest from having been used by the Pythagoreans as a sign—known as the triple triangle or pentagram star—by which they could recognize one another. It was considered symbolical of health, and probably the angles were denoted by the letters of the word ὑγίεια, the diphthong ει being replaced by a θ.

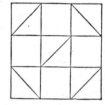

Iamblichus, who is our authority for this, tells us that a certain Pythagorean, when travelling, fell ill at a roadside inn where he had put up for the night; he was poor and sick, but the landlord, who was a kind-hearted fellow, nursed him carefully and spared no trouble or expense to relieve his pains. However, in spite of all efforts, the student got worse. Feeling that he was dying, and unable to make the landlord any pecuniary recompense, he asked for a board, on which he inscribed the pentagram star; this he gave to his host, begging him to hang it up outside so that all passers-by might see it, and assuring him that the result would recompense him for his charity. The scholar died and was honourably buried, and the board was duly exposed. After a considerable time had elapsed, a traveller one day riding by saw the sacred symbol; dismounting, he entered the inn, and after hearing the story, handsomely remunerated the landlord. Such is the anecdote, which, if not true, is at least well found.

As another example of a unicursal diagram, I may mention the geometrical figure formed by taking a $(2n + 1)$-gon and joining every angular point to every other angular point. The edges of an octahedron also form a unicursal figure. On the other hand, a chess-board, divided as usual by straight lines into 64 cells, has 28 odd nodes : hence it would require 14 separate pen-strokes to trace out all the boundaries without going over any more than once. Again, the diagram on page 169 has 20 odd nodes, and therefore would require 10 separate pen-strokes to trace it out.

I turn next to discuss in how many ways we can describe a unicursal figure, all of whose nodes are even.*

Let us consider first how the problem is affected by a path which starts from a node A of order $2n$ and returns to it, forming a closed loop L. If this loop were suppressed, we should have a figure with all its nodes even, the node A being now of the order $2(n-1)$. Suppose the original figure can be described in N ways, and the reduced figure in N' ways. Then each of these N' routes passes $(n-1)$ times through A, and in any of these passages we could describe the loop L in either sense as a part of the path. Hence $N = 2(n-1)N'$.

Similarly if the node A on the original figure is of the order $2(n + l)$, and there are l independent closed loops which start from and return to A, we shall have

$$N = 2^l n(n + 1)(n + 2) \ldots (n + l - 1)N',$$

where N' is the number of routes by which the figure obtained by suppressing these l loops can be described.

By the use of these results, we may reduce any unicursal figure to one in which there are no closed loops of the kind above described. Let us suppose that in this reduced figure there are k nodes. We can suppress one of these nodes, say A, provided we replace the figure by two or more separate figures each of which has not more than $k - 1$ nodes. For suppose

* See G. Tarry, *Association Française pour l'Avancement des Sciences*, 1886, pp. 49—53.

that the node A is of the order $2n$. Then the $2n$ paths which meet at A may be coupled in n pairs in $1 \cdot 3 \cdot 5 \ldots (2n-1)$ ways and each pair will constitute either a path through A, or (in the special case where both members of the pair abut on another node B) a loop from A. This path or loop will form a portion of the route through A in which this pair of paths are concerned. Hence the number of ways of describing the original figure is equal to the sum of the number of ways of describing $1 \cdot 3 \cdot 5 \ldots (2n-1)$ separate simpler figures.

It will be seen that the process consists in successively suppressing node after node. Applying this process continually we finally reduce the figure to a number of figures without loops and in each of which there are only two nodes. If in one of these figures these nodes are each of the order $2n$, it is easily seen that it can be described in $2 \times (2n-1)!$ ways.

We know that a figure with only two odd nodes, A and B, is unicursal if we start at A (or B) and finish at B (or A). Hence the number of ways in which it can be described unicursally will be the same as the number required to describe the figure obtained from it by joining A and B. For if we start at A, it is obvious that at the B end of each of the routes which cover the figure we can proceed along BA to the node A whence we started.

This theory has been applied by Monsieur Tarry* to determine the number of ways in which a set of dominoes, running up to even numbers, can be arranged. This example will serve to illustrate the general method.

A domino consists of a small rectangular slab, twice as long as it is broad, whose face is divided into two squares, which are either blank or marked with 1, 2, 3 ... dots. An ordinary set contains 28 dominoes marked 6–6, 6–5, 6–4, 6–3, 6–2, 6–1, 6–0, 5–5, 5–4, 5–3, 5–2, 5–1, 5–0, 4–4, 4–3, 4–2, 4–1, 4–0, 3–3, 3–2, 3–1, 3–0, 2–2, 2–1, 2–0, 1–1, 1–0, and 0–0. Dominoes are used in various games, in most, if not all, of

---

* See the second edition of the French Translation of this work, Paris, 1908, vol. II, pp. 253—263; see also Lucas, vol. IV, pp. 145—150.

which the pieces are played so as to make a line such that
consecutive squares of adjacent dominoes are marked alike.
Thus if 6–3 is on the table, the only dominoes which can be
placed next to the 6 end are 6–6, 6–5, 6–4, 6–2, 6–1, or 6–0.
Similarly the dominoes 3–5, 3–4, 3–3, 3–2, 3–1, or 3–0, can
be placed next to the 3 end. Assuming that the doubles
are played in due course, it is easy to see that such a set of
dominoes will form a closed circuit.* We want to determine
the number of ways in which such a line or circuit can be formed.

Let us begin by considering the case of a set of 15 dominoes
marked up to double-four. Of these 15 pieces, 5 are doubles.
The remaining 10 dominoes may be represented by the sides
and diagonals of a regular pentagon 01, 02, etc. The inter-
sections of the diagonals do not enter into the representation,

Figure A.

and accordingly are to be neglected. Omitting these from our
consideration, the figure formed by the sides and diagonals of
the pentagon has five even nodes, and therefore is unicursal.
Any unicursal route (*e.g.* 0–1, 1–3, 3–0, 0–2, 2–3, 3–4, 4–1,
1–2, 2–4, 4–0) gives one way of arranging these 10 dominoes.
Suppose there are a such routes. In any such route we may
put each of the five doubles in either of two positions (*e.g.*
in the route given above the double-two can be put between
0–2 and 2–3 or between 1–2 and 2–4). Hence the total
number of unicursal arrangements of the 15 dominoes is 2^5a.

---

* Hence if we remove one domino, say 5–4, we know that the line formed
by the rest of the dominoes must end on one side in a 5 and on the other in
a 4.

If we arrange the dominoes in a straight line, then as we
may begin with any of the 15 dominoes, the total number of
arrangements is $15 \cdot 2^5 \cdot a$.

We have next to find the number of unicursal routes of
the pentagon delineated above in figure A. At the node 0
there are four paths which may be coupled in three pairs. If
0 1 and 0 2 are coupled, as also 0 3 and 0 4, we get figure B.
If 0 1 and 0 3 are coupled, as also 0 2 and 0 4, we get figure C.
If 0 1 and 0 4 are coupled, as also 0 2 and 0 3, we get figure D.

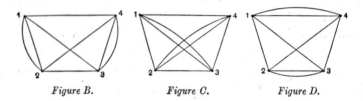

Figure B.   Figure C.   Figure D.

Let us denote the number of ways of describing figure B by b,
of describing figure C by c, and so on. The effect of suppressing
the node 0 in the pentagon A is to give us three quadrangles,
B, C, D. And, in the above notation, we have $a = b + c + d$.

Take any one of these quadrangles, for instance D. We
can suppress the node 1 in it by coupling the four paths which
meet there in pairs. If we couple 1 2 with the upper of the
paths 1 4, as also 1 3 with the lower of the paths 1 4, we get

Figure E.   Figure F.

the figure E. If we couple 1 2 with the lower of the paths 1 4,
as also 1 3 with the upper of the paths 1 4, we again get the
figure E. If we couple 1 2 and 1 3, as also the two paths 1 4,
we get the figure F. Then as above, $d = 2e + f$. Similarly

$b = 2e + f$, and $c = 2e + f$. Hence $a = b + c + d = 6e + 3f$.

We proceed to consider each of the reduced figures E and F. First take E, and in it let us suppress the node 4. For simplicity of description, denote the two paths 4 2 by β and β', and the two paths 4 3 by γ and γ'. Then we can couple β and γ, as also β' and γ', or we can couple β and γ', as also β' and γ : each of these couplings gives the figure G. Or we can couple β and β', as also γ and γ' : this gives the figure H. Thus $e = 2g + h$. Each of the figures G and H has only two nodes. Hence by the formulae given above, we have $g = 2 \cdot 3 \cdot 2 = 12$, and $h = 2 \cdot 2 \cdot 2 = 8$. Therefore $e = 2g + h = 32$. Next take the figure F. This has a loop at 4. If we suppress this

Figure G.   Figure H.   Figure J.

loop we get the figure J, and $f = 2j$. But the figure J, if we couple the two lines which meet at 4, is equivalent to the figure G. Thus $f = 2j = 2g = 24$. Introducing these results we have $a = 6e + 3f = 192 + 72 = 264$. And therefore $N = 15 \cdot 2^5 \cdot a = 126720$. This gives the number of possible arrangements in line of a set of 15 dominoes. In this solution we have treated an arrangement from right to left as distinct from one which goes from left to right : if these are treated as identical we must divide the result by 2. The number of arrangements in a closed ring is $2^5 a$, that is 8448.

We have seen that this number of unicursal routes for a pentagon and its diagonals is 264. Similarly the number for a heptagon is $h = 129{,}976320$. Hence the number of possible arrangements in line of the usual set of 28 dominoes, marked up to double-six, is $28 \cdot 3^7 \cdot h$, which is equal to $7{,}959229{,}931520$. The number of unicursal routes covering a polygon of nine sides is $n = 2^{17} . 3^{11} . 5^2 . 711 . 40787$. Hence the number of possible arrangements in line of a set of 45 dominoes marked up to double-eight is $48 . 4^9 . n$.*

MAZES

Everyone has read of the labyrinth of Minos in Crete and of Rosamund's Bower. A few modern mazes exist here and there—notably one, a very poor specimen of its kind, at Hampton Court—and in one of these, or at any rate on a drawing of one, most people have at some time threaded their way to the interior. I proceed now to consider the manner in which any such construction may be completely traversed even by one who is ignorant of its plan.

The theory of the description of mazes is included in Euler's theorems given above. The paths in the maze are what previously we have termed branches, and the places where two or more paths meet are nodes. The entrance to the maze, the end of a blind alley, and the centre of the maze are free ends and therefore odd nodes.

If the only odd nodes are the entrance to the maze and the centre of it—which will necessitate the absence of all blind alleys—the maze can be described unicursally. This follows from Euler's third proposition. Again, no matter how many odd nodes there may be in a maze, we can always find a route which will take us from the entrance to the centre without retracing our steps, though such a route will take us through only a part of the maze. But in neither of the cases mentioned in this paragraph can the route be determined without a plan of the maze.

A plan is not necessary, however, if we make use of Euler's suggestion, and suppose that every path in the maze is duplicated. In this case we can give definite rules for the complete description of the whole of any maze, even if we are entirely

* These numerical conclusions have also been obtained by algebraical analysis : see M. Reiss, *Annali di Matematica*, Milan, 1871, vol. v, pp. 63—120.

ignorant of its plan. Of course, to walk twice over every path
in a labyrinth is not the shortest way of arriving at the centre,
but, if it is performed correctly, the whole maze is traversed,
the arrival at the centre at some point in the course of the
route is certain, and it is impossible to lose one's way.

I need hardly explain why the complete description of
such a duplicated maze is possible, for now every node is even,
and hence, by Euler's second proposition, if we begin at the
entrance we can traverse the whole maze; in so doing we
shall at some point arrive at the centre, and finally shall
emerge at the point from which we started. This description
will require us to go over every path in the maze twice, and
as a matter of fact the two passages along any path will be
always made in opposite directions.

If a maze is traced on paper, the way to the centre is
generally obvious, but in an actual labyrinth it is not so easy
to find the correct route unless the plan is known. In order
to make sure of describing a maze without knowing its plan, it
is necessary to have some means of marking the paths which
we traverse and the direction in which we have traversed them
—for example, by drawing an arrow at the entrance and end
of every path traversed, or better perhaps by marking the
wall on the right-hand side, in which case a path may not be
entered when there is a mark on each side of it.

Of the various practical rules for threading a maze those
enunciated by M. Trémaux seem to be the simplest.* These
I proceed to explain. For brevity I shall describe a path or a
node as old or new according as it has been traversed once
before or not at all. Then the rules are : (i) whenever you come
to a new node, take any path you like ; (ii) whenever you come
by a new path to an old node or to the closed end of a blind
alley, turn back along the path by which you have just come ;
(iii) whenever you come by an old path to an old node, take a
new path, if there is one, but if not, an old path ; (iv) of course,
a path traversed twice must not be entered. I should add that

* Lucas, vol. I, part iii, pp. 47 *et seq.*

on emerging at any node then, of the various routes which are permitted by these rules, it will be convenient always to select that which lies next to one's right hand, or always that which lies next to one's left hand.

Few if any mazes of the type I have been considering (namely, a series of interlacing paths through which some route can be obtained leading to a space or building at the centre of the maze) existed in classical or medieval times. One class of what the ancients called mazes or labyrinths seems to have comprised any complicated buildings with numerous vaults and passages.* Such a building might be termed a labyrinth, but it is not what is now usually understood by the word. The above rules would enable anyone to traverse the whole of any structure of this kind. I do not know if there are any accounts or descriptions of Rosamund's Bower other than those by Drayton, Bromton, and Knyghton: in the opinion of some, these imply that the bower was merely a house, the passages in which were confusing and ill-arranged.

Another class of ancient mazes consisted of a tortuous path confined to a small area of ground and leading to a tree or shrine in the centre.† This is a maze in which there is no chance of taking a wrong turning; but, as the whole area can be occupied by the windings of one path, the distance to be traversed from the entrance to the centre may be considerable, even though the piece of ground covered by the maze is but small.

The traditional form of the labyrinth constructed for the Minotaur is a specimen of this class. It was delineated on

---

* For instance, see the descriptions of the labyrinth at Lake Moeris given by Herodotus, bk. ii, c. 148; Strabo, bk. xvii, c. 1, art. 37; Diodorus, bk. i, cc. 61, 66; and Pliny, *Hist. Nat.*, bk. xxxvi, c. 13, arts. 84—89. On these and other references see A. Wiedemann, *Herodots zweites Buch*, Leipzig, 1890, p. 522 *et seq.* See also Virgil, *Aeneid*, bk. v, c. v, 588; Ovid, *Met.*, bk. viii, c. 5, 159; Strabo, bk. viii, c. 6.

† On ancient and medieval labyrinths—particularly of this kind—see an article by Mr. E. Trollope in *The Archaeological Journal*, 1858, vol. xv, pp. 216—235, from which much of the historical information given above is derived.

the reverses of the coins of Cnossus, specimens of which are
not uncommon ; one form of it is indicated in the accompanying
diagram (figure i). The design really is the same as that
drawn in figure ii, as can be easily seen by bending round a
circle the rectangular figure there given.

Figure i.   *Figure* ii.

Mr. Inwards has suggested * that this design on the coins
of Cnossus may be a survival from that on a token given by
the priests as a clue to the right path in the labyrinth there.
Taking the circular form of the design shown above he supposed each circular wall to be replaced by two equidistant
walls separated by a path, and thus obtained a maze to which
the original design would serve as the key. The route thus
indicated may be at once obtained by noticing that when a
node is reached (*i.e.* a point where there is a choice of paths),
the path to be taken is that which is next but one to that
by which the node was approached. This maze may be also
threaded by the simple rule of always following the wall on
the right-hand side, or always that on the left-hand side.
The labyrinth may be somewhat improved by erecting a few
additional barriers, without affecting the applicability of the
above rules, but it cannot be made really difficult. This
makes a pretty toy, but though the conjecture on which it is
founded is ingenious, it has no historical justification. Another
suggestion is that the curved line on the reverse of the coins
indicated the form of the rope held by those taking part in
some rhythmic dance ; while others consider that the form was
gradually evolved from the widely prevalent swastika.

* *Knowledge*, London, October, 1892.

S

Copies of the maze of Cnossus were frequently engraved on Greek and Roman gems ; similar but more elaborate designs are found in numerous Roman mosaic pavements.* A copy of the Cretan labyrinth was embroidered on many of the state robes of the later Emperors, and, apparently thence, was copied on to the walls and floors of various churches.† At a later time in Italy and in France these mural and pavement decorations were developed into scrolls of great complexity, but consisting, as far as I know, always of a single line. Some of the best specimens now extant are on the walls of the

Maze at Hampton Court.

cathedrals at Lucca, Aix in Provence, and Poitiers ; and on the floors of the churches of Santa Maria in Trastevere at Rome, San Vitale at Ravenna, Notre Dame at St. Omer, and the cathedral at Chartres. It is possible that they were used to represent the journey through life as a kind of pilgrim's progress.

In England these mazes were usually, perhaps always, cut in the turf adjacent to some religious house or hermitage : and there are some slight reasons for thinking that, when traversed as a religious exercise, a *pater* or *ave* had to be repeated at every turning. After the Renaissance, such labyrinths were frequently termed Troy-Towns or Julian's Bowers. Some of the best specimens, which are still extant, or were so until recently, are those at Rockliff Marshes, Cumberland ; Asenby,

* See, *e.g.*, Breton's *Pompeia*, p. 303.
† Ozanam, *Graphia aureae urbis Romae*, pp. 92, 178.

Yorkshire; Alkborough, Lincolnshire; Wing, Rutlandshire; Boughton-Green, Northamptonshire; Comberton, Cambridge-shire; Saffron Walden, Essex; and Chilcombe, near Winchester.

The modern maze seems to have been introduced—probably from Italy—during the Renaissance, and many of the palaces and large houses built in England during the Tudor and the Stuart periods had labyrinths attached to them. Those adjoining the royal palaces at Southwark, Greenwich, and Hampton Court were well known from their vicinity to

the capital. The last of these was designed by London and Wise in 1690, for William III, who had a fancy for such conceits: a plan of it is given in various guide-books. For the majority of the sight-seers who enter, it is sufficiently elaborate; but it is an indifferent construction, for it can be described completely by always following the hedge on one side (either the right hand or the left hand), and no node is of an order higher than three.

Unless at some point the route to the centre forks and subsequently the two forks reunite, forming a loop in which the centre of the maze is situated, the centre can be reached by the rule just given—namely, by following the wall on one side, either on the right hand or on the left hand. No labyrinth is worthy of the name of a puzzle which can be threaded in this way. Assuming that the path forks as described above, the more numerous the nodes and the higher their order the more difficult will be the maze, and the difficulty might be increased considerably by using bridges and tunnels so as to construct a labyrinth in three dimensions. In an ordinary garden and on a small piece of ground, often of an inconvenient shape, it is not easy to make a maze which fulfils these conditions. On page 259 is a plan of one which I put up in my own garden on a plot of ground which would not allow of more than 36 by 23 paths, but it will be noticed that none of the nodes are of a high order.

GEOMETRICAL TREES

Euler's original investigations were confined to a closed network. In the problem of the maze it was assumed that there might be any number of blind alleys in it, the ends of which formed free nodes. We may now progress one step further, and suppose that the network or closed part of the figure diminishes to a point. This last arrangement is known as a *tree*.

We can illustrate the possible form of these trees by rods, having a hook at each end. Starting with one such rod, we can attach at either end one or more similar rods. Again, on any free hook we can attach one or more similar rods, and so on. Every free hook, and also every point where two or more rods meet, are what hitherto we have called nodes. The rods are what hitherto we have termed branches or paths.

The theory of trees—which already plays a somewhat important part in certain branches of modern analysis, and possibly may contain the key to certain chemical and biological theories—originated in a memoir by Cayley,* written in

* *Philosophical Magazine*, March, 1857, series 4, vol. XIII, pp. 172—176; or *Collected Works*, Cambridge, 1890, vol. III, no. 203, pp. 242—246 : see also the paper on double partitions, *Philosophical Magazine*, November, 1860, series 4, vol. XX, pp. 337—341. On the number of trees with a given number

1856.   The discussion of the theory has been analytical rather than geometrical.   I content myself with noting the following results.

The number of trees with n given nodes is n^{n-2}. If A_n is the number of trees with one special node, or *root*, and n other nodes (and therefore n branches), then

$$(1 - x)^{-1}(1 - x^2)^{-A_1}(1- x^3)^{-A_3} \ldots$$
$$= 1 + A_1 x + A_2 x^2 + A_3 x^3 + \ldots .$$

Using this formula we can find successively the values of $A_1, A_2, \ldots$ The values of A_n when $n = 1, 2, 3, 4, 5, 6, 7$ are 1, 2, 4, 9, 20, 48, 115.

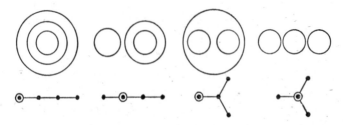

These results have an application to another topological problem : to find the number of ways in which n circles (or spheres) can be internal or external to one another.   For instance, two circles may be outside one another, or one inside the other.   The n circles can be put into correspondence with the nodes, other than the root, of a tree having n branches. Circles not contained in others correspond to nodes directly joined to the root.   Thereafter, every branch indicates that one circle is inside another.   This correspondence shows that the required number of ways is A_n.   In the above diagrams (for the case when $n = 3$), the root of each tree is ringed.

---

of nodes, see the *Quarterly Journal of Mathematics*, London, 1889, vol. XXIII, pp. 376—378.   The connection with chemistry was first pointed out in Cayley's paper on isomers, *Philosophical Magazine*, June, 1874, series 4, vol. XLVII, pp. 444—447, and was treated more fully in his report on trees to the British Association in 1875, *Reports*, pp. 257—305.

If we suppose the n circles to be numbered, so that the first might be inside the second, or the second inside the first, then the number of ways is increased to $(n + 1)^{n-1}$, this being the number of trees (regardless of roots) having $n + 1$ *given* nodes.

I turn next to consider some problems where it is desired to find a route which will pass once and only once through each node of a given geometrical figure. This is the reciprocal of the problem treated in the first part of this chapter, and is a far more difficult question. I am not aware that the general theory has been considered by mathematicians, though two special cases—namely, the *Hamiltonian* (or Icosian) *Game* and the *Knight's Path on a Chess-Board*—have been treated in some detail.

The Hamiltonian Game

The Hamiltonian Game consists in the determination of a route along the edges of a regular dodecahedron which will pass once and only once through every angular point. Sir William Hamilton,* who invented this game—if game is the right term for it—denoted the twenty angular points on the

solid by letters which stand for various towns. The thirty edges constitute the only possible paths. The inconvenience of using a solid is considerable, and the dodecahedron may be represented conveniently in perspective by a flat board marked as shown in the first of the above diagrams. The second and

* See *Quarterly Journal of Mathematics*, London, 1862, vol. v, p. 305; or *Philosophical Magazine*, January, 1884, series 5, vol. xvii, p. 42; also Lucas, vol. ii, part vii.

third diagrams will answer our purpose equally well and are
easier to draw.

The first problem is to go " all round the world," that is,
starting from any town, to go to every other town once and
only once and to return to the initial town; the order of the
n towns to be first visited being assigned, where n is not
greater than five.

Hamilton's rule for effecting this was given at the meeting
in 1857 of the British Association at Dublin. At each
angular point there are three and only three edges. Hence,
if we approach a point by one edge, the only routes open to
us are one to the right, denoted by r, and one to the left,
denoted by l. It will be found that the operations indicated
on opposite sides of the following equalities are equivalent,

$$lr^2l = rlr, \ rl^2r = lrl, \ lr^3l = r^2, \ rl^3r = l^2.$$

Also the operation l^5 or r^5 brings us back to the initial point:
we may represent this by the equations

$$l^5 = 1, \ r^5 = 1.$$

To solve the problem for a figure having twenty angular
points we must deduce a relation involving twenty successive
operations, the total effect of which is equal to unity. By
repeated use of the relation $l^2 = rl^3r$ we see that

$$1 = l^5 = l^2l^3 = (rl^3r)l^3 = \{rl^3\}^2 = \{r(rl^3r)l\}^2$$
$$= \{r^2l^3rl\}^2 = \{r^2(rl^3r)lrl\}^2 = \{r^3l^3rlrl\}^2.$$

Therefore $\{r^3l^3(rl)^2\}^2 = 1$ ....(i),

and similarly $\{l^3r^3(lr)^2\}^2 = 1$ ....(ii).

Hence on a dodecahedron either of the operations

$$r \, r \, r \, l \, l \, l \, r \, l \, r \, l \, r \, r \, r \, l \, l \, l \, r \, l \, r \, l \ldots \text{(i)},$$
$$l \, l \, l \, r \, r \, r \, l \, r \, l \, r \, l \, l \, l \, l \, r \, r \, r \, l \, r \, l \, r \ldots \text{(ii)},$$

indicates a route which takes the traveller through every town.
The arrangement is cyclical, and the route can be commenced
at any point in the series of operations by transferring the
proper number of letters from one end to the other. The

point at which we begin is determined by the order of certain towns which is given initially.

Thus, suppose that we are told that we start from F and then successively go to B, A, U, and T, and we want to find a route from T through all the remaining towns which will end at F. If we think of ourselves as coming into F from G, the path FB would be indicated by l, but if we think of ourselves as coming into F from E, the path FB would be indicated by r. The path from B to A is indicated by l, and so on. Hence our first paths are indicated either by $l\,l\,l\,r$ or by $r\,l\,l\,r$. The latter operation does not occur either in (i) or in (ii), and therefore does not fall within our solutions. The former operation may be regarded either as the 1st, 2nd, 3rd, and 4th steps of (ii), or as the 4th, 5th, 6th, and 7th steps of (i). Each of these leads to a route which satisfies the problem. These routes are

$$F\,B\,A\,U\,T\,P\,O\,N\,C\,D\,E\,J\,K\,L\,M\,Q\,R\,S\,H\,G\,F,$$
and $$F\,B\,A\,U\,T\,S\,R\,K\,L\,M\,Q\,P\,O\,N\,C\,D\,E\,J\,H\,G\,F.$$

It is convenient to make a mark or to put down a counter at each corner as soon as it is reached, and this will prevent our passing through the same town twice.

The operations denoted by l and r, and all combinations of them, form a closed set of sixty. For, if we start off along any one edge, the different operations take us in turn to each of the thirty edges in either direction. These sixty operations, or sixty symbols which have the same laws of combination, are said to constitute the *icosahedral group*, for which the relations

$$l^5 = 1, \quad r^5 = 1, \quad (l^3 r)^2 = 1, \quad (l r^3)^2 = 1$$

provide an *abstract definition*. This means that every true relation between the generators l and r (such as (i), or the relation $l r^2 l = r l r$ mentioned above) is an algebraic consequence of these four. Hamilton himself has given * a simpler

---

* *Philosophical Magazine*, 1856, series 4, vol. XII, p. 446. (That short paper is the foundation for an important branch of mathematics: the theory of Abstract Groups.)

abstract definition for the same group (in terms of generators differently selected from the sixty operations).

A similar game may be played with other solids, provided that at each vertex three and only three edges meet. The reader can make for himself any number of plane figures representing such solids, similar to those drawn on page 262. (For some of these the problem is insoluble.*) But the "group-theoretical" method remains applicable only when the faces of the solid all have the same number of sides. Besides the tetrahedron and the cube, this restriction admits certain regular networks on surfaces of higher genus, such as the map of seven hexagons on the torus (page 235).

For solids having angular points where more than three edges meet—such as the octahedron where at each angular point four edges meet, or the icosahedron where at each angular point five edges meet—we should at each point have more than two routes open to us; hence (unless we suppress some of the edges) the symbolical notation would have to be extended before it could be applied to these solids. I offer the suggestion to anyone who is desirous of inventing a new game.

Another and a very elegant solution of the Hamiltonian dodecahedron problem has been given by M. Hermary. It consists in unfolding the dodecahedron into its twelve pentagons, each of which is attached to the preceding one by only one of its sides; but the solution is geometrical, and not directly applicable to more complicated solids.

. Hamilton suggested as another problem to start from any town, to go to certain specified towns in an assigned order, then to go to every other town once and only once, and to end the journey at some given town. He also suggested the consideration of the way in which a certain number of towns should be blocked so that there was no passage through them, in order to produce certain effects. These problems have not, so far as I know, been subjected to mathematical analysis.

* Dénes König, *Theorie der endlichen und unendlichen Graphen*, Leipzig, 1936, p. 28.

Hamilton's problem has been extended to certain cases where the number of towns is infinite (the required route having no beginning and no end). For a route along the edges of the tessellation of squares (4^4), see König's book on graphs.* A

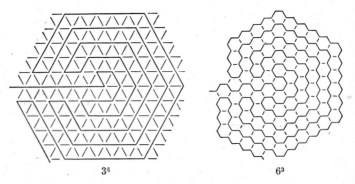

3^6 6^3

similar treatment of the other regular tessellations (3^6 and 6^3) is shown above.

The problem of the knight's path on a chess-board is somewhat similar in character to the Hamiltonian game. This I have already discussed in Chapter VI.

* Dénes König, *op. cit.*, p. 32.

CHAPTER X

The Fifteen School-Girls Problem—first enunciated by T. P. Kirkman, and commonly known as *Kirkman's Problem* —consists in arranging fifteen things in different sets of triplets. It is usually presented in the form that a school-mistress was in the habit of taking her girls for a daily walk. The girls were fifteen in number, and were arranged in five rows of three each, so that each girl might have two companions. The problem is to dispose them so that for seven consecutive days no girl will walk with any of her school-fellows in any triplet more than once.

In the general problem, here discussed, we require to arrange n girls, where n is an odd multiple of 3, in triplets to walk out for y days, where $y = (n - 1)/2$, so that no girl will walk with any of her school-fellows in any triplet more than once.

The theory of the formation of all such possible triplets in the case of nine girls is comparatively easy, but the general theory involves considerable difficulties. Before describing any methods of solution, I will give briefly the leading facts in the history of the problem. For this and much of the material of this chapter I am indebted to O. Eckenstein. Detailed references to the authorities mentioned are given in the bibliography mentioned in the footnote.*

The question was propounded in 1850, and in the same year

---

* The problem was first published in the *Lady's and Gentleman's Diary* for 1850, p. 48, and has been the subject of numerous memoirs. A bibliography of the problem by O. Eckenstein appeared in the *Messenger of Mathematics*, Cambridge, July, 1911, vol. XLI, pp. 33—36.

solutions were given for the cases when $n = 9, 15$, and 27; but the methods used were largely empirical.

The first writer to subject it to mathematical analysis was R. R. Anstice who, in 1852 and 1853, described a method for solving all cases of the form $12m + 3$ when $6m + 1$ is prime. He gave solutions for the cases when $n = 15, 27, 39$. Substantially, his process, in a somewhat simplified form, is covered by that given below under the heading Analytical Methods.

The next important advance in the theory was due to B. Peirce who, in 1860, gave cyclical methods for solving all cases of the form $12m + 3$ and $24m + 9$. But the processes used were complicated and partly empirical.

In 1871 A. H. Frost published a simple method applicable to the original problem when $n = 15$ and to all cases when n is of the form $2^{2m} - 1$. It has been applied to find solutions when $n = 15$ and $n = 63$.

In 1883 A. Bray (a name assumed by G. D. L. Harison) and E. Marsden gave three-step cyclical solutions for 21 girls. These were interesting because Kirkman had expressed the opinion that this case was insoluble.

Another solution when $n = 21$, by T. H. Gill, was given in the fourth edition of this book in 1905. His method though empirical appears to be applicable to all cases, but for high values of n it involves so much preliminary work by trial and error as to be of little value.

A question on the subject which I propounded in the *Educational Times* in 1906, attracted the attention of L. A. Legros, H. E. Dudeney and O. Eckenstein, and I received from them a series of interesting and novel solutions. As illustrations of the processes used, Dudeney published new solutions for $n = 27, 33, 51, 57, 69, 75, 87, 93, 111$; and Eckenstein for $n = 27, 33, 39, 45, 51, 57, 69, 75, 93, 99, 111, 123, 135$.

I now proceed to describe some of the methods applicable to the problem. We can use cycles and combinations of them. I confine my discussion to processes where the steps of the cycles do not exceed three symbols at a time. It will be convenient to begin with the easier methods, where, however, a certain amount of arrangement has to be made empirically, and then to go on to the consideration of the more general method.

One-Step Cycles. As illustrating solutions by one-step cyclical permutations I will first describe Legros's method. Solutions obtained by it can be represented by diagrams, and their use facilitates the necessary arrangements. It is always applicable when n is of the form $24m + 3$, and seems to be also applicable when n is of the form $24m + 9$. Somewhat similar methods were used by Dudeney, save that he made no use of geometrical constructions.

We have $n = 2y + 1 = 24m + 3$ or $n = 2y + 1 = 24m + 9$. We may denote one girl by k, and the others by the numbers $1, 2, 3, \ldots 2y$. Place k at the centre of a circle, and the numbers $1, 2, 3, \ldots 2y$ at equidistant intervals on the circumference. Thus the centre of the circle and each point on its circumference will indicate a particular girl. A solution in which the centre of the circle is used to denote one girl is termed a central solution.

The companions of k are to be different on each day. If we uppose that on the first day they are 1 and $y + 1$, on the second 2 and $y + 2$, and so on, then the diameters through k will give for each day a triplet in which k appears. On each day we have to find $2(y - 1)/3$ other triplets satisfying the conditions of the problem. Every triplet formed from the remaining $2y - 2$ girls will be represented by an inscribed triangle joining the points representing these girls. The sides of the triangles are the chords joining these $2y - 2$ points. These chords may be represented symbolically by [1], [2], [3], ... $[y - 1]$; these numbers being proportional to the smaller arcs subtended. I will denote the sides of a triangle so represented by the letters p, q, r, and I will use the term triad or grouping to denote any group of p, q, r which determines the dimensions of an inscribed triangle. I shall place the numbers of a triad in square brackets. If p, q, r are proportional to the smaller arcs subtended, it is clear that if $p + q$ is less than y, we have $p + q = r$; and if $p + q$ is greater than y we have $p + q + r = 2y$. If we like to use arcs larger than the semi-circumference we may confine ourselves to the relation $p + q = r$. In the geometrical methods described below, we usually first determine the dimensions of the triangles to be used in the solution, and then find how they are to be arranged in the circle.

If $(y - 1)/3$ scalene triangles, whose sides are p, q, r, can be inscribed in the circle so that to each triangle corresponds an equal complementary triangle having its equal sides parallel to those of the first and with its vertices at free points, then the system of $2(y - 1)/3$ triangles with the corresponding diameter will give an arrangement for one day. If the system be permuted cyclically $y - 1$ times we get arrangements for the other $y - 1$ days. No two girls will walk together twice, for each chord occupies a different position after each permutation, and as all the chords forming the $(y - 1)/3$ triangles are unequal the same combination cannot occur twice. Since the triangles are placed in complementary pairs, one being y points in front of the other, it follows that after $y - 1$ permutations we shall come to a position like the initial one, and the cycle will be completed. If the circle be drawn and the triangles cut out to scale, the arrangement of the triangles is facilitated. The method will be better understood if I apply it to one or two of the simpler cases.

The first case is that of three girls, a, b, c, walking out for one day, that is, $n = 3$, $m = 0$, $y = 1$. This involves no discussion, the solution being $(a.\ b.\ c)$.

The next case is that of nine girls walking out for four days, that is, $n = 9$, $m = 0$, $y = 4$. The first triplet on the first day is $(1.\ k.\ 5)$. There are six other girls represented by the points 2, 3, 4, 6, 7, 8. These points can be joined so as to form triangles, and each triangle will represent a triplet. We want to find one such triangle, with unequal sides, with its vertices at three of these points, and such that the triangle formed by the other three points will have its sides equal and parallel to the sides of the first triangle.

The sides of a triangle are p, q, r. The only possible values are 1, 2, 3, and they satisfy the condition $p + q = r$. If a triangle of this shape is placed with its vertices at the points 3, 4, 6, we can construct a complementary equal triangle, four points further on, having 7, 8, 2 for its vertices. All the points in the figure are now joined, and form the three triplets for the first day, namely $(k. 1. 5)$, $(3. 4. 6)$, $(7. 8. 2)$. It is only necessary to rotate the figure one step at a time in order to obtain the triplets for the remaining three days. Another similar solution is obtained from the diameter $(1. k. 5)$, and the triangles $(2. 3. 8)$, $(6. 7. 4)$. It is the reflection of the former solution.

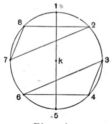

Figure i.

The next case to which the method is applicable is when $n = 27$, $m = 1$, $y = 13$. Proceeding as before, the 27 girls must be arranged with one of them, k, at the centre and the other 26 on the circumference of a circle. The diameter $(1. k. 14)$ gives the first triplet on the first day. To obtain the other triplets we have to find four dissimilar triangles which satisfy the conditions mentioned above. The chords used as sides of these triangles may be of the lengths represented symbolically by [1], [2], . . . [12]. We have to group these lengths so that $p + q = r$ or $p + q + r = 2y$; if the first condition can be satisfied it is the easier to use, as the numbers are smaller. In this instance the triads [3, 8, 11], [5, 7, 12], [2, 4, 6], [1, 9, 10] will be readily found. Now if four triangles with their sides of these lengths can be arranged in a system so that all the vertices fall on the ends of different diameters (exclusive of the ends of the diameter 1, k, 14), it follows that the opposite ends of those diameters can be joined by chords giving a series of equal triangles, symmetrically placed, each having its sides parallel to those of a triangle of the first system.   The following arrangement of triangles satisfies the conditions : (4. 11. 25), (5. 8. 23), (6. 7. 16), (9. 13. 15).   The complementary system is (17. 24. 12), (18. 21. 10), (19. 20. 3), (22. 26. 2).   These triplets with (k. 1. 14) give an arrangement for the first day ; and, by rotating the system cyclically, the arrangements for the remaining 12 days can be found immediately.

I proceed to give one solution of this type for every remaining case where n is less than 100.   From the result the triads or groupings used can be obtained. It is sufficient in each case to give an arrangement on the first day, since the arrangements on the following days are at once obtainable by cyclical permutations.

I take first the three cases, 33, 57, 81, where n is of the form $24m + 9$. In these cases the arrangements on the other days are obtained by one-step cyclical permutations.

For 33 girls, a solution is given by the system of triplets (2, 11. 16), (4. 6. 10), (5. 13. 30), (7. 8. 19), (9. 28. 31), and the complementary system (18. 27. 32), (20. 22. 26), (21. 29. 14), (23. 24. 3), (25. 12. 15).   These 10 triplets, together with that represented by (k. 1. 17), will give an arrangement for the first day.

For 57 girls, a possible arrangement of triplets is (18. 13. 50), (20. 11. 28), (21. 52. 3), (8. 10. 51), (4. 25. 26), (2. 6. 12), (7. 19. 33), (27. 43. 16), (37. 14. 17). These, with the 9 complementary triplets, and the diameter triplet (1. k. 29), give an arrangement for the first day.

For 81 girls an arrangement for the first day consists of the diameter triplet (1. k. 41), the 13 triplets (3. 35. 42), (4. 10. 29), (5. 28. 56), (6. 26. 39), (7. 15. 17), (8. 11. 32), (13. 27. 49), (14. 19. 30), (20. 37. 38), (21. 25. 52), (24. 36. 62), (18. 33. 63), (31. 40. 74), and the 13 complementary triplets.

I take next the three cases, 51, 75, 99, where n is of the form $24m + 3$.   In these cases the arrangements on the other days are obtained either by one-step or by two-step cyclical permutations.

For 51 girls, an arrangement for the first day consists of the diameter triplet (k. 1. 26), the 8 triplets (2. 9. 36), (4. 7. 25), (6. 10. 19), (8. 14. 22), (12. 17. 45), (13. 24. 48), (15. 16. 46), (18, 28. 30), and the 8 complementary triplets.

For 75 girls, an arrangement for the first day consists of the diameter triplet (k. 1. 38), the 12 triplets (2. 44. 55), (4. 11. 19), (5. 50. 66), (6. 52. 57), (8. 46. 58), (10. 59. 65), (12. 60. 64), (14. 24. 68), (16. 25. 72), (17. 3. 74), (33. 34. 73), (30. 32. 63), and the 12 complementary triplets.

For 99 girls an arrangement for the first day consists of the diameter triplet (1. k. 50), the 16 triplets (2. 17. 47), (3. 9. 68), (4. 44. 82), (5. 12. 75), (6. 32. 42), (7. 23. 97), (8. 21. 30), (15. 20. 76), (16. 35. 85), (18. 45. 62), (22. 40. 63), (25. 37. 92), (28. 29. 80), (34. 38. 59), (39. 41. 73), (46. 49. 60), and the 16 complementary triplets.

It is also possible to obtain, for numbers of the form $24m + 3$, solutions which are uniquely two-step, but in these the complementary triangles are not placed symmetrically to each other. I give 27 girls as an instance, using the same triads as in the solution of this case given above. The triplets for the first day are (k. 1. 14), (2. 12. 3), (21. 5. 22), (20. 24. 26), (11. 15. 17), (8. 16. 19), (25. 7. 10), (6. 18. 13), and (23. 9. 4). From this the arrangements on the other days can be obtained by a two-step (but not by a one-step) cyclical permutation.

It is unnecessary to give more examples, or to enter on the question of how from one solution others can be deduced, or how many solutions of each case can be obtained in this way. The types of the possible triangles are found analytically, but their geometrical arrangement is empirical. The defect of this method is that it may not be possible to arrange a given grouping. Thus when $n = 27$, we easily obtain 24 different groupings, but two of them cannot be arranged geometrically to give solutions; and whether any particular grouping will give a solution can, in many cases, be determined only by long and troublesome empirical work. The same objection applies to the two-step and three-step methods which are described below.

Two-Step Cycles. The method used by Legros was extended by Eckenstein to cases where n is of the form $12m + 3$. When n is of this form and m is odd we cannot get sets of complementary triangles as is required in Legros's method; hence, to apply a similar method, we have to find $2(y - 1)/3$ different dissimilar inscribed triangles having no vertex in common and satisfying the condition $p + q = r$ or $p + q + r = 2y$. These solutions are also central. Since there are $2y$ points on the circumference of the circle, the permutations, if they are to be cyclical, must go in steps of two numbers at a time. In Legros's method we represent one triplet by a diameter. But obviously it will answer our purpose equally well to represent it by a triangle with k as vertex and two radii as sides, one

T

drawn to an even number and the other to an odd number : in fact, this will include the diameter as a particular case.

I begin by considering the case where we use the diameter (1. *k*. *y* + 1) to represent one triplet on the first day. Here the chords used for sides of the triangles representing the other triplets must be of lengths [1], [2], . . . [*y* − 1]. Also each given length must appear twice, and the two equal lines so represented must start one from an even number and the other

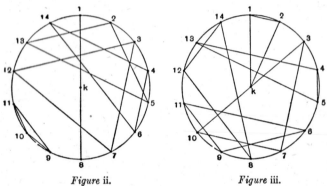

Figure ii.   *Figure* iii.

from an odd number, so as to avoid the same combination of points occurring again when the system is rotated cyclically. Of course, a vertex cannot be at the point 1 or *y*, as these points will be required for the diameter triplet (1. *k*. *y* + 1).

These remarks will be clearer if we apply them to a definite example. I take as an instance the case of 15 girls. As before, we represent 14 of them by equidistant points numbered 1, 2, 3, . . . 14 on the circumference of a circle, and one by a point *k* at its centre. Take as one triplet the diameter (1. *k*. 8). Then the sides *p*, *q*, *r* may have any of the values [1], [2], [3], [4], [5], [6], and each value must be used twice. On examination it will be found that there are only two possible groupings—namely, [1, 1, 2], [2, 4, 6], [3. 3. 6], [5. 5. 4], and [1, 2, 3], [1, 4, 5], [3, 5, 6], [2, 4, 6]. One of the solutions to which the first set of groupings leads is defined by the diameter (1. *k*. 8) and the four triplets (9. 10. 11), (4. 6. 14), (2. 5. 13), (3. 7. 12) ; see figure ii, above: of the four triangles used, three are isosceles. The second set leads to solutions defined by the triplets $(k. 1. 8)$ $(4. 5. 7)$, $(13. 14. 9)$, $(3. 6. 11)$, $(10. 12. 2)$, or by the triplets $(k. 1. 8)$, $(6. 7. 9)$, $(3. 4. 13)$, $(5. 11. 14)$, $(10. 12. 2)$: in these solutions all the triangles used are scalene. If any one of these three sets of triplets is rotated cyclically two steps at a time, we get a solution of the problem for the seven days required. Each of these solutions by reflection and inversion gives rise to three others.

Next, if we take $(k. 1. 2)$ for one triplet on the first day, we shall have the points $3, 4, \ldots 14$ for the vertices of the four triangles denoting the other triplets on that day. The sides must be of the lengths $[1], [2], \ldots [7]$, of which $[2], \ldots [6]$ must be used not more than twice and $[1], [7]$ must be used only once. The $[1]$ used must start from an even number, for otherwise the chord denoted by it would, when the system was rotated, occupy the position joining the points 1 and 2, which has been already used. The only possible groupings are $[2, 4, 6], [2, 3, 5], [3, 4, 7], [1, 5, 6]$; or $[2, 4, 6], [2, 5, 7]$, $[1, 4, 5], [3, 3, 6]$; or $[2, 4, 6], [2, 5, 7], [1, 3, 4], [3, 5, 6]$. Each of these groupings gives rise to various solutions. For instance, the first grouping gives a set of triplets $(k. 1. 2)$, $(3. 7. 10)$, $(4. 5. 13)$, $(6. 9. 11)$, $(8. 12. 14)$. From this by a cyclical two-step permutation we get a solution. This solution is represented in figure iii. If we take $(k. 1. 4)$ or $(k. 1. 6)$ as one triplet on the first day, we get other sets of solutions.

Solutions involving the triplets $(k. 1. 2)$, $(k. 1. 4)$, $(k. 1. 6)$, $(k. 1. 8)$, and other analogous solutions can be obtained from the solutions illustrated in the above diagrams by rearranging the symbols denoting the girls. For instance, if in figure iii, where all the triangles used are scalene, we replace the numbers $2, 8, 3, 13, 4, 6, 5, 11, 7, 9, 10, 14$ by $8, 2, 13, 3, 6, 4, 11, 5, 9$, $7, 14, 10$, we get the solution $(k. 1. 8)$, $(4. 5. 7)$, etc., given above. Again, if in figure iii we replace the symbols $1, 2, 3, 4, 5, 6$, $7, 8, 9, 10, 11, 12, 13, 14, k$ by $12, 2, 10, 6, 1, 14, 5, 13, 9$, $15, 4, 3, 11, 8, 7$, we obtain a solution equivalent to that given by T. H. Gill and printed in the fourth edition of this book.   In this the arrangement on the first day is (1. 6. 11), (2. 7. 12), (3. 8. 13), (4. 9. 14), (5. 10. 15).   The arrangements on the other days are obtained as before by rotating the system so delineated round 7 as a centre two steps at a time.   Gill's arrangement is thus presented in its canonical form as a central two-step cyclical solution.

I proceed to give one solution of this type for every remaining case where n is less than 100. In each case I give an arrangement on the first day; the arrangements for the other days can be got from it by a two-step cyclical permutation of the numbers.

In the case of 27 girls, one arrangement on the first day is (k. 1. 14), (19. 21. 20), (3. 9. 6), (13. 23. 18), (5. 17. 24), (7. 25. 16), (11. 15. 26), (10. 4. 2), (12. 22. 8).

In the case of 39 girls, one arrangement for the first day is (k. 1. 20), (35. 37. 36), (7. 13. 10), (19. 29. 24), (11. 25. 18), (3. 21. 12), (17. 33. 6), (15. 27. 2), (23. 31. 8), (5. 9. 26), (4. 16. 32), (14. 34. 38), (22. 28. 30).

In the case of 51 girls, one arrangement for the first day is (k. 1. 26), (21. 23. 22), (11. 17. 14), (35. 45. 40), (25. 39. 32), (15. 33. 24), (13. 41. 2), (5. 31. 18), (19. 49. 34), (27. 43. 10), (9. 47. 28), (29. 37. 8), (3. 7. 30), (4. 20. 46), (6. 36. 42), (12. 16. 44), (38. 48. 50).

In the case of 63 girls, one arrangement for the first day is (k. 1. 32), (57. 59. 58), (23. 29. 26), (37. 47. 42), (5. 53. 60), (17. 61. 8), (3. 43. 54), (7. 33. 20), (9. 39. 24), (27. 55. 10), (21. 45. 2), (11. 31. 52), (35. 51. 12), (13. 25. 50), (41. 49. 14), (15. 19. 48), (16. 18. 36), (6. 34. 38), (46. 56. 62), (22. 30. 44), (4. 28. 40).

In the case of 75 girls, one arrangement for the first day is (k. 1. 38), (23. 25. 24), (3. 9. 6), (29. 39. 34), (7. 21. 14), (51. 69. 60), (33. 55. 44), (11. 59. 72), (35. 65. 50), (37. 71. 54), (27. 63. 8), (15. 57. 36), (13. 41. 64), (43. 67. 18), (19. 73. 46), (31. 47. 2), (5. 17. 48), (53. 61. 20), (45. 49. 10), (30. 32. 52), (22. 26. 66), (56. 62. 70), (12. 28. 74), (16. 40. 58), (4. 42. 68).

In the case of 87 girls, one arrangement for the first day is (k. 1. 44), (61. 63. 62), (73. 79. 76), (35. 45. 40), (11. 83. 4), (25. 43. 34), (59. 81. 70), (7. 33. 20), (41. 71. 56), (23. 75. 6), (27. 65. 46), (13. 57. 78), (5. 51. 28), (3. 39. 64), (15. 47. 74), (9. 67. 38), (31. 55. 86), (19. 85. 52), (21. 37. 72), (17. 29. 66), (69. 77. 30), (49. 53. 8), (10. 12. 24), (22. 26. 84), (18. 54. 60), (2. 50. 80), (32. 42. 58), (14. 36. 82), (16. 48. 68).

In the case of 99 girls, one arrangement for the first day is (k. 1. 50), (47. 49. 48), (53. 59. 56), (55. 65. 60), (57. 71. 64), (23. 41. 32), (17. 39. 28), (63. 89. 76), (5. 35. 20), (3. 67. 84), (9. 69. 88), (29. 85. 8), (27. 79. 4), (25. 73. 98), (33. 77. 6), (21. 61. 90), (45. 81. 14), (51. 83. 18), (15. 43. 78), (13. 37. 74), (11. 31. 70), (75. 91. 34), (7. 19. 62), (87. 95. 42), (93. 97. 46), (58. 94. 96), (40. 44. 66), (10. 16. 26), (30. 38. 82). (68. 80. 2), (22. 36. 92), (24. 54. 72), (12. 52. 86).

This method may be also represented as a one-step cycle. For if we denote the girls by a point k at the centre of the circle, and points a_1, b_1, a_2, b_2, a_3, b_3, ... placed in that order on the circumference, we can re-write the solutions in the suffix notation, and then the cyclical permutation of the numbers denoting the suffixes is by one step at a time.

The one-step and two-step methods described above cover all cases except those where n is of the form $24m + 21$. These I have failed to bring under analogous rules, but we can solve them by recourse to the three-step cycles next described.

Three-Step Cycles. The fact that certain cases are soluble by one-step cycles, and others by two-step cycles, suggests the use of three-step cycles, and the fact that n is a multiple of 3 points to the same conclusion. On the other hand, if we denote the n girls by 1, 2, 3, ... n, and make a cyclical permutation of three steps at a time (or if we denote the girls by a_1, b_1, c_1, a_2, b_2, c_2, ..., and make a cyclical permutation of the suffixes one step at a time), we cannot get arrangements for more than $n/3$ days. Hence there will remain $(n-1)/2 - n/3$ days, that is, $(n-3)/6$ days, for which we have to find other arrangements. In fact, however, we can arrange the work so that in addition to the cyclical arrangements for $n/3$ days we can find $(n-3)/6$ single triplets from each of which by a cyclical permutation of the numbers or suffixes an arrangement for one of these remaining days can be obtained; other methods are also sometimes available.

For instance, take the case of 21 girls. An arrangement for the first day is (1. 4. 10), (2. 5. 11), (3. 6. 12), (7. 14. 18), (8. 15. 16), (9. 13. 17), (19. 20. 21). From this by cyclical permutations of the numbers three steps at a time, we can get arrangements for 7 days in all. The arrangement for the 8th day can be got from the triplet (1. 6. 11) by a three-step cyclical permutation of the numbers in it. Similarly the arrangement for the 9th day can be got from the triplet (2. 4. 12), and that for the 10th day from the triplet (3. 5. 10), by three-step cyclical permutations.

This method was first used by A. Bray in 1883, and was subsequently developed by Dudeney and Eckenstein. It gives a solution for every value of n except 15, but it is not so easy to use as the methods already described, partly because the solution is in two parts, and partly because the treatment varies according as n is of the form $18m + 3$, or $18m + 9$, or $18m + 15$. Most of the difficulties in using it arise in the case when n is of the form $18m + 15$.

The geometrical representation is sufficiently obvious. In the methods used by Legros and Eckenstein, previously described, the girls were represented by $2y$ equidistant points on the circumference of a circle and a point at its centre. It is evident that we may with equal propriety represent all the girls by symbols placed at equidistant intervals round the circumference of a circle : such solutions are termed non-central. The symbols may be 1, 2, 3, ... n, or letters a_1, b_1, c_1, a_2, b_2, c_2, ... Any triplet will be represented by a triangle whose sides are chords of the circle. The arrangement on any day is to include all the girls, and therefore the triangles representing the triplets on that day are $n/3$ in number, and as each girl appears in only one triplet, no two triangles can have a common vertex.

The complete three-step solution will require the determination of a system of $(n - 1)/2$ inscribed triangles. In the first part of the solution $n/3$ of these triangles must be selected to form an arrangement for the first day, so that by rotating this arrangement three steps at a time we obtain triplets for $n/3$ days in all. In the second part of the solution we must assure ourselves that the remaining $(n - 3)/6$ triangles are such that from each of them, by a cyclical permutation of three steps at a time, an arrangement for one of the remaining $(n - 3)/6$ days is obtainable.

As before, we begin by tabulating the possible differences $[1], [2], [3], ... [(n - 1)/2]$, whose values denote the lengths of the sides p, q, r of the possible triangles ; also, we have either $p + q = r$ or $p + q + r = n$. From these values of p, q, r

are formed triads, and in these triads each difference must be used three times and only three times. Triangles of these types must be then formed and placed in the circle so that the side denoting any assigned difference p must start once from a number of the form $3m$, once from a number of the form $3m + 1$, and once from a number of the form $3m + 2$. Also an isosceles triangle, one of whose sides is a multiple of three, cannot be used : thus in any particular triad a 3, 6, 9, . . . cannot appear more than once. Save in some exceptional cases of high values of n, every triangle, one of whose sides is a multiple of 3, must be used in the first part of the solution. In the whole arrangement every possible difference will occur n times, and, since any two assigned numbers can occur together only once, each difference when added to a number must start each time from a different number. I will not go into further details as to how these triangles are determined, but I think the above rules will be clear if I apply them to one or two easy examples.

For 9 girls, the possible differences are [1], [2], [3], [4], each of which must be used three times in the construction of four triangles the lengths of whose sides p, q, r are such that $p + q = r$ or $p + q + r = 9$. One possible set of triads formed from these numbers is [1, 2, 3], [1, 2, 3], [2, 3, 4], and [1, 4, 4]. Every triangle with a side of the length [3] must appear in the first part of the solutions ; thus the triplets used in the first part of the solution must be obtained from the first three of these triads. Hence we obtain as an arrangement for the first day the triplets (1. 3. 9), (2. 4. 7), (5. 6. 8). From this, three-step cyclical permutations give arrangements for other two days. The remaining triad [1, 4, 4] leads to a triplet (1. 2. 6) which, by a three-step cyclical permutation, gives an arrangement for the remaining day.

If we use the suffix notation, an arrangement for the first day is $a_1 b_2 a_3$, $b_1 c_2 b_3$, $c_1 a_2 c_3$. From this, by simple cyclical permutations of the suffixes, we get arrangements for the second and third days. Lastly, the triplet $a_1 b_1 c_1$ gives, by cyclical permutation of the suffixes, the arrangement for the fourth day—namely, $a_1b_1c_1$, $a_2b_2c_2$, $a_3b_3c_3$.

For 15 girls, the three-step process is inapplicable. The explanation of this is that two triads are required in the second part of the solution, and in neither of them may a 3 appear. The triads are to be formed from the differences [1], [2], ... [7], each of which is to be used three times, and the condition that in any particular triad only one 3 or one 6 may appear necessitates that six of the triads shall involve a 3 or a 6. Hence only one triad will be available for the second part of the solution.

I proceed to give one solution of this type for every remaining case where n is less than 100. I give some in the numerical, others in the suffix notation. The results will supply an indication of the process used.

First, I consider those cases where n is of the form $18m + 3$. In these cases it is always possible to find $2m$ triads each repeated thrice, and one equilateral triad, and to use the equilateral and m triads in the first part of the solution, the 3 triplets representing any one of these m triads being placed in the circle at equal intervals from each other in the first day's arrangement. From this, three-step or one-step cyclical permutations give arrangements for $6m + 1$ days in all. In the second part of the solution each of the m remaining triads is used thrice; it suffices to give the first triplet on each day, since from it the other triplets on that day are obtained by a three-step cyclical permutation.

For 21 girls an arrangement for the first day, for the first part of the solution, is (1. 4. 10), (8. 11. 17), (15. 18. 3), (2. 6. 7), (9. 13. 14), (16. 20. 21), (5. 12. 19). From this, three-step or one-step cyclical permutations give arrangements for 7 days in all. The first triplets used in the second part of the solution are (1. 3. 11), (2. 4. 12), (3. 5. 13). Each of these three triplets gives by a three-step cyclical permutation an arrangement for one of the remaining 3 days.

For 39 girls, arrangements for 13 days can be obtained from the following arrangement of triplets for the first day : (1. 4. 13), (14. 17. 26), (27. 30. 39), (2. 8. 23), (15. 21. 36), (28. 34. 10), (7. 11. 12), (20. 24. 25), (33. 37. 38), (3. 5. 19), (16. 18. 32), (29. 31. 6), (9. 22. 35). From each of the 6 triplets (1. 8. 18), (2. 9. 19), (3. 10. 20), (1. 9. 20), (2. 10. 21), (3. 11. 22), an arrangement for one of the remaining 6 days is obtainable.

For 57 girls, arrangements for 19 days can be obtained from the following arrangement of triplets for the first day : (1. 4. 25), (20. 23. 44), (39. 42. 6), (2. 8. 17), (21. 27. 36), (40. 46. 55), (3. 15. 33), (22. 34. 52), (41. 53. 14), (18. 19. 26), (37. 38. 45), (56. 57. 7), (13. 30. 35), (32. 49. 54), (51. 11. 16), (9. 29. 43), (28. 48. 5), (47. 10. 24), (12. 31. 50). From each of the 9 triplets (1. 3. 14), (2. 4. 15), (3. 5. 16), (1. 5. 30), (2. 6. 31), (3. 7. 32), (1. 11. 27),

(2. 12. 28), (3. 13. 29), an arrangement for one of the remaining 9 days is obtainable.

For 75 girls, arrangements for 25 days can be obtained from the following arrangement of triplets for the first day : (1. 4. 10), (26. 29. 35), (51. 54. 60), (3. 15. 36), (28. 40. 61), (53. 65. 11), (2. 17. 41), (27. 42. 66), (52. 67. 16), (13. 31. 58), (38. 56. 8), (63. 6. 33), (14. 21. 22), (39. 46. 47), (64. 71. 72), (7. 18. 20), (32. 43. 45), (57. 68. 70), (5. 9. 37), (30. 34. 62), (55. 59. 12), (19. 24. 50), (44. 49. 75), (69. 74. 25), (23. 48. 73). From each of the 12 triplets (1. 11. 30), (2. 12. 31), (3. 13. 32), (1. 15. 35), (2. 16. 36), (3. 17. 37), (1. 17. 39), (2. 18. 40), (3. 19. 41), (1. 18. 41), (2. 19. 42), (3. 20. 43), an arrangement for one of the remaining 12 days is obtainable.

For 93 girls, arrangements for 31 days can be obtained from the following arrangement of triplets for the first day : (1. 76. 79), (32. 14. 17), (63. 45. 48), (13. 25. 55), (44. 56. 86), (75. 87. 24), (29. 50. 74), (60. 81. 12), (91. 19. 43), (20. 26. 59), (51. 57. 90), (82. 88. 28), (3. 30. 39), (34. 61. 70), (65. 92. 8), (27. 64. 71), (58. 2. 9), (89. 33. 40), (35. 36. 52), (66. 67. 83), (4. 5. 21), (11. 15. 37), (42. 46. 68), (73. 77. 6), (16. 18. 41), (47. 49. 72), (78. 80. 10), (23. 31. 69), (54. 62. 7), (85. 93. 38), (22. 53. 84). From each of the 15 triplets (1. 14. 42), (2. 15. 43), (3. 16. 44), (1. 33. 44), (2. 34. 45), (3. 35. 46), (1. 11. 30), (2. 12. 31), (3. 13. 32), (1. 6. 41), (2. 7. 42), (3. 8. 43), (1. 15. 35), (2. 16. 36), (3. 17. 37), an arrangement for one of the remaining 15 days is obtainable by a three-step cyclical permutation.

Before leaving the subject of numbers of this type, I give two other solutions of the case when $n = 21$, one to illustrate the use of the suffix notation, and the other a cyclical solution which is uniquely three-step.

If we employ the suffix notation, the suffixes, with the type here used, are somewhat trying to read. Accordingly hereafter I shall write $a1$, $a2$, ..., instead of a_1, a_2, ... In the case of 21 girls, an arrangement for the first day is $(a1. a2. a4)$, $(b1. b2. b4)$, $(c1. c2. c4)$, $(a3, b6. c5)$, $(b3. c6. a5)$, $(c3. a6. b5)$, $(a7. b7. c7)$. From this, by one-step cyclical permutations of the suffixes, we get arrangements for the 2nd, 3rd, 4th, 5th, 6th and 7th days. The arrangement for the 8th day can be obtained from the triplet $(a1. b2. c4)$ by permuting the suffixes cyclically one step at a time. Similarly the arrangement for the 9th day can be obtained from the triplet $(b1. c2. a4)$ and that for the 10th day from the triplet $(c1. a2. b4)$. Thus with seven suffixes we keep 7 for each symbol in one triplet, and every other triplet depends on one or other of only two arrangements—namely, (1. 2. 4) or (3. 6. 5). If the solution be written out at length the principle of the method used will be clear.

Cyclical solutions which are uniquely three-step can also be obtained for numbers of the form $18m + 3$; in them the same triads can be used as before, but they are not placed at equal intervals in the circle. I give 21 girls as instance. The arrangements on the first 7 days can be obtained from the arrangement (1. 4. 10), (2. 20. 14), (15. 18. 3), (16. 17. 21), (8. 9. 13), (6. 7. 11), (5. 12. 19) by a three-step (but not by a one-step) cyclical permutation. From each of the triplets (1. 3. 11), (2. 4. 12), (3. 5. 13) an arrangement for one of the remaining 3 days is obtainable.

Next, I consider those cases where n is of the form $18m + 9$. Here, regular solutions in the suffix notation can be obtained in all cases except in that of 27 girls, but if the same solutions are expressed in the numerical notation, the triads are irregular. Accordingly, except when $n = 27$, it is better to use the suffix notation. I will deal with the case when $n = 27$ after considering the cases when $n = 45, 63, 81, 99$.

For 45 girls, an arrangement for the first day consists of the 5 triplets $(a1.\ a12.\ a13)$, $(a2.\ a9.\ a11)$, $(a5.\ a10.\ b15)$, $(a4.\ b3.\ c7)$, $(a8.\ b6.\ c14)$, and the 10 analogous triplets—namely, $(b1.\ b12.\ b13)$, $(c1.\ c12.\ c13)$, $(b2.\ b9.\ b11)$, $(c2.\ c9.\ c11)$, $(b5.\ b10.\ c15)$, $(c5.\ c10.\ a15)$, $(b4.\ c3.\ a7)$, $(c4.\ a3.\ b7)$, $(b8.\ c6.\ a14)$, $(c8.\ a6.\ b14)$. From these, by one-step cyclical permutations of the suffixes, the arrangements for 15 days can be got. Each of the 2 triplets $(c4.\ b3.\ a7)$, $(c8.\ b6.\ a14)$, the 4 analogous triplets—namely, $(a4.\ c3.\ b7)$, $(b4.\ a3.\ c7)$, $(a8.\ c6.\ b14)$, $(b8.\ a6.\ c14)$—and the triplet $(a1.\ b1.\ c1)$, gives, by a one-step cyclical permutation of the suffixes, an arrangement for one of the remaining 7 days.

For 63 girls, an arrangement for the first day consists of the 7 triplets $(a1.\ a10.\ a9)$, $(a5.\ a8.\ a3)$, $(a4.\ a19.\ a15)$, $(a7.\ a14.\ b21)$, $(a20.\ b11.\ c12)$, $(a16.\ b13.\ c18)$, $(a17.\ b2.\ c6)$, and the 14 analogous triplets. From these, by one-step cyclical permutations of the suffixes, the arrangements for 21 days can be got. Each of the 10 triplets, consisting of the 3 triplets $(c20.\ b11.\ a12)$, $(c16.\ b13, a18)$, $(c17.\ b2.\ a6)$, the 6 analogous triplets, and the triplet $(a1.\ b1.\ c1)$, gives, by a one-step cyclical permutation of the suffixes, an arrangement for one of the remaining 10 days.

For 81 girls, an arrangement for the first day consists of the 9 triplets $(a5.\ a7.\ a8)$, $(a3.\ a10.\ a14)$, $(a11.\ a21.\ a26)$, $(a4.\ a12.\ a25)$, $(a9.\ a18.\ b27)$, $(a22.\ b20.\ c19)$, $(a24.\ b17.\ c13)$, $(a16.\ b6.\ c1)$, $(a23.\ b15.\ c2)$, and the 18 analogous triplets. From these, by cyclical permutations of the suffixes, the arrangements for 27 days can be got. Each of the 13 triplets consisting of the 4 triplets $(c22.\ b20.\ a19)$, $(c24.\ b17.\ a13)$, $(c16.\ b6.\ a1)$, $(c23.\ b15.\ a2)$, the 8 analogous triplets, and the triplet $(a1.\ b1.\ c1)$, gives, by a cyclical permutation of the suffixes, an arrangement for one of the remaining 13 days.

For 99 girls, an arrangement for the first day consists of the 11 triplets $(a1.\ a3.\ a10)$, $(a2.\ a6.\ a20)$, $(a4.\ a12.\ a7)$, $(a8.\ a24.\ a14)$, $(a16.\ a15.\ a28)$, $(a11.\ a22.\ b33)$, $(a32.\ b30.\ c23)$, $(a31.\ b27.\ c13)$, $(a29.\ b21.\ c26)$, $(a25.\ b9.\ c19)$, $(a17.\ b18.\ c5)$, and the 22 analogous triplets. From these, by cyclical permutations of the suffixes, the arrangements for 33 days can be got. Each of the 16 triplets consisting of the 5 triplets $(c32.\ b30.\ a23)$, $(c31.\ b27.\ a13)$, $(c29.\ b21.\ a26)$, $(c25.\ b9.\ a19)$, $(c17.\ b18.\ a5)$, the 10 analogous triplets, and the triplet $(a1.\ b1.\ c1)$, gives, by a cyclical permutation of the suffixes, an arrangement for one of the remaining 16 days.

For 27 girls, an arrangement of triplets for the first day is $(1.\ 7.\ 10)$, $(14.\ 17.\ 8)$, $(27.\ 6.\ 9)$, $(13.\ 20.\ 25)$, $(11.\ 23.\ 18)$, $(12.\ 16.\ 24)$, $(21.\ 2.\ 4)$, $(15.\ 22.\ 26)$, $(19.\ 3.\ 5)$. From this, three-step cyclical permutations give arrangements for 9 days in all. The first triplets on the remaining 4 days are $(1.\ 2.\ 3)$, $(1.\ 6.\ 20)$, $(1.\ 11.\ 15)$, $(1.\ 17.\ 27)$, from each of which, by a three-step cyclical permutation, an arrangement for one of those days is obtainable.

Regular solutions in the numerical notation can also be obtained for all values of n, except 9, where n is of the form $18m + 9$. I give 27 girls as an instance. The first day's arrangement is $(1.\ 2.\ 4)$, $(10.\ 11.\ 13)$, $(19.\ 20.\ 22)$, $(8.\ 15.\ 23)$, $(17.\ 24.\ 5)$, $(26.\ 6.\ 14)$, $(3.\ 25.\ 9)$, $(12.\ 7.\ 18)$, $(21.\ 16.\ 27)$; from this arrangements for 9 days in all are obtained by one-step cyclical permutations. Each of the three triplets (1. 5. 15), (2. 6. 16), (3. 7. 17) gives an arrangement for one day by a three-step cyclical permutation. Finally the triplet (1. 10. 19), represented by an equilateral triangle, gives the arrangement on the last day by a one-step cyclical permutation.

Lastly, I consider those cases where n is of the form $18m + 15$. As before, the solution is divided into two parts. In the first part, we obtain an arrangement of the triplets for the first day, from which arrangements for $6m + 5$ days are obtained by three-step cyclical permutations. In the second part, we obtain the first triplet on each of the remaining $3m + 2$ days, from which the other triplets on that day are obtained by three-step cyclical permutations.

For 33 girls, an arrangement in the first part is (1. 13. 19), (23. 11. 5), (3. 15. 21), (2. 4. 7), (12. 14. 17), (28. 30. 33), (6. 16. 25), (10. 20. 29), (8. 18. 27), (24. 31. 32), (9. 22. 26). The triplets in the second part are (25. 32. 33), (26. 33. 1), (10. 23. 27), (11. 24. 28), (1. 12. 23).

For 51 girls, an arrangement in the first part is (17. 34. 51), (49. 16. 10), (11. 44. 50), (15. 33. 27), (19. 4. 46), (2. 38. 29), (21. 36. 45), (22. 25. 24), (5. 8. 7), (39. 42. 41), (43. 13. 20), (26. 47. 3), (9. 30. 37), (1. 14. 6), (35. 48. 40), (18. 31. 23), (28. 32. 12). The triplets in the second part are (29. 33. 13), (30. 34. 14), (1. 26. 12), (2. 27. 13), (3. 28. 14), (1. 11. 30), (2. 12. 31), (3. 13. 32).

For 69 girls, an arrangement in the first part is (23. 46. 69), (31. 34. 43), (11. 8. 68), (54. 57. 66), (58. 52. 28), (35. 29. 5), (45. 51. 6), (16. 1. 49), (62. 47. 26), (39. 24. 3), (4. 55. 42), (50. 32. 19), (27. 9. 65), (40. 67. 18), (17. 44. 64), (63. 21. 41), (10. 14. 15), (33. 37. 38), (56. 60. 61), (25. 53. 36), (2. 30. 13), (48. 7. 59), (22. 20. 12). The triplets in the second part are (23. 21. 13), (24. 22. 14), (1. 8. 33), (2. 9. 34), (3. 10. 35), (1. 17. 36), (2. 18. 37), (3. 19. 38), (1. 41. 15), (2. 42. 16), (3. 43. 17).

For 87 girls, an arrangement in the first part is (29. 58. 87), (76. 82. 73), (47. 53. 44), (15. 9. 18), (70. 1. 13), (41. 59. 71), (12. 30. 42), (4. 67. 31), (2. 26. 62), (60. 84. 33), (40. 79. 25), (11. 50. 83), (69. 21. 54), (43. 64. 63), (14. 35. 34), (72. 6. 5), (61. 16. 77), (32. 74. 48), (3. 45. 19), (28. 68. 66), (37. 86. 39), (10. 8. 57), (46. 80. 36), (22. 65. 75), (7. 17. 51), (85. 23. 78), (52. 20. 27), (49. 56. 81), (55. 38. 24). The triplets in the second part are (56. 39. 25), (57. 40. 26), (1. 5. 42), (2. 6. 43), (3. 7. 44), (1. 29. 6), (2. 30. 7), (3. 31. 8), (1. 9. 20), (2. 10. 21), (3. 11. 22), (1. 14. 36), (2. 15. 37), (3. 16. 38).

Before proceeding to the consideration of other methods I should add that it is also possible to obtain irregular solutions of cases where n is of any of these three forms. As an instance I give a three-step solution of 33 girls. A possible arrangement in the first part is (1. 4. 10), (14. 23. 26), (9. 15. 30), (3. 28. 33), (2. 6. 8), (11. 18. 27), (13. 24. 25), (5. 16. 20), (7. 17. 22), (21. 29. 31), (12. 19. 32). The triplets in the second part are (1. 2. 21), (1. 8. 30), (1. 3. 26), (1. 15. 20), (1. 17. 18). I describe this solution as irregular, since all, save one, of the triads used are different.

The Focal Method. Another method of attacking the problem, comparatively easy to use in practice, is applicable

when n is of the form $24m + 3p$, where $p = 6q + 3$. It is due to Eckenstein. Here it is convenient to use a geometrical representation by denoting $24m + 2p$ girls by equidistant numbered points on the circumference of a circle, and the remaining p girls by lettered points placed inside the circle; these p points are termed foci. The solution is in two parts. In the first part, we obtain an order from which the arrangements for $12m + p$ days are deducible by a two-step cycle of the numbers: in none of these triplets does more than one focus appear. In the second part, we find the arrangements for the remaining $3q + 1$ days; here the foci and the numbered points are treated separately, the former being arranged by any of the methods used for solving the case of $6q + 3$ girls, while of the latter a typical triplet is used on each of those days, from which the remaining triplets on that day are obtained by cyclical permutations.

This method covers all cases except when $n = 15, 21, 39$; and solutions by it for all values of n less than 200 have been written out. Sets of all the triplets required can be definitely determined. One way of doing this is by finding the primitive roots of the prime factors of $4m + 2q + 1$, though in the simpler cases the triplets can be written down empirically without much trouble. An advantage of this method is that solutions of several cases are obtained by the same work. Suppose that we have arranged suitable triangles in a circle, having on its circumference $12m + p$ or $3c$ equidistant points, and let y be the greatest integer satisfying the indeterminate equation $2x + 4y + 1 = c$, where $x = 0$ or $x = 1$, and α the highest multiple of 6 included in $x + y$, then solutions of not less than $y + 1 - \alpha$ cases can be deduced. Thus from a 27 circle arrangement, where $c = 9$, $y = 2$, $x = 0$, $\alpha = 0$, we can by this method deduce three solutions—namely, when $n = 57, 69, 81$; from a 39 circle arrangement where $c = 13$, $y = 3$, $x = 0$, $\alpha = 0$, we can deduce four solutions—namely, when $n = 81, 93, 105, 117$.

I have no space to describe the method fully, but I will

give solutions for two cases—namely, for 33 girls ($n = 33$, $m = 1$, $p = 3$) where there are 3 foci, and for 51 girls ($n = 51$, $m = 1$, $p = 9$) where there are 9 foci.

For 33 girls, we have 3 foci which we may denote by a, b, c, and 30 points which we may denote by the numbers 1 to 30 placed at equidistant intervals on the circumference of a circle. Then if the arrangement on the first day is (a. 5. 10), (b. 20, 25), (c. 15. 30), (1. 2. 14), (16. 17. 29), (4. 23. 26), (19. 8. 11), (9. 7. 3), (24. 22. 18), (6. 27. 13), (21. 12. 28), a two-step cyclical permutation of the numbers gives arrangements for 15 days; that on the second day being (a. 7. 12), (b. 22. 27), etc. The arrangement on the 16th day is (a. b. c), (1. 11. 21). (2. 12. 22), (3. 13. 23), ... (10. 20. 30).

For 51 girls, we have 9 foci, which we may denote by a, b, c, d, e, f, g, h, j, and 42 points denoted by 1, 2, ... 42, placed at equidistant intervals on the circumference of a circle. Then if the arrangement on the first day is (a. 5. 6), (b. 26. 27), (c. 3. 10), (d. 24. 31), (e. 19. 34), (f. 40. 13), (g. 39. 16), (h. 18. 37), (j. 21. 42), (9. 11. 22), (30. 32. 1), (35. 41. 2), (14. 20. 23), (17. 29. 12), (38. 8. 33), (7. 15. 25), (28. 36. 4), a two-step cyclical permutation of the numbers gives arrangements for 21 days. Next, arrange the 9 foci in triplets by any of the methods already given so as to obtain arrangements for 4 days. From the numbers 1 to 42 we can obtain four typical triplets not already used—namely, (1. 5. 21), (2. 6. 22), (3. 7. 23), (14. 28. 42). From each of these triplets we can, by a three-step cyclical permutation, obtain an arrangement of the 42 girls for one day, thus getting arrangements for 4 days in all. Combining these results of letters and numbers, we obtain arrangements for the 4 days. Thus an arrangement for the first day would be (a. c. j), (b. d. g), (e. f. h), (1. 5. 21), (4. 8. 24), (7. 11. 27), (10. 14. 30), (13. 17. 33), (16. 20. 36), (19. 23. 39), (22. 26. 42), (25. 29. 3), (28. 32. 6), (31. 35. 9), (34. 38. 12), (37. 41. 15), (40. 2. 18). For the second day the corresponding arrangement would be (d. f. c), (e. g. a), (h. j. b), (2. 6. 22), (5. 9. 25), etc.

Analytical Methods. The methods described above, under the headings One-Step, Two-Step and Three-Step Cycles, involve some empirical work. It is true that with a little practice it is not difficult to obtain solutions by them when n is a low number, but the higher the value of n the more troublesome is the process and the more uncertain its success. A general arithmetical process has, however, been given by which it is claimed that *some* solutions for *any* value of n can be always obtained. Most of the solutions given earlier in this chapter can be obtained in this way.

The essential feature of the method is the arrangement of the numbers by which the girls are represented in an order such that definite rules can be laid down for grouping them in pairs and triplets, so that the differences of the numbers in each pair or triplet either are all different or are repeated as often as may be required. The process depends on finding primitive roots of the prime factors of whatever number is taken as the base of the solution. When $(n-1)/2$ is prime, of the form $6u+1$, and is taken as base, the order is obtainable at once, and the rules for grouping the numbers are easy of application; owing to considerations of space, I here confine myself to such instances, but similar though somewhat longer methods are applicable to all cases.

I use the geometrical representation already explained. We have $n = 2y + 1$, and y is a prime of the form $6u + 1$. In forming the triplets we either proceed directly by arranging all the points in threes, or we arrange some of them in pairs and make the selection of the third point dependent on those of the two first chosen, leaving only a few triplets to be obtained otherwise. In the former case we have to arrange the numbers in triplets so that each difference will appear twice, and so that no two differences will appear together more than once. In the latter case we have to arrange the numbers so that the differences between the numbers in each pair comprise consecutive integers from 1 upwards and are all different. In both cases we commence by finding a primitive root of y, say x. The residues to the modulus y of the $6u$ successive powers of x form a series of numbers, $e1$, $e2$, $e3$, . . ., comprising all the integers from 1 to $6u$, and when taken in the order of the successive powers, they can be arranged in the manner required by definite rules.

I will apply the method to the case of 27 girls from which the general theory, in the restricted case where y is a prime of the form $6u + 1$, will be sufficiently clear. In this case we have $n = 27$, $y = 13$, $u = 2$, and $x = 2$. I take 13 as the base of the analysis. I will begin by pairing the points, and this being so, it is convenient to represent the girls by a point k at the centre of a circle and points $a1$, $b1$, $a2$, $b2$, . . . at equidistant intervals on the circumference. We reserve k, $a13$, $b13$ for one triplet, and we have to arrange the other 24 points so as to form 8 triangles of certain types. The residues are in the order 2, 4, 8, 3, 6, 12, 11, 9, 5, 10, 7, 1, and these may be taken as the suffixes of the remaining " a "s and " b "s.

First arrange these residues in pairs so that every difference between the numbers in a pair occurs once. One rule by which this can be effected is to divide the residues into two equal sections and pair the numbers in the two sections. This gives (2. 11), (4. 9), (8. 5), (3. 10), (6. 7), (12. 1) as possible pairs. Another such rule is to divide the residue into six equal sections, and pair the numbers in the first and second sections, those in the third and fourth sections, and those in the fifth and sixth sections. This gives (2. 8), (4. 3), (6. 11), (12. 9), (5. 7), (10. 1) as possible pairs. Either arrangement can be used, but the first set of pairs leads only to scalene triangles. In none of the pairs of the latter set does the sum of the numbers in a pair add up to 13, and since this may allow the formation of isosceles as well as of scalene triangles, and thus increase the variety of the resulting solutions, I will use the latter set of pairs. We use these basic pairs as suffixes of the " a "s, and each pair thus determines two points of one of the triangles required. We have now used up all the " a "s. The third point associated with each of these six pairs of points must be a " b," and the remaining six " b "s must be such that they can be arranged in suitable triplets.

Next, then, we must arrange the $6u$ residues $e1$, $e2$, $e3$ . . . in possible triplets. To do this arrange them cyclically in triplets, for instance, as shown in the first column of the left half of the table on page 289. We write in the second column the differences between the first and second numbers in each triplet, in the third column the differences between the second and third numbers in each triplet, and in the fourth column the differences between the third and first numbers in each triplet. If any of these differences d is greater than $3u$ we may replace it by the complementary number $y - d$: that this is permissible is obvious from the geometrical representation. By shifting cyclically the symbols in any vertical line in the first column we change these differences. We can, however, in this way always displace the second and third vertical lines in the first column so that the numbers in the second, third, and fourth columns include the numbers 1 to $3u$ twice over. This can be effected thus. If any term in the residue series is greater than $3u$, replace it by its complementary number $y - e$. In this way, from the residue series, we get a derivative series $d1$, $d2$, $d3$, . . . such that any $3u$ consecutive terms comprise all the integers from 1 to $3u$. The first half of this series may be divided into three equal divisions thus : (1) $d1$, $d4$, $d7$, . . . ; (2) $d2$, $d5$, $d8$, . . . ; (3) $d3$, $d6$, $d9$, ... If the displacement is such that the first numbers in the second, third, and fourth columns are contained in different divisions, each difference must occur twice, and it will give a possible solution. Other possible regular arrangements give other solutions. Applying this to our case, we have the residue series, 2, 4, 8, 3, 6, 12, 11, 9, 5, 10, 7, 1. The derivative series is 2, 4, 5, 3, 6, 1, 2, 4, 5, 3, 6, 1. The three divisions are : (i) 2, 3 ; (ii) 4, 6, ; (iii) 5, 1. The cyclical arrangement we started with and the consequent differences are shown in the left half of the accompanying table. A cyclical change as described above of the vertical lines of the symbols in the first column gives the arrangement in the right half of the table. Here each difference occurs twice, and accordingly this gives a possible arrangement of the triplets—namely, 2, 6, 5; 3, 9, 1; 11, 7, 8; 10, 4, 12. These are the suffixes of the "b"s. We have now to use six of these "b"s in connection with the basic "a"s already determined, keeping the other six "b"s for the remaining two triangles.

For instance we may obtain a scalene solution by taking as a suffix of the "b" associated with any pair of "a"s, a number equal to the sum of the suffixes of the "a"s. We

2.	4.	8	2	4	6	2.	6.	5	4	1	3
3.	6.	12	3	6	4	3.	9.	1	6	5	2
11.	9.	5	2	4	6	11.	7.	8	4	1	3
10.	7.	1	3	6	4	10.	4.	12	6	5	2

thus get as a solution (a2. a8. b10), (a4. a3. b7), (a6. a11. b4), (a12. a9. b8), (a5. a7. b12), (a10. a1. b11), (b2. b6. b5), (b3. b9, b1), (k. a13. b13). Or we might take as a suffix of the "b" associated with any pair of "a"s, the number midway between the suffixes of the "a"s on the 13 circle. This gives the following solution, in which the first six triangles are isosceles: (a2. a8. b5), (a4. a3. b10), (a6. a11. b2), (a12. a9. b4), (a5. a7. b6), (a10. a1. b12), (b3. b9. b1), (b11. b7. b8), (k. a13. b13).

In the case of 27 girls, we may equally well represent the points by k at the centre of the circle and 26 equidistant points 1, 2, ... 26 on the circumference. The points previously denoted by a and b with the suffix h are now denoted by the numbers $2h - 1$ and $2h$. Hence the basic pairs (2. 8), (4. 3), ... become (3. 15), (7. 5), (11. 21), (23. 17), (9. 13), (19. 1), and the corresponding scalene arrangement for the first day is (3. 15. 20), (7. 5. 14), ... (k. 25. 26). From this, by a two-step cyclical permutation of the numbers, an arrangement for 13 days can be got.

The case of 27 girls can also be treated by the direct formation of triplets. The triplets must be such that each difference

U

is represented twice, but so that the groups of differences are different. There are analytical rules for forming such triplets somewhat analogous to those I have given for forming basic pairs, but their exposition would be lengthy, and I will not discuss them here. One set which will answer our purpose is (1. 12. 5), (2. 3. 10), (4. 6. 9), (8. 11. 7), giving respectively the differences [2, 6, 4], [1, 6, 5], [2, 3, 5], [3, 4, 1]. Now every difference d in a 13 circle will correspond to d or $13 - d$ in a 26 circle, and every residue e in a 13 circle will correspond to e or $13 + e$ in a 26 circle. Further, a triplet in the 26 circle must either have three even differences, or one even and two odd differences. Hence from the above sets we can get the following arrangement for the first day: (1. 25. 5) and (14. 12. 18) with differences [2, 6, 4], (15. 3. 10) and (2. 16. 23) with differences [12, 7, 5], (17. 6. 9) and (4. 19. 22) with differences [11, 3, 8], (21. 11. 20) and (8. 24. 7) with differences [10, 9, 1], (k. 13. 26). From this, by either a one-step or a two-step cyclical permutation of the numbers, an arrangement for 13 days can be got. I will not go into further details about the deduction of other similar solutions. A similar method is always applicable when n is of the form $24m + 3$.

The process by pairing when y is a prime of the form $6u + 1$ is extremely rapid. For instance, in the case of 15 girls we have $n = 15$, $y = 7$, $u = 1$, $x = 5$. The order of the residues is 5, 4, 6, 2, 3, 1. By our rule we can at once arrange basic pairs (5. 4), (6. 2), (3. 1). From these pairs we can obtain numerous solutions. Thus, using scalene triangles as above explained, we get as an arrangement for the first day ($a5. a4. b2$), ($a6. a2. b1$), ($a3. a1. b4$), ($b3. b5. b6$), ($k. a7. b7$), from which, by a one-step cyclical permutation of the numbers, arrangements for the seven days can be obtained. Using the basic pairs as bases of isosceles triangles, we get as an arrangement for the first day ($a5. a4. b1$), ($a6. a2. b4$), ($a3. a1. b2$), ($b3. b5. b6$), ($k. a7. b7$).

Again, take the case of 39 girls. Here we have $n = 39$, $y = 19$, $u = 3$, $x = 3$. The order of the residues is 3, 9, 8;

5, 15, 7 ; 2, 6, 18 ; 16, 10, 11 ; 14, 4, 12 ; 17, 13, 1. The basic
pairs are (3. 5), (9. 15), (8. 7), (2. 16), etc. These are the suffixes
of the " a "s. The possible triplets which determine what
" b "s are to be associated with these, and what " b "s are to
be left for the remaining three triangles, can be determined as
follows : From the residue series we obtain the derivative
series 3, 9, 8, 5, 4, 7, 2, 6, 1, etc. The divisions are (i) 3, 5, 2 ;
(ii) 9, 4, 6 ; (iii) 8, 7, 1. A cyclical arrangement like that given
above leads to the result in the left half of the following table,
which does not satisfy our condition. A cyclical displacement
of the symbols in the vertical lines in the first column leads to
the arrangement given in the right half of the table, and shows

3.	9.	8	6	2	5	3.	15.	18	7	3	4
5.	15.	7	9	8	2	5.	6.	11	1	5	6
2.	6.	18	4	7	3	2.	10.	12	8	2	9
16.	10.	11	6	1	5	16.	4.	1	7	3	4
14.	4.	12	9	8	2	14.	13.	8	1	5	6
17.	13.	1	6	7	3	17.	9.	7	8	2	9

that (3. 15. 18), (5. 6. 11), etc., are possible triplets. From
these results numerous solutions can be deduced in the same
way as above. For instance, one solution is (a3. a.5 b4),
(a9. a15. b12), (a8. a7. b17), (a2. a16. b9), (a6. a10. b8),
(a18. a11. b5), (a14. a17. b6), (a4. a13. b18), (a12. a1. b16),
(b3. b10. b1), (b2. b13. b7), (b14. b15. b11), (k. a19. b19).

In the case of 39 girls, we may also extend the method
used above by which for 27 girls we obtained the solution
(1. 25. 5), (14. 12. 18), ... We thus get a solution for 39 girls
as follows : (1. 25. 18), (14. 38. 31), (27. 12. 5); (15. 16. 10),
(28. 29. 23), (2. 3. 36) ; (17. 19. 35), (30. 32. 9), (4. 6. 22) ;
(21. 24. 33), (34. 37. 7), (8. 11. 20) ; (13. 26. 39). From this
the arrangements for the first 13 days are obtained either by
a one-step or a three-step cyclical permutation of the numbers.
The single triplets from each of which an arrangement for one
of the other six days is obtainable are (1. 5. 15), (2. 6. 16),

(3. 7. 17); (1. 9. 20), (2. 10. 21), (3. 11. 22). From each of these the arrangement for one day is obtainable by a three-step cyclical permutation of the numbers.

These examples of the use of the Focal and Analytical Methods are given only by way of illustration, but they will serve to suggest the applications to other cases. When the number taken as base is composite, the formations of the series used in the Analytical Method may be troublesome, but the principle of the method is not affected, though want of space forbids my going into further details. Eckenstein, to whom the development of this method is mainly due, can, with the aid of a table of primitive roots and sets of numbers written on cards, within half an hour obtain a solution for any case in which n is less than 500, and can within one hour obtain a solution for any case in which n lies between 500 and 900.

Number of Solutions. The problem of 9 girls has been subjected to an exhaustive examination. The number of solutions is 840, if an arrangement on Monday, Tuesday, Wednesday and Thursday, and the same arrangement on (say) Monday, Tuesday, Thursday and Wednesday are regarded as identical. [If they are regarded as different the number of possible independent solutions is 20,160.] Any of these 840 solutions can, however, be deduced from any other of them by interchanges, and thus there is only one fundamental solution. The total number of possible arrangements of the girls in triplets for four days is $(280)^4/(4!)$; hence the probability of obtaining a solution by a chance arrangement is about 1 in 300,000.

In the case of 15 girls, the number of solutions, according to Mulder,* is $65 \times 13!$. The number of fundamental solutions, according to Mulder and Cole,† is seven. The total number of ways in which the girls can walk out for a week in triplets is

* P. Mulder, *Kirkman-Systemen* (Groningen Dissertation), Leiden, 1917.
† F. N. Cole, *Bulletin of the American Mathematical Society*, 1922, vol. XXVIII, pp. 435—437.

$(1401400)^7/(7!)$; so the probability that any chance way satisfies the conditions of the problem is less than one in 10^{27}.

Harison's Theorem. If we know solutions for Kirkman's Problem for $3l$ girls and for $3m$ girls we can find a solution for $3lm$ girls. The particular case of this when $l = 1$ was established by Walecki and given in the earlier editions of this work. Harison's proof, given in 1916, of the more general theorem is as follows :—

If the school-girls be denoted by the consecutive numbers from 1 to $3lm$ and the numbers be divided into $3l$ sets, each of m consecutive numbers, each of these sets can, by the method for the $3l$ problem, be divided in $(3l - 1)/2$ collections of groups of three sets, so that every set shall be included once in the same group with every other set.

In one of these collections, each group of three sets (involving $3m$ numbers) can, by the method for the $3m$ problem, be arranged in triplets for $(3m - 1)/2$ days, so as to have each number in each of the sets composing the group included once in the same triplet with every other number in the set to which it belongs and with every number in the other two sets in the group. This will give arrangements of all the numbers for that number of days.

In the remaining $(3l - 3)/2$ collections, each group can be arranged in triplets for m days, so as to have each number in each of the sets composing the group included once in the same triplet with each number of the other two sets. In the first arrangement in each collection, the first triplet in each group is composed of the first number of each set. In the second arrangement, the first triplet is composed of the first number of the first set, the second number of the second set, and the last number of the third set. In every other arrangement the first triplet is formed from the first triplet in the next preceding arrangement, by adding unity to the number of the second set, subtracting unity from the number of the third set, and leaving the number of the first set unchanged. In every arrangement the second and all subsequent triplets are formed cyclically from the next preceding triplet.

The arrangements thus made of the numbers in all the groups of all the collections will give arrangements of all the numbers for $(3lm-1)/2$ days, and will provide a solution of the problem.

Harison's Theorem provides solutions, alternative to those given above, for the cases when $n = 27, 45, 63, 75, 81, 99$. Also we can, by it, from the solutions already given for all values of n less than 100, at once deduce solutions for the cases when $n = \cdot105, 117, 135, 147, 153, 165, 171, 189, 195$, etc.

Extension to n^2 Girls. Peirce suggested the corresponding problem of arranging n^2 girls in n groups, each group containing n girls on $n + 1$ days, so that no two girls will be together in a group on more than one day. We may conveniently represent the girls by a point k at the centre of a circle and $n^2 - 1$ equidistant points, numbered 1, 2, 3, ..., on the circumference.

When $n = 2$, we may arrange initially the 4 points in two pairs, one pair consisting of k and one of the points (say) 3, and the other pair of the remaining points (1. 2). These two pairs give the arrangement for the first day. From them, the solution for the other days is obtained by one-step cyclical permutations.

When $n = 3$, we may arrange initially the 9 points in three triplets—namely, k and the ends of a diameter $(k. 4. 8)$; a triangle (1. 2. 7); and the similar triangle (5. 6. 3) obtained by a four-step cyclical permutation. These three triplets give an arrangement for the first day. From them the solutions for the other days are obtained by one-step cyclical permutations.

When $n = 4$, we may arrange initially the 16 points in four quartets—namely, k and three equidistant points, $(k. 5. 10. 15)$; a quadrilateral (1. 2. 4. 8); and the two similar quadrilaterals (6. 7. 9. 13) and (11. 12. 14. 3) obtained by five-step cyclical permutations. These four quartets give an arrangement for the first day. From them the solutions for the other days are obtained by one-step cyclical permutations.

When $n = 5$, we may arrange initially the 25 points in five quintets—namely, k and four equidistant points, (k. 6. 12. 18. 24); a pentagon (2. 3. 5. 13. 22); and the three similar pentagons (8. 9. 11. 19. 4), (14. 15. 17. 1. 10), (20. 21. 23. 7. 16) obtained by six-step cyclical permutations. These five quintets give an arrangement for the first day. From them the solutions for the other days are obtained by one-step cyclical permutations. There is a second solution (k. 6. 12. 18. 24), (1. 2. 15. 17. 22), etc.

Hitherto the case when $n = 6$ has baffled all attempts to find a solution.

When $n = 7$, we may initially arrange the 49 points in seven groups—namely (k. 8. 16. 24. 32. 40. 48), a group (1. 2. 5. 11. 31. 36. 38) and five similar groups obtained by successive additions of 8 to these numbers. There are three other solutions: in these the second group is either (2. 3. 17. 28. 38. 45. 47), or (3. 4. 6. 18. 23. 41. 45), or (3. 4. 14. 17. 26. 45. 47).

When $n = 8$, there are three solutions. If the first group is (k. 9. 18. 27. 36. 45. 54. 63), the second group is either (1. 2. 4. 8. 16. 21. 32. 42), or (2. 3. 16. 22. 24. 50. 55. 62), or (3. 4. 7. 19. 24. 26. 32. 56), the other groups in each solution being obtained by successive addition of 9 to the numbers in the second group.

When $n = 9$, one solution is as follows. Divide the girls into nine classes, each containing nine girls, denoted by $a1, a2, \ldots a9$; $b1, b2, \ldots b9$; and similarly for the letters c, d, e, f, g, h, k. The arrangement on the first day is made up of the a group, the b group, etc. The arrangement on the second day is of nine groups, as follows: first group, $k1, a5, b3, c8, d7, e9, f4, g6, h2$; second group, $k2, a3, b6, c4, d1, e8, f9, g5, h7$; third group, $k3, a8, b4, c7, d5, e2, f1, g9, h6$; fourth group, $k4, a7, b1, c5, d8, e6, f3, g2, h9$; fifth group, $k5, a9, b8, c2, d6, e1, f7, g4, h3$; sixth group, $k6, a4, b9, c1, d3, e7, f2, g8, h5$; seventh group, $k7, a6, b5, c9, d2, e4, f8, g3, h1$; eighth group, $k8, a2, b7, c6, d9, e3, f5, g1, h4$; ninth group, $k9, a1, b2, c3, d4, e5, f6, g7, h8$. The arrangements for the other eight days are got by shifting the numbers attached to the letters $a, b, \ldots h$ (but not k) in each group cyclically. Thus the first group on the third day will be, $k1$, $a3$, $b8$, $c7$, $d9$, $e4$, $f6$, $g2$, $h5$.

When n is composite, no general method of attacking the problem has been discovered, though solutions for various particular cases have been given. But when n is prime, we can proceed thus. Denote the n^2 girls by the suffixed letters

$k1$,	$k2$,	.... kn.		$k1$,	$a1$,	$b2$,	$c3$,	....
$a1$,	$a2$,	.... an.		$k2$,	$a2$,	$b4$,	$c6$,	....
$b1$,	$b2$,	.... bn,		$k3$,	$a3$,	$b6$,	$c9$,	....
....				....				
....				kn,	an,	bn,	cn,	....
Arrangement on First Day				*Arrangement on Second Day*				

shown in the left half of the above table. Take this as giving the arrangement on the first day. Then on the second day we may take as an arrangement that shown in the right half of the table. From the arrangement on the second day, the arrangements for the other days are obtained by one-step cyclical permutations of the suffixes of a, b, etc.; the suffixes of k being unaltered.

Kirkman's Problem in Quartets. The problem of arranging $4m$ girls, where m is of the form $3n + 1$, in quartets to walk out for $(4m - 1)/3$ days, so that no girl will walk with any of her school-fellows in any quartet more than once, has been attacked. Methods similar to those given above are applicable, and solutions for all cases where m does not exceed 49 have been written out. One example will suffice: for 16 girls (*i.e.* when $m = 4$, $n = 1$), arrangements in quartets for five days can be obtained from the following arrangement for the first day, $(k. 5. 10. 15)$, $(8. 2. 1. 4)$, $(13. 7. 6. 9)$, $(3. 12. 11. 14)$; from which three-step cyclical permutations of the numbers give arrangements for the other days. I conjecture that similar methods are applicable to corresponding problems about quintets, sextets, etc.

Bridge Problem. Another analogous question is where we deal with arrangements in pairs instead of triplets. One problem of this kind is to arrange $4m$ members of a bridge club for $4m - 1$ rubbers so that (i) no two members shall play together as partners more than once, and (ii) each member shall meet every other member as opponent twice. The general theory has been discussed by E. H. Moore, O. Eckenstein and G. A. Miller. A typical method for obtaining cyclic solutions is as follows. Denote the members by a point k at the centre of a circle and by $4m - 1$ equidistant points, numbered 1, 2, 3, . . ., on the circumference. We can join the points 2, 3, 4, . . . by chords, and these chords with $(k.\ 1)$ give possible partners at the m tables in the first rubber. A one-step cyclical permutation of the numbers will give the arrangements for the other rubbers if, in the initial arrangement, (i) the lengths of the chords representing every pair of partners are unequal and thus appear only once, and (ii) the lengths of the chords representing every pair of opponents appear only twice. Since the chords representing pairs of partners are unequal, their lengths are uniquely determined, but the selection of the chords is partly empirical. Solutions for many values of m have been given. In the following examples for $m = 2, 3, 4$, I give an arrangement of the card-tables for the first rubber, the arrangements for the subsequent rubbers being thence obtained by one-step cyclical permutations of the numbers. If $m = 2$, such an initial arrangement is $(k.\ 1$ against $5.\ 6)$ and $(2.\ 4$ against $3.\ 7)$. If $m = 3$, one such initial arrangement is $(k.\ 1$ against $5.\ 6)$, $(2.\ 11$ against $3.\ 9)$ and $(4.\ 8$ against $7.\ 10)$. If $m = 4$, one such initial arrangement is $(k.\ 1$ against $6.\ 11)$, $(2.\ 3$ against $5.\ 9)$, $(4.\ 12$ against $13.\ 15)$, and $(7.\ 10$ against $8.\ 14)$. There are also solutions by other methods.

Sylvester's Corollary. To the original theorem J. J. Sylvester added the corollary that the school of 15 girls could walk out in triplets on 91 days until every possible triplet had walked abreast once, and he published a solution in 1861.

The generalized problem of finding the number of ways in

which x girls walking in rows of a abreast can be arranged so
that every possible combination of b of them may walk abreast
once and only once is as yet unsolved. Suppose that this
number of ways is y. It is obvious that, if all the x girls are to
walk out each day in rows of a abreast, then x must be an exact
multiple of a, and the number of rows formed each day is x/a.
If such an arrangement can be made for z days, then we have a
solution of the problem to arrange x girls to walk out in rows of
a abreast for z days so that they all go out each day and so that
every possible combination of b girls may walk together once
and only once. For instance, if $x = 2n$, $a = 2$, $b = 2$, we have
$y = n(2n - 1)/2$, $z = 2n - 1$. If $x = 15$, $a = 3$, $b = 2$, we
have $y = 35$; and these 35 rows can be divided into 7 sets,
each of which contains all the symbols; hence $z = 7$.

ADDENDUM

Note. Page 267. Here is an explicit solution of Kirkman's Problem in
its original form.

Sun.	Mon.	Tues.	Wed.	Thurs.	Fri.	Sat.
1, 2, 3	1, 4, 5	1, 6, 7	1, 8, 9	1, 10, 11	1, 12, 13	1, 14, 15
4, 8, 12	2, 8, 10	2, 9, 11	2, 12, 14	2, 13, 15	2, 4, 6	2, 5, 7
5, 10, 15	3, 13, 14	3, 12, 15	3, 5, 6	3, 4, 7	3, 9, 10	3, 8, 11
6, 11, 13	6, 9, 15	4, 10, 14	4, 11, 15	5, 9, 12	5, 11, 14	4, 9, 13
7, 9, 14	7, 11, 12	5, 8, 13	7, 10, 13	6, 8, 14	7, 8, 15	6, 10, 12

Michael Goldberg has pointed out that these triplets are " safe combinations " in the game of Nim (page 37).

CHAPTER XI

MISCELLANEOUS PROBLEMS

I PROPOSE to discuss in this chapter the mathematical theory of a few common mathematical amusements and games. I might have dealt with them in the first four chapters, but, since most of them involve mixed geometry and algebra, it is rather more convenient to deal with them apart from the problems and puzzles which have been described already; the arrangement is, however, based on convenience rather than on any logical distinction.

The majority of the questions here enumerated have no connection one with another, and I jot them down almost at random.

I shall discuss in succession the *Fifteen Puzzle*, the *Tower of Hanoï*, *Chinese Rings*, and some miscellaneous *Problems connected with a Pack of Cards*.

THE FIFTEEN PUZZLE *

Some years ago the so-called *Fifteen Puzzle* was on sale in all toy-shops. It consists of a shallow wooden box—one side being marked as the top—in the form of a square, and contains fifteen square blocks or counters numbered 1, 2, 3, . . . up to 15. The box will hold just sixteen such counters, and, as it contains only fifteen, they can be moved about in the box relatively to one another. Initially they are put in the box in any order, but leaving the sixteenth cell or small square empty; the

---

* There are two articles on the subject in the *American Journal of Mathematics*, 1879, vol. II, by Professors Woolsey Johnson and Storey; but the whole theory is deducible immediately from the proposition I give in the text.

puzzle is to move them so that finally they occupy the position shown in the first of the annexed figures.

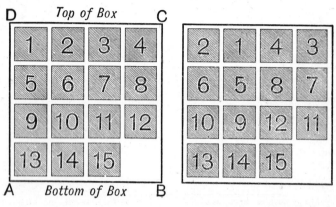

We may represent the various stages in the game by supposing that the blank space, occupying the sixteenth cell, is moved over the board, ending finally where it started.

The route pursued by the blank space may consist partly of tracks followed and again retraced, which have no effect on the arrangement, and partly of closed paths travelled round, which necessarily are cyclical permutations of an odd number of counters. No other motion is possible.

Now, a cyclical permutation of n letters is equivalent to $n-1$ simple interchanges; accordingly an odd cyclical permutation is equivalent to an even number of simple interchanges. Hence, if we move the counters so as to bring the blank space back into the sixteenth cell, the new order must differ from the initial order by an even number of simple interchanges. If therefore the order we want to get can be obtained from this initial order only by an odd number of interchanges, the problem is incapable of solution; if it can be obtained by an even number, the problem is possible.

Thus the order in the second of the diagrams given above is deducible from that in the first diagram by six interchanges—namely, by interchanging the counters 1 and 2, 3 and 4, 5 and

6, 7 and 8, 9 and 10, 11 and 12. Hence the one can be deduced from the other by moving the counters about in the box.

If, however, in the second diagram the order of the last three counters had been 13, 15, 14, then it would have required seven interchanges of counters to bring them into the order given in the first diagram. Hence in this case the problem would be insoluble.

The easiest way of finding the number of simple interchanges necessary in order to obtain one given arrangement from another is to make the transformation by a series of cycles. For example, suppose that we take the counters in the box in any definite order, such as taking the successive rows from left to right, and suppose the original order and the final order to be respectively

1, 13, 2, 3, 5, 7, 12, 8, 15, 6, 9, 4, 11, 10, 14,
and   11, 2, 3, 4, 5, 6, 7, 1, 9, 10, 13, 12, 8, 14, 15.

We can deduce the second order from the first by 12 simple interchanges. The simplest way of seeing this is to arrange the process in three separate cycles as follows :—

| 1, 11, 8 ; | 13, 2, 3, 4, 12, 7, 6, 10, 14, 15, 9 ; | 5. |
| 11, 8, 1 ; | 2, 3, 4, 12, 7, 6, 10, 14, 15, 9, 13 ; | 5. |

Thus, if in the first row of figures 11 is substituted for 1, then 8 for 11, then 1 for 8, we have made a cyclical interchange of 3 numbers, which is equivalent to 2 simple interchanges (namely, interchanging 1 and 11, and then 1 and 8). Thus the whole process is equivalent to one cyclical interchange of 3 numbers, another of 11 numbers, and another of 1 number. Hence it is equivalent to $(2 + 10 + 0)$ simple interchanges. This is an even number, and thus one of these orders can be deduced from the other by moving the counters about in the box.

It is obvious that, if the initial order is the same as the required order except that the last three counters are in the order 15, 14, 13, it would require one interchange to put them in the order 13, 14, 15 ; hence the problem is insoluble.

If, however, the box is turned through a right angle, so as to make AD the top, this rotation will be equivalent to 13 simple interchanges. For, if we keep the sixteenth square always blank, then such a rotation would change any order such as

$$1, 2, 3, 4, \quad 5, \quad 6, 7, 8, \quad 9, 10, 11, 12, 13, 14, 15,$$
to $\quad$ $13, 9, 5, 1, 14, 10, 6, 2, 15, 11, \quad 7, \quad 3, 12, \quad 8, \quad 4,$

which is equivalent to 13 simple interchanges. Hence it will change the arrangement from one where a solution is impossible to one where it is possible, and *vice versa*.

Again, even if the initial order is one which makes a solution impossible, yet if the first cell and not the last is left blank, it will be possible to arrange the fifteen counters in their natural order. For, if we represent the blank cell by b, this will be equivalent to changing the order

$$1, 2, 3, 4, 5, 6, 7, 8, 9, 10, 11, 12, 13, 14, 15, \quad b,$$
to $\quad$ $b, 1, 2, 3, 4, 5, 6, 7, 8, \quad 9, 10, 11, 12, 13, 14, 15 :$

this is a cyclical interchange of 16 things, and therefore is equivalent to 15 simple interchanges. Hence it will change the arrangement from one where a solution is impossible to one where it is possible, and *vice versa*.

So, too, if it were permissible to turn the 6 and the 9 upside down, thus changing them to 9 and 6 respectively, this would be equivalent to one simple interchange, and therefore would change an arrangement where a solution is impossible to one where it is possible.

It is evident that the above principles are applicable equally to a rectangular box containing mn cells or spaces and $mn - 1$ counters which are numbered. Of course, m may be equal to n. When m and n are both even (and in certain other cases, such as $m = 3$, $n = 5$), the operation of turning the box through a right angle is equivalent to an odd number of simple interchanges, and thus will change an impossible position to a possible one, and *vice versa*. Similarly, if m and n are not both odd, and it is impossible to solve the problem when the

last call is left blank, then it will be possible to solve it by
leaving the first cell blank.

The problem may be made more difficult by limiting the
possible movements by fixing bars inside the box which will
prevent the movement of a counter transverse to their directions.   We can conceive also of a similar cubical puzzle, but we
could not work it practically except by sections.

The Tower of Hanoï

I may mention next the ingenious puzzle known as the
Tower of Hanoï. It was brought out in 1883 by M. Claus
(Lucas).

It consists of three pegs fastened to a stand, and of eight
circular discs of wood or cardboard, each of which has a hole in
the middle through which a peg can be passed.   These discs
are of different radii, and initially they are placed all on one
peg, so that the biggest is at the bottom, and the radii of the
successive discs decrease as we ascend : thus the smallest disc
is at the top. This arrangement is called the *Tower*. The
problem is to shift the discs from one peg to another in such
a way that a disc shall never rest on one smaller than itself,
and finally to transfer the tower (*i.e.* all the discs in their
proper order) from the peg on which they initially rested to one
of the other pegs.

The method of effecting this is as follows.   (i) If initially
there are n discs on the peg A, the first operation is to transfer
gradually the top $n-1$ discs from the peg A to the peg B,
leaving the peg C vacant : suppose that this requires x separate
transfers.   (ii) Next, move the bottom disc to the peg C.   (iii)
Then, reversing the first process, transfer gradually the $n-1$
discs from B to C, which will necessitate x transfers.   Hence,
if it requires x transfers of simple discs to move a tower of
$n-1$ discs, then it will require $2x+1$ separate transfers of
single discs to move a tower of n discs. Now, with 2 discs it
requires 3 transfers, *i.e.* 2^2-1 transfers ; hence with 3 discs

the number of transfers required will be $2(2^2 - 1) + 1$, that is, $2^3 - 1$. Proceeding in this way, we see that with a tower of n discs it will require $2^n - 1$ transfers of single discs to effect the complete transfer. Thus the eight discs of the puzzle will require 255 single transfers. It will be noticed that every alternate move consists of a transfer of the smallest disc from one peg to another, the pegs being taken in cyclical order; further, if the discs be numbered consecutively 1, 2, 3, ... beginning with the smallest, all those with odd numbers rotate in one direction, and all those with even numbers in the other direction.

Obviously, the discs may be replaced by cards numbered 1, 2, 3, ... n; and if n is not greater than 10, playing-cards may be conveniently used.

De Parville gave an account of the origin of the toy which is a sufficiently pretty conceit to deserve repetition.* In the great temple at Benares, says he, beneath the dome which marks the centre of the world, rests a brass plate in which are fixed three diamond needles, each a cubit high and as thick as the body of a bee. On one of these needles, at the creation, God placed sixty-four discs of pure gold, the largest disc resting on the brass plate, and the others getting smaller and smaller up to the top one. This is the Tower of Bramah. Day and night unceasingly the priests transfer the discs from one diamond needle to another according to the fixed and immutable laws of Bramah, which require that the priest on duty must not move more than one disc at a time and that he must place this disc on a needle so that there is no smaller disc below it. When the sixty-four discs shall have been thus transferred from the needle on which at the creation God placed them to one of the other needles, tower, temple, and Brahmins alike will crumble into dust, and with a thunderclap the world will vanish.

The number of separate transfers of single discs which the Brahmins must make to effect the transfer of the tower is

* *La Nature*, Paris, 1884, part I, pp. 285—286.

$2^{64} - 1$, that is, is 18,446744,073709,551615 : a number which, even if the priests never made a mistake, would require many thousands of millions of years to carry out.

CHINESE RINGS *

A somewhat more elaborate toy, known as *Chinese Rings*, which is on sale in most English toy-shops, is represented in the accompanying figure. It consists of a number of rings hung upon a bar in such a manner that the ring at one end (say *A*)

can be taken off or put on the bar at pleasure; but any other ring can be taken off or put on only when the one next to it towards *A* is on, and all the rest towards *A* are off the bar. The order of the rings cannot be changed.

Only one ring can be taken off or put on at a time. [In the toy, as usually sold, the first two rings form an exception to the rule. Both these can be taken off or put on together. To simplify the discussion I shall assume at first that only one ring is taken off or put on at a time.] I proceed to show that, if there are *n* rings, then, in order to disconnect them from the

* This was described by Cardan in 1550 in his *De Subtilitate*, bk. xv, paragraph 2, ed. Sponius, vol. iii, p. 587; by Wallis in his *Algebra*, Latin edition, 1693, *Opera*, vol. ii, chap. cxi, pp. 472—478; and allusion is made to it also in Ozanam's *Récréations*, 1723 edition, vol. iv, p. 439.

bar, it will be necessary to take a ring off or to put a ring on either $\frac{1}{3}(2^{n+1} - 1)$ times or $\frac{1}{3}(2^{n+1} - 2)$ times, according as n is odd or even.

Let the taking a ring off the bar or putting a ring on the bar be called a *step*. It is usual to number the rings from the free end A. Let us suppose that we commence with the first m rings off the bar and all the rest on the bar; and suppose that then it requires $x - 1$ steps to take off the next ring—that is, it requires $x - 1$ additional steps to arrange the rings so that the first $m + 1$ of them are off the bar and all the rest are on it. Before taking these steps we can take off the $(m + 2)$th ring, and thus it will require x steps from our initial position to remove the $(m + 1)$th and $(m + 2)$th rings.

Suppose that these x steps have been made, and that thus the first $m + 2$ rings are off the bar and the rest on it, and let us find how many additional steps are now necessary to take off the $(m + 3)$th and $(m + 4)$th rings. To take these off, we begin by taking off the $(m + 4)$th ring : this requires 1 step. Before we can take off the $(m + 3)$th ring we must arrange the rings so that the $(m + 2)$th ring is on and the first $m + 1$ rings are off : to effect this, (i) we must get the $(m + 1)$th ring on and the first m rings off, which requires $x - 1$ steps, (ii) then we must put on the $(m + 2)$th ring, which requires 1 step, (iii) and lastly we must take the $(m + 1)$th ring off, which requires $x - 1$ steps : these movements require in all $\{2(x - 1) + 1\}$ steps. Next we can take the $(m + 3)$th ring off, which requires 1 step; this leaves us with the first $m + 1$ rings off, the $(m + 2)$th on, the $(m + 3)$th and $(m + 4)$th off, and all the rest on. Finally, to take off the $(m + 2)$th ring, (i) we get the $(m + 1)$th ring on and the first m rings off, which requires $x - 1$ steps, (ii) we take off the $(m + 2)$th ring, which requires 1 step, (iii) we take the $(m + 1)$th ring off, which requires $x - 1$ steps : these movements require $\{2(x - 1) + 1\}$ steps.

Therefore, if when the first m rings are off it requires x steps to take off the $(m + 1)$th and $(m + 2)$th rings, then the number of additional steps required to take off the $(m + 3)$th

and $(m+4)$th rings is $1 + \{2(x-1)+1\} + 1 + \{2(x-1)+1\}$
—that is, is $4x$.

To find the whole number of steps necessary to take off an odd number of rings we proceed as follows.

To take off the first ring requires 1 step;

∴ to take off the first 3 rings requires 4 additional steps;

∴ „   „   5 „   „ 4^2 „   „

In this way we see that the number of steps required to take off the first $2n + 1$ rings is $1 + 4 + 4^2 + \ldots + 4^n$, which is equal to $\frac{1}{3}(2^{2n+2} - 1)$.

To find the number of steps necessary to take off an even number of rings we proceed in a similar manner.

To take off the first 2 rings requires 2 steps;

∴ to take off the first 4 rings requires 2×4 additional steps;

∴ „   „   „ 6 „   „ 2×4^2 „   „

In this way we see that the number of steps required to take off the first $2n$ rings is $2 + (2 \times 4) + (2 \times 4^2) + \ldots + (2 \times 4^{n-1})$, which is equal to $\frac{1}{3}(2^{2n+1} - 2)$.

If we take off or put on the first two rings in one step instead of two separate steps, these results become respectively 2^{2n} and $2^{2n-1} - 1$.

I give the above analysis because it is the direct solution of a problem attacked unsuccessfully by Cardan in 1550 and by Wallis in 1693, and which at one time attracted some attention.

I proceed next to give another solution, more elegant, though rather artificial. This, which is due to Monsieur Gros,* depends on a convention by which any position of the rings is denoted by a certain number expressed in the binary scale of notation in such a way that a step is indicated by the addition or subtraction of unity.

Let the rings be indicated by circles : if a ring is on the bar, it is represented by a circle drawn above the bar; if the ring is off the bar, it is represented by a circle below the bar. Thus figure i below represents a set of seven rings, of which the first

---

* *Théorie du Baguenodier*, by L. Gros, Lyons, 1872. I take the account of this from Lucas, vol. I, part 7.

two are off the bar, the next three are on it, the sixth is off it, and the seventh is on it.

Denote the rings which are on the bar by the digits 1 or 0 alternately, reckoning from left to right, and denote a ring which is off the bar by the digit assigned to that ring on the bar which is nearest to it on the left of it, or by a 0 if there is no ring to the left of it.

Thus the three positions indicated below are denoted respectively by the numbers written below them. The position represented in figure ii is obtained from that in figure i by putting the first ring on to the bar, while the position represented in figure iii is obtained from that in figure i by taking the fourth ring off the bar.

It follows that every position of the rings is denoted by a number expressed in the binary scale: moreover, since in going from left to right every ring on the bar gives a variation (that is, 1 to 0, or 0 to 1) and every ring off the bar gives a continuation, the effect of a step by which a ring is taken off or put on the bar is either to subtract unity from this number or to add unity to it. For example, the number denoting the position of the rings in figure ii is obtained from the number denoting that in figure i by adding unity to it. Similarly the number denoting the position of the rings in figure iii is obtained from the number denoting that in figure i by subtracting unity from it.

| 1101000 | 1101001 | 1100111 |
| Figure i. | Figure ii. | Figure iii. |

The position when all the seven rings are off the bar is denoted by the number 0000000 : when all of them are on the bar, by the number 1010101. Hence to change from one position to the other requires a number of steps equal to the difference between these two numbers in the binary scale. The first of these numbers is 0 : the second is equal to $2^6 +$

$2^4 + 2^2 + 1$—that is, to 85.   Therefore 85 steps are required.
In a similar way we may show that to put on a set of $2n + 1$
rings requires $(1 + 2^2 + \ldots + 2^{2n})$ steps—that is, $\frac{1}{3}(2^{2n+2} - 1)$
steps—and to put on a set of $2n$ rings requires $(2 + 2^3 + \ldots + 2^{2n-1})$ steps—that is, $\frac{1}{3}(2^{2n+1} - 2)$ steps.

I append a table indicating the steps necessary to take off
the first four rings from a set of five rings.   The diagrams in
the middle column show the successive position of the rings

Initial position		10101
After 1st step		10110 ⎫
,, 2nd ,,		10111 ⎭
,, 3rd ,,		11000
,, 4th ,,		11001 ⎫
,, 5th ,,		11010 ⎭
,, 6th ,,		11011
,, 7th ,,		11100
,, 8th ,,		11101
,, 9th ,,		11110 ⎫
,, 10th ,,		11111 ⎭

after each step.   The number following each diagram indicates
that position, each number being obtained from the one above
it by the addition of unity.   The steps which are bracketed
together can be made in one movement, and, if thus effected,
the whole process is completed in 7 movements instead of 10
steps : this is in accordance with the formula given above.

Gros asserted that it is possible to take from 64 to 80 steps a
minute, which in my experience is a rather high estimate.   If
we accept the lower of these numbers, it would be possible to
take off 10 rings in less than 8 minutes ; to take off 25 rings
would require more than 582 days, each of ten hours'

work; and to take off 60 rings would necessitate no less than 768614,336404,564650 steps, and would require nearly 55000,000000 years' work—assuming, of course, that no mistakes were made.

PROBLEMS CONNECTED WITH A PACK OF CARDS

An ordinary pack of playing-cards can be used to illustrate many questions depending on simple properties of numbers, or involving the relative position of the cards. In problems of this kind, the principle of solution generally consists in re-arranging the pack in a particular manner so as to bring the card into some definite position. Any such rearrangement is a species of shuffling.

I shall treat in succession of problems connected with *Shuffling a Pack*, *Arrangements by Rows and Columns*, the *Determination of a Pair out of* $\frac{1}{2}n(n+1)$ *Pairs*, *Gergonne's Pile Problem*, the *Window Reader*, and the game known as the *Mouse Trap*.

SHUFFLING A PACK

Any system of *shuffling a pack* of cards, if carried out consistently, leads to an arrangement which can be calculated; but tricks that depend on it generally require considerable technical skill.

Suppose, for instance, that a pack of n cards is shuffled, as is not unusual, by placing the second card on the first, the third below these, the fourth above them, and so on. The theory of this system of shuffling is due to Monge.* The following are some of the results, and are not difficult to prove directly.

* Monge's investigations are printed in the *Mémoires de l'Académie des Sciences*, Paris, 1773, pp. 390—412. Among those who have studied the subject afresh I may in particular mention V. Bouniakowski, *Bulletin physico-mathématique de St. Pétersbourg*, 1857, vol. xv. pp. 202—205, summarized in the *Nouvelles annales de mathématiques*, 1858, *Bulletin*, pp. 66—67; T. de St. Laurent, *Mémoires de l'Académie de Gard*, 1865; L. Tanner, *Educational Times Reprints*, 1880, vol. xxxii, pp. 73—75; M. J. Bourget, *Liouville's Journal*, 1882, pp. 413—434; H. F. Baker, *Transactions of the British Association for* 1910, pp. 526—528; and P. H. Cowell, *The Field* 2 April, 1921, p. 444.

One shuffle of a pack of $2p$ cards will move the card which was in the x_0th place to the x_1th place, where $x_1 = \frac{1}{2}(2p + x_0 + 1)$ if x_0 is odd, and $x_1 = \frac{1}{2}(2p - x_0 + 2)$ if x_0 is even. For instance, if a complete pack of 52 cards is shuffled as described above, the eighteenth card will remain the eighteenth card. If an écarté pack of 32 cards is so shuffled, the seventh and the twentieth cards will change places.

By repeated applications of the above formulae we can show that the effect of m such shuffles is to move the card which was initially in the x_0th place to the x_mth place, where

$$2^{m+1}x_m = (4p+1)(2^{m-1} \pm 2^{m-2} \pm \ldots \pm 2 \pm 1) \pm 2x_0 + 2^m \pm 1,$$

the sign $\pm$ representing an ambiguity of sign.

Again, in any pack of n cards, after a certain number of shufflings, not greater than n, the cards will return to their primitive order. This will always be the case as soon as the original top card occupies that position again. To determine the number of shuffles required for a pack of $2p$ cards, it is sufficient to put $x_m = x_0$ and find the smallest value of m which satisfies the resulting equation for all values of x_0 from 1 to $2p$.

The result can, however, be obtained more easily if the cards are numbered from the bottom of the original pack. Doing this, we can show that if after s shuffles a card is in the rth place from the bottom, its original number from the bottom was the difference between $2^s \times r$ and the nearest multiple of $4p + 1$. Hence, if m shuffles are required to restore the original order, m is the least number for which $2^m + 1$ or $2^m - 1$ is divisible by $4p + 1$. The number for a pack of $2p + 1$ cards is the same as that for a pack of $2p$ cards. With an écarté pack of 32 cards, six shuffles are sufficient; with a pack of 2^n cards, $n + 1$ shuffles are sufficient; with a full pack of 52 cards, twelve shuffles are sufficient; with a pack of 13 cards, ten shuffles are sufficient; while with a pack of 50 cards, fifty shuffles are required; and so on.

W. H. H. Hudson * has also shown that, whatever is the law

* *Educational Times Reprints*, London, 1865, vol. II, p. 105.

of shuffling, yet if it is repeated again and again on a pack of n cards, the cards will ultimately fall into their initial positions after a number of shufflings not greater than the greatest possible L.C.M. of all numbers whose sum is n.

For suppose that any particular position is occupied after the 1st, 2nd, ..., pth shuffles by the cards A_1, A_2, ..., A_p respectively, and that initially the position is occupied by the card A_0. Suppose further that after the pth shuffle A_0 returns to its initial position, therefore $A_0 = A_p$. Then at the second shuffling A_2 succeeds A_1 by the same law by which A_1 succeeded A_0 at the first; hence it follows that previous to the second shuffling A_2 must have been in the place occupied by A_1 previous to the first. Thus the cards which after the successive shuffles take the place initially occupied by A_1 are A_2, A_3, ..., A_p, A_1—that is, after the pth shuffle A_1 has returned to the place initially occupied by it : and so for all the other cards A_2, A_3, ..., A_{p-1}.

Hence the cards A_1, A_2, ..., A_p form a cycle of p cards, one or other of which is always in one or other of p positions in the pack, and which go through all their changes in p shufflings. Let the number n of the pack be divided into p, q, r, ... such cycles, whose sum is n; then the L.C.M. of p, q, r, ... is the utmost number of shufflings necessary before all the cards will be brought back to their original places. In the case of a pack of 52 cards, the greatest L.C.M. of numbers whose sum is 52 is 180180.

ARRANGEMENTS BY ROWS AND COLUMNS

A not uncommon trick, which rests on a species of shuffling, depends on the obvious fact that if n^2 cards are arranged in the form of a square of n rows, each containing n cards, then any card will be defined if the row and the column in which it lies are mentioned.

This information is generally elicited by first asking in which row the selected card lies, and noting the extreme left-hand card of that row. The cards in each column are then taken up, face upwards, one at a time, beginning with the lowest card of each column and taking the columns in their order from right to left—each card taken up being placed on the top of those previously taken up. The cards are then dealt out again in rows, from left to right, beginning with the top left-hand corner, and a question is put as to which row contains the card. The selected card will be that card in the row mentioned which is in the same vertical column as the card which was originally noted.

The trick is improved by allowing the pack to be cut as often as is liked before the cards are re-dealt, and then giving one cut at the end so as to make the top card in the pack one of those originally in the top row. For instance, take the case of 16

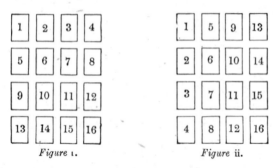

Figure i. Figure ii.

cards. The first and second arrangements may be represented by figures i and ii. Suppose we are told that in figure i the card is in the third row, it must be either 9, 10, 11, 12 : hence, if we know in which row of figure ii it lies, it is determined. If we allow the pack to be cut between the deals, we must secure somehow that the top card is either 1, 2, 3, or 4, since that will leave the cards in each row of figure ii unaltered though the positions of the rows will be changed.

DETERMINATION OF A SELECTED PAIR OF CARDS OUT OF $\frac{1}{2}n(n + 1)$ GIVEN PAIRS *

Another common trick is to throw twenty cards on to a table in ten couples, and ask someone to select one couple. The cards

* Bachet, problem xvii, avertissement, pp. 146 et seq.

are then taken up, and dealt out in a certain manner into four rows each containing five cards. If the rows which contain the given cards are indicated, the cards selected are known at once.

This depends on the fact that the number of homogeneous products of two dimensions which can be formed out of four things is 10. Hence the homogeneous products of two dimensions formed out of four things can be used to define ten things.

Suppose that ten couples of cards are placed on a table and

someone selects one couple. Take up the cards in their couples. Then the first two cards form the first couple, the next two the second couple, and so on. Deal them out in four rows each containing five cards according to the scheme shown above.

The first couple (1 and 2) are in the first row. Of the next couple (3 and 4), put one in the first row and one in the second. Of the next couple (5 and 6), put one in the first row and one in the third, and so on, as indicated in the diagram. After filling up the first row proceed similarly with the second row, and so on.

Enquire in which rows the two selected cards appear. If only one line, the mth, is mentioned as containing the cards, then the required pair of cards are the mth and $(m + 1)$th cards in that line. These occupy the clue squares of that line. Next, if two lines are mentioned, then proceed as follows. Let the two lines be the pth and the qth and suppose $q > p$. Then that one of the required cards which is in the qth line will be the $(q - p)$th card which is below the first of the clue squares in the pth line. The other of the required cards is in the pth line, and is the $(q - p)$th card to the right of the second of the clue squares.

Bachet's rule, in the form in which I have given it, is applicable to a pack of $n(n + 1)$ cards divided into couples, and dealt in n rows each containing $n + 1$ cards; for there are $\frac{1}{2}n(n + 1)$ such couples, also there are $\frac{1}{2}n(n + 1)$ homogeneous products of two dimensions which can be formed out of n things. Bachet gave the diagrams for the cases of 20, 30, and 42 cards : these the reader will have no difficulty in constructing for himself, and I have enunciated the rule for 20 cards in a form which covers all the cases.

I have seen the same trick performed by means of a sentence and not by numbers. If we take the case of ten couples, then, after collecting the pairs, the cards must be dealt in four rows each containing five cards, in the order indicated by the sentence *Matas dedit nomen Cocis*. This sentence must be imagined as written on the table, each word forming one line. The first card is dealt on the M. The next card (which is the pair of the first) is placed on the second m in the sentence—that is, third in the third row. The third card is placed on the a. The fourth card (which is the pair of the third) is placed on the second a—that is, fourth in the first row. Each of the next two cards is placed on a t, and so on. Enquire in which rows the two selected cards appear. If two rows are mentioned, the two cards are on the letters common to the words that make these rows. If only one row is mentioned, the cards are on the two letters common to that row.

The reason is obvious : let us denote each of the first pair by an a, and similarly each of any of the other pairs by an e, i, o, c, d, m, n, s, or t respectively. Now the sentence *Matas dedit nomen Cocis* contains four words each of five letters; ten letters are used, and each letter is repeated only twice. Hence, if two of the words are mentioned, they will have one letter in common, or, if one word is mentioned, it will have two like letters.

To perform the same trick with any other number of cards we should require a different sentence.

The number of homogeneous products of three dimensions which can be formed out of four things is 20, and of these the number consisting of products in which three things are alike and those in which three things are different is 8. This leads to a trick with 8 trios of things, which is similar to that last given—the cards being arranged in the order indicated by the sentence *Lanata levete livini novoto*.

I believe that these arrangements by sentences are well-known, but I am not aware who invented them.

GERGONNE'S PILE PROBLEM

Before discussing Gergonne's theorem I will describe the familiar three-pile problem, the theory of which is included in his results.

The Three-Pile Problem.* This trick is usually performed as follows. Take 27 cards and deal them into three piles, face upwards. By " dealing " is to be understood that the top card is placed as the bottom card of the first pile, the second card in the pack as the bottom card of the second pile, the third card as the bottom card of the third pile, the fourth card on the top of the first one, and so on: moreover, I assume that throughout the problem the cards are held in the hand face upwards. The result can be modified to cover any other way of dealing.

Request a spectator to note a card, and remember in which pile it is. After finishing the deal, ask in which pile the card is. Take up the three piles, placing that pile between the other two. Deal again as before, and repeat the question as to which pile contains the given card. Take up the three piles again, placing the pile which now contains the selected card between the other two. Deal again as before, but in dealing note the middle card of each pile. Ask again, for the third

* The trick is mentioned by Bachet, problem xviii, p. 143, but his analysis of it is insufficient.

time, in which pile the card lies, and you will know that the
card was the one which you noted as being the middle card of
that pile. The trick can be finished then in any way that you
like. The usual method—but a very clumsy one—is to take
up the three piles once more, placing the named pile between
the other two as before, when the selected card will be the
middle one in the pack—that is, if 27 cards are used it will be
the 14th card.

The trick is often performed with 15 cards or with 21 cards,
in either of which cases the same rule holds.

Gergonne's Generalization. The general theory for a pack
of m^m cards was given by M. Gergonne.* Suppose the pack is
arranged in m piles, each containing m^{m-1} cards, and that, after
the first deal, the pile indicated as containing the selected card
is taken up ath; after the second deal, is taken up bth; and so
on, and finally after the mth deal, the pile containing the card
is taken up kth. Then when the cards are collected after the
mth deal, the selected card will be nth from the top where

$$\text{if } m \text{ is even, } n = km^{m-1} - jm^{m-2} + \ldots + bm - a + 1,$$
$$\text{if } m \text{ is odd, } n = km^{m-1} - jm^{m-2} + \ldots - bm + a.$$

For example, if a pack of 256 cards (*i.e.* $m = 4$) was given,
and anyone selected a card out of it, the card could be determined by making four successive deals into four piles of
64 cards each, and after each deal asking in which pile the
selected card lay. The reason is that after the first deal you
know it is one of 64 cards. In the next deal these 64 cards
are distributed equally over the four piles, and therefore, if
you know in which pile it is, you will know that it is one of
16 cards. After the third deal you know it is one of 4 cards.
After the fourth deal you know which card it is.

Moreover, if the pack of 256 cards is used, it is immaterial
in what order the pile containing the selected card is taken up
after a deal. For, if after the first deal it is taken up ath,

* Gergonne's *Annales de Mathématiques*, Nîmes, 1813—1814, vol. IV,
pp. 276—283.

after the second bth, after the third cth, and after the fourth dth, the card will be the $(64d - 16c + 4b - a + 1)$th from the top of the pack, and thus will be known. We need not take up the cards after the fourth deal, for the same argument will show that it is the $(64 - 16c + 4b - a + 1)$th in the pile then indicated as containing it. Thus if $a = 3, b = 4, c = 1, d = 2$, it will be the 62nd card in the pile indicated after the fourth deal as containing it, and will be the 126th card in the pack as then collected.

In exactly the same way a pack of 27 cards may be used, and three successive deals, each into three piles of 9 cards, will suffice to determine the card. If after the deals the pile indicated as containing the given card is taken up ath, bth, and cth, respectively, then the card will be the $(9c - 3b + a)$th in the pack or will be the $(9 - 3b + a)$th card in the pile indicated after the third deal as containing it.

The method of proof will be illustrated sufficiently by considering the usual case of a pack of 27 cards, for which $m = 3$, which are dealt into three piles each of 9 cards.

Suppose that, after the first deal, the pile containing the selected card is taken up ath : then (i) at the top of the pack there are $a - 1$ piles each containing 9 cards ; (ii) next there are 9 cards, of which one is the selected card ; and (iii) lastly there are the remaining cards of the pack. The cards are dealt out now for the second time : in each pile the bottom $3(a - 1)$ cards will be taken from (i), the next 3 cards from (ii), and the remaining $9 - 3a$ cards from (iii).

Suppose that the pile now indicated as containing the selected card is taken up bth : then (i) at the top of the pack are $9(b - 1)$ cards ; (ii) next are $9 - 3a$ cards ; (iii) next are 3 cards, of which one is the selected card ; and (iv) lastly are the remaining cards of the pack. The cards are dealt out now for the third time : in each pile the bottom $3(b - 1)$ cards will be taken from (i), the next $3 - a$ cards will be taken from (ii), the next card will be one of the 3 cards in (iii), and the remaining $8 - 3b + a$ cards are from (iv).

Hence, after this deal, as soon as the pile is indicated, it is known that the card is the $(9 - 3b + a)$th from the top of that pile. If the process is continued by taking up this pile as cth, then the selected card will come out in the place $9(c - 1) + (8 - 3b + a) + 1$ from the top—that is, will come out as the $(9c - 3b + a)$th card.

Since, after the third deal, the position of the card in the pile then indicated is known, it is easy to notice the card, in which case the trick can be finished in some way more effective than dealing again.

If we put the pile indicated always in the middle of the pack, we have $a = 2$, $b = 2$, $c = 2$, hence $n = 9c - 3b + a = 14$, which is the form in which the trick is usually presented, as was explained above on page 316.

I have shown that if a, b, c are known, then n is determined. We may modify the rule so as to make the selected card come out in any assigned position—say the nth. In this case we have to find values of a, b, c which will satisfy the equation $n = 9c - 3b + a$, where a, b, c can have only the values 1, 2, or 3.

Hence, if we divide n by 3 and the remainder is 1 or 2, this remainder will be a; but, if the remainder is 0, we must decrease the quotient by unity so that the remainder is 3, and this remainder will be a. In other words, a is the smallest positive number (exclusive of zero) which must be subtracted from n to make the difference a multiple of 3.

Next let p be this multiple—i.e. p is the next lowest integer to $n/3$: then $3p = 9c - 3b$, therefore $p = 3c - b$. Hence b is the smallest positive number (exclusive of zero) which must be added to p to make the sum a multiple of 3, and c is that multiple.

A couple of illustrations will make this clear. Suppose we wish the card to come out 22nd from the top, therefore $22 = 9c - 3b + a$. The smallest number which must be subtracted from 22 to leave a multiple of 3 is 1, therefore $a = 1$. Hence $22 = 9c - 3b + 1$, therefore $7 = 3c - b$. The smallest number which must be added to 7 to make a multiple of 3 is 2, therefore $b = 2$. Hence $7 = 3c - 2$, therefore $c = 3$. Thus $a = 1, b = 2, c = 3$.

Again, suppose the card is to come out 21st. Hence $21 = 9c - 3b + a$. Therefore a is the smallest number which subtracted from 21 makes a multiple of 3, therefore $a = 3$. Hence $6 = 3c - b$. Therefore b is the smallest number which added to 6 makes a multiple of 3, therefore $b = 3$. Hence $9 = 3c$, therefore $c = 3$. Thus $a = 3, b = 3, c = 3$.

If any difficulty is experienced in this work, we can proceed thus. Let $a = x + 1$, $b = 3 - y$, $c = z + 1$; then x, y, z may have only the values 0, 1, or 2. In this case Gergonne's equation takes the form $9z + 3y + x = n - 1$. Hence, if $n - 1$ is expressed in the ternary scale of notation, x, y, z will be determined, and therefore a, b, c will be known.

The rule in the case of a pack of m^m cards is exactly similar. We want to make the card come out in a given place. Hence, in Gergonne's formula, we are given n and we have to find $a, b, \ldots, k$. We can effect this by dividing n continually by m, with the convention that the remainders are to be alternately positive and negative, and that their numerical values are to be not greater than m or less than unity.

An analogous theorem with a pack of lm cards can be constructed. C. T. Hudson and L. E. Dickson * have discussed the general case where such a pack is dealt n times, each time into l piles of m cards; and they have shown how the piles must be taken up in order that after the nth deal the selected card may be rth from the top.

The principle will be sufficiently illustrated by one example treated in a manner analogous to the cases already discussed. For instance, suppose that an écarté pack of 32 cards is dealt into four piles each of 8 cards, and that the pile which contains some selected card is picked up ath. Suppose that on dealing

---

* *Educational Times Reprints*, 1868, vol. IX, pp. 89—91; and *Bulletin* of the American Mathematical Society, New York, April, 1895, vol. I, pp. 184—186.

again into four piles, one pile is indicated as containing the selected card, the selected card cannot be one of the bottom $2(a - 1)$ cards, or of the top $8 - 2a$ cards, but must be one of the intermediate 2 cards, and the trick can be finished in any way, as for instance by the common conjuring ambiguity of asking someone to choose one of them, leaving it doubtful whether the one he takes is to be rejected or retained.

M. R. Goormaghtigh * has determined the condition which l and m must satisfy in order that a selected card may be located by dealing three times into l piles of m, the indicated pile being taken up second every time. The condition is $[(m + h)/l] = [(m + k)/l]$ ($= p$, say), where $h = [m/l]$ and and $k = [(2m - 1)/l]$. The selected card is then the $(p + 1)$th in the pile indicated after the third deal. For an ordinary pack of 52 cards, we may take $l = 4$, $m = 13$; then $h = 3$, $k = 6$, and $p = 4$, so that after three deals the selected card will be the fifth in the indicated pile.

THE WINDOW READER

Some years ago a set of 8 numbered and perforated cards was brought out which enabled an operator to state a number chosen by a spectator. Of the 8 cards each of the first 7 was pierced with window-like openings, each of the last 7 contained some of the numbers less than 100 headed by the word *Yes*, each of the last 3 had also certain digits on its back, and the first of the cards was headed with the word *Top*. Each card if turned upside down bore on what was then its top the word *No*.

The cards were employed to determine any number less than 100 chosen by someone—say, A. They were used by B thus. B first laid on the table the card numbered 1 with the side marked *Top* uppermost. B then took the second card, and asked A if the chosen number was on it; if A said yes, B placed the card 2 on the top of the card 1 with the *Yes* uppermost; and if A said no, B turned the card round and

* *Sphinx*, 1936, pp. 113—115.

Y

placed it with the *No* uppermost.   *B* then asked if the chosen number was on the third card, and placed it on the top of 2 with the appropriate end uppermost; and so on with the rest of the cards 4 to 8.   Finally, on turning the whole pile over, the chosen number was seen through the windows.

The puzzle must have been widely circulated.   It was sold in Italy and Germany as well as in London.   The method used is fairly obvious, and I will leave to any reader, sufficiently interested, the task of constructing cards suitable for the purpose.

Evidently, however, any number not exceeding 128 can be determined by only 7 cards, each bearing 64 selected numbers. For the first card serves to divide the numbers into two sets of 64 numbers, numbers on the second card can be chosen so as to divide each of these into two sets of 32 cards, the third divides each of these into two sets of 16 cards, and so on. The numbers must be written on the cards and the windows cut so that after arranging the cards in their proper order, and turning the pack over, the chosen number appears on the back of the seventh card as seen through the windows cut in the first 6 cards.   To arrange the numbers in this way presents no difficulty, but the geometrical problem of cutting the windows is less easy.   I give one solution.

If we work with 7 cards, one way of preparing them is as follows.   We write under the word *Yes* on the first card, the 64 numbers 1 to 32, 65 to 96 ; on the second card, the numbers 1 to 16, 33 to 48, 65 to 80, 97 to 112 ; on the third card, the numbers in four arithmetical progressions starting from 1, 2, 5, 6, each of 16 terms, with 8 as difference ; on the fourth card, the numbers in eight arithmetical progressions starting from 1, 2, 3, 4, 5, 6, 7, 8, each of 8 terms, with 16 as difference ; on the fifth card, the odd numbers from 1 to 127 ; on the sixth card, the numbers in four arithmetical progressions starting from 1, 2, 3, 4, each of 16 terms, with 8 as difference ; and on the seventh card the consecutive numbers from 1 to 64 ; on this card, however, the *No* must be written on the left-hand edge of the card, and not on its lowest edge. On the back of the last card we must now write the numbers from 1 to 128 in their natural order, 1 to 32 occupying the first quarter, 33 to 64 the fourth quarter, 65 to 96 the second quarter rotated through a right angle, and 97 to 128 the third quarter also rotated through a right angle. The spacing of the figures requires care, but is not difficult if the principle of construction is grasped and squared paper used.

The windows should be cut as follows. We will suppose that we use squared paper dividing each card into four equal quadrants with margins. In the first card, we form the window by cutting out the whole of the second quadrant. In the second card, we get two windows by cutting out the top half of the second quadrant and the top half of the third quadrant. In the third card, we get two windows by cutting out the right half of the second quadrant and the right half of the third quadrant. In the fourth card, we divide the second and third quadrants into four equal horizontal strips, and from each of these quadrants cut out the first and third strips. In the fifth card, we divide the second and third quadrants into four equal vertical strips, and from each of these quadrants cut out the second and fourth of these strips. In the sixth card, we divide the second and third quadrants into eight horizontal strips, and from each of these quadrants cut out the first, third, fifth, and seventh strips.

It will be noticed that no windows are cut in the first or fourth quarter of any card; hence they are free for insertion of the 64 numbers written on the face of each card. The construction here given is due to my friend R. A. L. Cole.

Possibly the puzzle is better presented by omitting all numbers exceeding 100, for the introduction of 128 at once suggests the method of construction. With that restriction I think the use of only 7 cards is better and more elegant than the form in which I have seen it on sale.

THE MOUSE TRAP.   TREIZE

I will conclude this chapter with the bare mention of another game of cards, known as the *Mouse Trap*, the discussion of which involves some rather difficult algebraic analysis.

It is played as follows. A set of cards, marked with the numbers 1, 2, 3, ..., n, is dealt in any order, face upwards, in the form of a circle. The player begins at any card and counts round the circle always in the same direction. If the kth card has the number k on it—which event is called a *hit*—the player takes up the card and begins counting afresh. According to Cayley, the player wins if he thus takes up all the cards, and the cards win if at any time the player counts up to n without being able to take up a card.

For example, if a pack of only 4 cards is used, and these cards come in the order 3214, then the player would obtain the second card 2 as a hit, next he would obtain 1 as a hit, but if he went on for ever, he would not obtain another hit. On the other hand, if the cards in the pack were initially in the order 1423, the player would obtain successively all four cards in the order 1, 2, 3, 4.

The problem may be stated as the determination of what hits and how many hits can be made with a given number of cards; and what permutations will give a certain number of hits in a certain order.

Cayley * showed that there are 9 arrangements of a pack of 4 cards in which no hit will be made, 7 arrangements in which only one hit will be made, 3 arrangements in which only two hits will be made, and 5 arrangements in which four hits will be made.

Prof. Steen † has investigated the general theory for a pack of n cards. He has shown how to determine the number of arrangements in which x is the first hit [Arts. 3—5]; the number of arrangements in which 1 is the first hit and x is the

---

* *Quarterly Journal of Mathematics*, 1878, vol. xv, pp. 8—10.
† *Ibid.*, vol. xv, pp. 230—241.

second hit [Art. 6]; and the number of arrangements in which 2 is the first hit and x the second hit [Arts. 7—8]; but beyond this point the theory has not been carried. It is obvious that, if there are $n - 1$ hits, the nth hit will necessarily follow.

The French game of *treize* is very similar. It is played with a full pack of fifty-two cards (knave, queen, and king counting as 11, 12, and 13 respectively) The dealer calls out 1, 2, 3, . . ., 13, as he deals the 1st, 2nd, 3rd, . . ., 13th cards respectively. At the beginning of a deal the dealer offers to lay or take certain odds that he will make a hit in the thirteen cards next dealt. (Cf. page 47.)

CHAPTER XII

THREE CLASSICAL GEOMETRICAL PROBLEMS

AMONG the more interesting geometrical problems of anti-quity are three questions which attracted the special attention of the early Greek mathematicians. Our knowledge of geometry is derived from Greek sources, and thus these questions have attained a classical position in the history of the subject. The three questions to which I refer are : (i) the duplication of a cube—that is, the determination of the side of a cube whose volume is double that of a given cube ; (ii) the trisection of an angle; and (iii) the squaring of a circle—that is, the determination of a square whose area is equal to that of a given circle; each problem to be solved by a geometrical construction involving the use of straight lines and circles only—that is, by Euclidean geometry.

This limitation to the use of straight lines and circles implies that the only instruments available in Euclidean geometry are compasses and rulers. But the compasses must be capable of opening as wide as is desired, and the ruler must be of unlimited length. Further, the ruler must not be graduated, for if there were two fixed marks on it we could obtain constructions equivalent to those obtained by the use of the conic sections.

With the Euclidean restriction all three problems are in-soluble.* To duplicate a cube the length of whose side is a, we have to find a line of length x, such that $x^3 = 2a^3$. Again,

---

* See F. C. Klein, *Vorträge über ausgewählte Fragen der Elementargeometrie*, Leipzig, 1895; and F. G. Texeira, *Sur les Problèmes célèbres de la Géométrie Élémentaire non resolubles avec la Règle et le Compas*, Coimbra, 1915. It is said that the earliest rigorous proof that the problems were insoluble by Euclidean geometry was given by P. L. Wantzell in 1837.

to trisect a given angle, we may proceed to find the sine of the angle—say a—then, if x is the sine of an angle equal to one-third of the given angle, we have $4x^3 = 3x - a$. Thus the first and second problems, when considered analytically, require the solution of a cubic equation; and since a construction by means of circles (whose equations are of the form $x^2 + y^2 + ax + by + c = 0$) and straight lines (whose equations are of the form $ax + \beta y + \gamma = 0$) cannot be equivalent to the solution of a cubic equation, it is inferred that the problems are insoluble if in our constructions we are restricted to the use of circles and straight lines. If the use of the conic sections is permitted, both of these questions can be solved in many ways. The third problem is different in character, but under the same restrictions it also is insoluble.

I propose to give some of the constructions which have been proposed for solving the first two of these problems. To save space I shall not draw the necessary diagrams, and in most cases I shall not add the proofs: the latter present but little difficulty. I shall conclude with some historical notes on approximate solutions of the quadrature of the circle.

THE DUPLICATION OF THE CUBE *

The problem of the duplication of the cube was known in ancient times as the Delian problem, in consequence of a legend that the Delians had consulted Plato on the subject. In one form of the story, which is related by Philoponus,† it is asserted that the Athenians in 430 B.C., when suffering from the plague of eruptive typhoid fever, consulted the oracle at Delos as to how they could stop it. Apollo replied that they must double the size of his altar, which was in the form of a cube. To the unlearned suppliants nothing seemed more easy,

---

* See *Historia Problematis de Cubi Duplicatione* by N. T. Reimer, Göttingen, 1798; and *Historia Problematis Cubi Duplicandi* by C. H. Biering, Copenhagen, 1844; also *Das Delische Problem*, by A. Sturm, Linz, 1895–7. Some notes on the subject are given in my *History of Mathematics*.

† *Philoponus ad Aristotelis Analytica Posteriora*, bk. i, chap. vii.

and a new altar was constructed either having each of its edges double that of the old one (from which it followed that the volume was increased eight-fold) or by placing a similar cube altar next to the old one. Whereupon, according to the legend, the indignant god made the pestilence worse than before, and informed a fresh deputation that it was useless to trifle with him, as his new altar must be a cube and have a volume exactly double that of his old one. Suspecting a mystery, the Athenians applied to Plato, who referred them to the geometricians. The insertion of Plato's name is an obvious anachronism. Eratosthenes * relates a somewhat similar story, but with Minos as the propounder of the problem.

In an Arab work, the Greek legend was distorted into the following extraordinarily impossible piece of history, which I cite as a curiosity of its kind. "Now in the days of Plato," says the writer, "a plague broke out among the children of Israel. Then came a voice from heaven to one of their prophets, saying, 'Let the size of the cubic altar be doubled, and the plague will cease'; so the people made another altar like unto the former, and laid the same by its side. Nevertheless the pestilence continued to increase. And again the voice spake unto the prophet, saying, 'They have made a second altar like unto the former, and laid it by its side, but that does not produce the duplication of the cube.' Then applied they to Plato, the Grecian sage, who spake to them, saying, 'Ye have been neglectful of the science of geometry, and therefore hath God chastised you, since geometry is the most sublime of all the sciences.' Now, the duplication of a cube depends on a rare problem in geometry, namely . . ." And then follows the solution of Apollonius, which is given later.

If a is the length of the side of the given cube and x that of the required cube, we have $x^3 = 2a^3$—that is, $x : a = \sqrt[3]{2} : 1$.

---

* *Archimedis Opera cum Eutocii Commentariis*, ed. Torelli, Oxford, 1792, p. 144; ed. Heiberg, Leipzig, 1880–1, vol. III, pp. 104—107.

It is probable that the Greeks were aware that the latter ratio is incommensurable—in other words, that no two integers can be found whose ratio is the same as that of $\sqrt[3]{2} : 1$—but it did not therefore follow that they could not find the ratio by geometry : in fact, the side and diagonal of a square are instances of lines whose numerical measures are incommensurable.

I proceed now to give some of the geometrical constructions which have been proposed for the duplication of the cube.* With one exception, I confine myself to those which can be effected by the aid of the conic sections.

Hippocrates † (*circ.* 420 B.C.) was perhaps the earliest mathematician who made any progress towards solving the problem. He did not give a geometrical construction, but he reduced the question to that of finding two means between one straight line (a), and another twice as long ($2a$). If these means are x and y, we have $a : x = x : y = y : 2a$, from which it follows that $x^3 = 2a^3$. It is in this form that the problem is always presented now. Formerly any process of solution by finding these means was called a mesolabum.

One of the first solutions of the problem was that given by Archytas ‡ in or about the year 400 B.C. His construction is equivalent to the following. On the diameter OA of the base of a right circular cylinder describe a semicircle whose plane is perpendicular to the base of the cylinder. Let the plane containing this semicircle rotate round the generator through O, then the surface traced out by the semicircle will cut the cylinder in a tortuous curve. This curve will itself be cut by a right cone, whose axis is OA and semi-vertical angle is (say) 60°, in a point P, such that the projection of OP on the base

---

* On the application to this problem of the traditional Greek methods of analysis by Hero and Philo (leading to the solution by the use of Apollonius's circle), by Nicomedes (leading to the solution by the use of the conchoid), and by Pappus (leading to the solution by the use of the cissoid), see *Geometrical Analysis* by J. Leslie, Edinburgh, second edition, 1811, pp. 247—250, 453.   † Proclus, ed. Friedlein, pp. 212—213.

‡ *Archimedis Opera*, ed. Torelli, p. 143 ; ed. Heiberg, vol. III, pp. 98—103.

of the cylinder will be to the radius of the cylinder in the ratio of the side of the required cube to that of the given cube. Of course, the proof given by Archytas is geometrical; and it is interesting to note that in it he shows himself familiar with the results of the propositions Euc. III, 18, III, 35, and XI, 19. To show analytically that the construction is correct, take OA as the axis of x, and the generator of the cylinder drawn through O as axis of z, then with the usual notation, in polar co-ordinates, if a is the radius of the cylinder, we have for the equation of the surface described by the semicircle $r = 2a \sin \theta$; for that of the cylinder $r \sin \theta = 2a \cos \phi$; and for that of the cone $\sin \theta \cos \phi = \frac{1}{2}$. These three surfaces cut in a point such that $\sin^3 \theta = \frac{1}{2}$, and therefore $(r \sin \theta)^3 = 2a^3$. Hence the volume of the cube whose side is $r \sin \theta$ is twice that of the cube whose side is a.

The construction attributed to Plato * (*circ.* 360 B.C.) depends on the theorem that, if CAB and DAB are two right-angled triangles, having one side, AB, common, their other sides, AD and BC, parallel, and their hypotenuses, AC and BD, at right angles, then if these hypotenuses cut in P, we have $PC : PB = PB : PA = PA : PD$. Hence, if such a figure can be constructed having $PD = 2PC$, the problem will be solved. It is easy to make an instrument by which the figure can be drawn.

The next writer whose name is connected with the problem is Menaechmus,† who in or about 340 B.C. gave two solutions of it.

In the first of these he pointed out that two parabolas having a common vertex, axes at right angles, and such that the latus rectum of the one is double that of the other, will intersect in another point whose abscissa (or ordinate) will give a solution. If we use analysis, this is obvious; for, if the equations of the parabolas are $y^2 = 2ax$ and $x^2 = ay$, they intersect in a point whose abscissa is given by $x^3 = 2a^3$. It is

* *Archimedis Opera*, ed. Torelli, p. 135; ed. Heiberg, vol. III, pp. 66—71.
† *Ibid.*, ed. Torelli, pp. 141—143; ed. Heiberg, vol. III, pp. 92—99.

probable that this method was suggested by the form in which Hippocrates had cast the problem—namely, to find x and y so that $a : x = x : y = y : 2a$, whence we have $x^2 = ay$ and $y^2 = 2ax$.

The second solution given by Menaechmus was as follows. Describe a parabola of latus rectum l. Next describe a rectangular hyperbola, the length of whose real axis is $4l$, and having for its asymptotes the tangent at the vertex of the parabola and the axis of the parabola. Then the ordinate and the abscissa of the point of intersection of these curves are the mean proportionals between l and $2l$. This is at once obvious by analysis. The curves are $x^2 = ly$ and $xy = 2l^2$. These cut in a point determined by $x^3 = 2l^3$ and $y^3 = 4l^3$. Hence

$$l : x = x : y = y : 2l.$$

The solution of Apollonius,[*] which was given about 220 B.C., was as follows. The problem is to find two mean proportionals between two given lines. Construct a rectangle $OADB$, of which the adjacent sides OA and OB are respectively equal to the two given lines. Bisect AB in C. With C as centre describe a circle cutting OA produced in a and cutting OB produced in b, so that aDb shall be a straight line. If this circle can be so described, it will follow that $OA : Bb = Bb : Aa = Aa : OB$—that is, Bb and Aa are the two mean proportionals between OA and OB. It is impossible to construct the circle by Euclidean geometry, but Apollonius gave a mechanical way of describing it.

The only other construction of antiquity to which I will refer is that given by Diocles and Sporus.[†] It is as follows. Take two sides of a rectangle OA, OB, equal to the two lines between which the means are sought. Suppose OA to be the greater. With centre O and radius OA describe a circle. Let

---

[*] *Archimedis Opera*, ed. Torelli, p. 137; ed. Heiberg, vol. III, pp. 76—79. The solution is given in my *History of Mathematics*, London, 1901, p. 84.

[†] *Ibid.*, ed. Torelli, pp. 138, 139, 141; ed. Heiberg, vol. III, pp. 78—84, 90—93.

OB produced cut the circumference in *C* and let *AO* produced
cut it in *D*. Find a point *E* on *BC* so that if *DE* cuts *AB*
produced in *F* and cuts the circumference in *G*, then *FE* =
EG. If *E* can be found, then *OE* is the first of the means
between *OA* and *OB*. Diocles invented the cissoid in order
to determine *E*, but it can be found equally conveniently by
the aid of conics.

In more modern times several other solutions have been
suggested. I may allude in passing to three given by
Huygens,* but I will enunciate only those proposed respectively by Vieta, Descartes, Gregory of St. Vincent, and
Newton.

Vieta's construction is as follows.† Describe a circle, centre
O, whose radius is equal to half the length of the larger of the
two given lines. In it draw a chord *AB* equal to the smaller
of the two given lines. Produce *AB* to *E* so that *BE* = *AB*.
Through *A* draw a line *AF* parallel to *OE*. Through *O* draw
a line *DOCFG*, cutting the circumference in *D* and *C*, cutting
AF in *F*, and cutting *BA* produced in *G*, so that *GF* = *OA*.
If this line can be drawn then *AB* : *GC* = *GC* : *GA* = *GA* : *CD*.

Descartes pointed out ‡ that the curves

$$x^2 = ay \text{ and } x^2 + y^2 = ay + bx$$

cut in a point (*x*, *y*) such that *a* : *x* = *x* : *y* = *y* : *b*. Of course,
this is equivalent to the first solution given by Menaechmus,
but Descartes preferred to use a circle rather than a second
conic.

Gregory's construction was given in the form of the following
theorem.§ The hyperbola drawn through the point of intersection of two sides of a rectangle so as to have the two other
sides for its asymptotes meets the circle circumscribing the
rectangle in a point whose distances from the asymptotes are

* *Opera Varia*, Leyden, 1724, pp. 393—396.
† *Opera Mathematica*, ed. Schooten, Leyden, 1646, prop. v, pp. 242—243.
‡ *Geometria*, bk. III, ed. Schooten, Amsterdam, 1659, p. 91.
§ Gregory of St. Vincent, *Opus Geometricum Quadraturae Circuli*, Antwerp,
1647, bk. VI, prop. 138, p. 602.

the mean proportionals between two adjacent sides of the rectangle. This is the geometrical expression of the proposition that the curves $xy = ab$ and $x^2 + y^2 = ay + bx$ cut in a point (x, y) such that $a : x = x : y = y : b$.

One of the constructions proposed by Newton is as follows.* Let OA be the greater of two given lines. Bisect OA in B. With centre O and radius OB describe a circle. Take a point C on the circumference so that BC is equal to the other of the two given lines. From O draw ODE cutting AC produced in D, and BC produced in E, so that the intercept $DE = OB$. Then $BC : OD = OD : CE = CE : OA$. Hence OD and CE are two mean proportionals between any two lines BC and OA.

The Trisection of an Angle †

The trisection of an angle is the second of these classical problems, but tradition has not enshrined its origin in romance. The following two constructions are among the oldest and best known of those which have been suggested; they are quoted by Pappus,‡ but I do not know to whom they were due originally.

The first of them is as follows. Let AOB be the given angle. From any point P in OB draw PM perpendicular to OA. Through P draw PR parallel to OA. On MP take a point Q so that if OQ is produced to cut PR in R then $QR = 2 . OP$. If this construction can be made, then $AOR = \frac{1}{3}AOB$. The solution depends on determining the position of R. This was effected by a construction which may be expressed analytically thus. Let the given angle be $\tan^{-1}(b/a)$. Construct the hyperbola $xy = ab$, and the circle $(x - a)^2 + $

---

* *Arithmetica Universalis*, Ralphson's (second) edition, 1728, p. 242; see also pp. 243, 245.

† On the bibliography of the subject see the supplements to *L'Intermédiaire des Mathématiciens*, Paris, May and June, 1904.

‡ Pappus, *Mathematicae Collectiones*, bk. IV, props. 32, 33 (ed. Commandino, Bonn, 1670, pp. 97—99). On the application to this problem of the traditional Greek methods of analysis see *Geometrical Analysis*, by J. Leslie, Edinburgh, second edition, 1811, pp. 245—247.

$(y - b)^2 = 4(a^2 + b^2)$. Of the points where they cut, let x be the abscissa which is greatest, then $PR = x - a$, and $\tan^{-1}(b/x) = \frac{1}{3}\tan^{-1}(b/a)$.

The second construction is as follows. Let AOB be the given angle. Take $OB = OA$, and with centre O and radius OA describe a circle. Produce AO indefinitely and take a point C on it external to the circle, so that if CB cuts the circumference in D then CD shall be equal to OA. Draw OE parallel to CDB. Then, if this construction can be made, $AOE = \frac{1}{3}AOB$. The ancients determined the position of the point C by the aid of the conchoid : it could be also found by the use of the conic sections.

I proceed to give a few other solutions, confining myself to those effected by the aid of conics.

Among other constructions given by Pappus * I may quote the following. Describe a hyperbola whose eccentricity is two. Let its centre be C and its vertices A and A'. Produce CA' to S so that $A'S = CA'$. On AS describe a segment of a circle to contain the given angle. Let the orthogonal bisector of AS cut this segment in O. With centre O and radius OA or OS describe a circle. Let this circle cut the branch of the hyperbola through A' in P. Then $SOP = \frac{1}{3}SOA$.

In modern times one of the earliest of the solutions by a direct use of conics was suggested by Descartes, who effected it by the intersection of a circle and a parabola. His construction † is equivalent to finding the points of intersection, other than the origin, of the parabola $y^2 = \frac{1}{4}x$ and the circle $x^2 + y^2 - \frac{13}{4}x + 4ay = 0$. The ordinates of these points are given by the equation $4y^3 = 3y - a$. The smaller positive root is the sine of one-third of the angle whose sine is a. The demonstration is ingenious.

One of the solutions proposed by Newton is practically equivalent to the third one which is quoted above from Pappus. It is as follows.‡ Let A be the vertex of one

* Pappus, *Mathematicae Collectiones*, bk. IV, prop. 34, pp. 99—104.

† *Geometria*, bk. III, ed. Schooten, Amsterdam, 1659, p. 91.

‡ *Arithmetica Universalis*, problem XLII, Ralphson's (second) edition, London, 1728, p. 148; see also pp. 243—245.

branch of a hyperbola whose eccentricity is two, and let S be the focus of the other branch. On AS describe the segment of a circle containing an angle equal to the supplement of the given angle. Let this circle cut the S branch of the hyperbola in P. Then PAS will be equal to one-third of the given angle.

The following elegant solution is due to Clairaut.* Let AOB be the given angle. Take $OA = OB$, and with centre O and radius OA describe a circle. Join AB, and trisect it in H, K, so that $AH = HK = KB$. Bisect the angle AOB by OC cutting AB in L. Then $AH = 2 . HL$. With focus A, vertex H, and directrix OC, describe a hyperbola. Let the branch of this hyperbola which passes through H cut the circle in P. Draw PM perpendicular to OC and produce it to cut the circle in Q. Then by the focus and directrix property we have $AP : PM = AH : HL = 2 : 1$, $\therefore$ $AP = 2 . PM = PQ$. Hence, by symmetry, $AP = PQ = QB$. $\therefore AOP = POQ = QOB$.

I may conclude by giving the solution which Chasles † regards as the most fundamental. It is equivalent to the following proposition. If OA and OB are the bounding radii of a circular arc AB, then a rectangular hyperbola having OA for a diameter and passing through the point of intersection of OB with the tangent to the circle at A will pass through one of the two points of trisection of the arc.

Several instruments have been constructed by which mechanical solutions of the problem can be obtained.

The Quadrature of the Circle ‡

The object of the third of the classical problems was the determination of a side of a square whose area should be equal to that of a given circle.

* I believe that this was first given by Clairaut, but I have mislaid my reference. The construction occurs as an example in the *Geometry of Conics*, by C. Taylor, Cambridge, 1881, No. 308, p. 126.

† *Traité des sections coniques*, Paris, 1865, art. 37, p. 36.

‡ See Montucla's *Histoire des Recherches sur la Quadrature du Cercle*, edited by P. L. Lacroix, Paris, 1831; also various articles by A. De Morgan,

The investigation, previous to the last two hundred years, of this question was fruitful in discoveries of allied theorems, but in more recent times it has been abandoned by those who are able to realize what is required. The history of this subject has been treated by competent writers in such detail that I shall content myself with a very brief allusion to it.

Archimedes showed * (what possibly was known before) that the problem is equivalent to finding the area of a right-angled triangle whose sides are equal respectively to the perimeter of the circle and the radius of the circle. Half the ratio of these lines is a number, usually denoted by π.

That this number is incommensurable had been long suspected, and has been now demonstrated. The earliest analytical proof of it was given by Lambert † in 1761; in 1803 Legendre ‡ extended the proof to show that π^2 was also incommensurable; and in 1882 Lindemann § showed that π cannot be the root of a rational algebraical equation.

An earlier attempt by James Gregory to give a geometrical demonstration of this is worthy of notice. Gregory proved ‖ that the ratio of the area of any arbitrary sector to that of

and especially his *Budget of Paradoxes*, London, 1872. A popular sketch of the subject has been compiled by H. Schubert, *Die Quadratur des Zirkels*, Hamburg, 1889; and since the publication of the earlier editions of these *Recreations* Prof. F. Rudio of Zurich has given an analysis of the arguments of Archimedes, Huygens, Lambert, and Legendre on the subject, with an introduction on the history of the problem, Leipzig, 1892.

* *Archimedis Opera*, Κύκλου μέτρησις, prop. I, ed. Torelli, pp. 203—205; ed. Heiberg, vol. I, pp. 258—261, vol. III, pp. 269—277.

† *Mémoires de l'Académie de Berlin* for 1761, Berlin, 1768, pp. 265—322.

‡ Legendre's *Geometry*, Brewster's translation, Edinburgh, 1824, pp. 239—245.

§ Ueber die Zahl π, *Mathematische Annalen*, Leipzig, 1882, vol. xx, pp. 213—225. The proof leads to the conclusion that, if x is a root of a rational integral algebraical equation, then e^x cannot be rational: hence, if πi was the root of such an equation, $e^{\pi i}$ could not be rational; but $e^{\pi i}$ is equal to -1, and therefore is rational; hence πi cannot be the root of such an algebraical equation, and therefore neither can π.

‖ *Vera Circuli et Hyperbolae Quadratura*, Padua, 1668: this is reprinted in Huygens's *Opera Varia*, Leyden, 1724, pp. 405—462.

the inscribed or circumscribed polygons is not expressible by a finite number of algebraical terms. Hence he inferred that the quadrature was impossible. This was accepted by Montucla, but it is not conclusive, for it is conceivable that some particular sector might be squared, and this particular sector might be the whole circle.

In connection with Gregory's proposition above cited, I may add that Newton * proved that in any closed oval an arbitrary sector bounded by the curve and two radii cannot be expressed in terms of the co-ordinates of the extremities of the arc by a finite number of algebraical terms. The argument is condensed and difficult to follow : the same reasoning would show that a closed oval curve cannot be represented by an algebraical equation in polar co-ordinates. From this proposition no conclusion as to the quadrature of the circle is to be drawn, nor did Newton draw any. In the earlier editions of this work I expressed an opinion that the result presupposed a particular definition of the word oval, but on more careful reflection I think that the conclusion is valid without restriction.

With the aid of the quadratrix, or the conchoid, or the cissoid, the quadrature of the circle is easy, but the construction of those curves assumes a knowledge of the value of π, and thus the question is begged.

I need hardly add that, if π represented merely the ratio of the circumference of a circle to its diameter, the determination of its numerical value would have but slight interest. It is, however, a mere accident that π is defined usually in that way, and it really represents a certain number which would enter into analysis from whatever side the subject was approached.

I recollect a distinguished professor explaining how different would be the ordinary life of a race of beings born, as easily they might be, so that the fundamental processes of arithmetic, algebra and geometry were different from those which seem

* *Principia*, bk. I, section VI, emma XXVIII.

z

to us so evident; but, he added, it is impossible to conceive of a universe in which e and π should not exist.

I have quoted elsewhere an anecdote, which perhaps will bear repetition, that illustrates how little the usual definition of π suggests its properties. De Morgan was explaining to an actuary what was the chance that a certain proportion of some group of people would at the end of a given time be alive; and quoted the actuarial formula, involving π, which, in answer to a question, he explained stood for the ratio of the circumference of a circle to its diameter. His acquaintance, who had so far listened to the explanation with interest, interrupted him and exclaimed, "My dear friend, that must be a delusion; what can a circle have to do with the number of people alive at the end of a given time?" In reality the fact that the ratio of the length of the circumference of a circle to its diameter is the number denoted by π does not afford the best analytical definition of π, and is only one of its properties.

The use of a single symbol to denote this number $3.14159\ldots$ seems to have been introduced about the beginning of the eighteenth century. William Jones * in 1706 represented it by π; a few years later † John Bernoulli denoted it by c; Euler in 1734 used p, and in 1736 used c; Christian Goldback in 1742 used π; and after the publication of Euler's *Analysis* the symbol π was generally employed.

The numerical value of π can be determined by either of two methods with as close an approximation to the truth as is desired.

The first of these methods is geometrical. It consists in calculating the perimeters of polygons inscribed in and circumscribed about a circle, and assuming that the circumference of the circle is intermediate between these perimeters.‡ The

---

* *Synopsis Palmariorum Matheseos*, London, 1706, pp. 243, 263 *et seq.*

† See notes by G. Eneström in the *Bibliotheca Mathematica*, Stockholm, 1889, vol. III, p. 28; *ibid.*, 1890, vol. IV, p. 22.

‡ The history of this method has been written by K. E. I. Selander, *Historik öfver Ludolphska Talet*, Upsala, 1868.

approximation would be closer if the areas and not the perimeters were employed. The second and modern method rests on the determination of converging infinite series for π.

We may say that the π-calculators who used the first method regarded π as equivalent to a geometrical ratio, but those who adopted the modern method treated it as the symbol for a certain number which enters into numerous branches of mathematical analysis.

It may be interesting if I add here a list of some of the approximations to the value of π given by various writers.* This will indicate incidentally those who have studied the subject to the best advantage.

The ancient Egyptians † took 256/81 as the value of π; this is equal to 3·1605 . . .; but the rougher approximation of 3 was used by the Babylonians ‡ and by the Jews.§ It is not unlikely that these numbers were obtained empirically.

We come next to a long roll of Greek mathematicians who attacked the problem. Whether the researches of the members of the Ionian School, the Pythagoreans, Anaxagoras, Hippias, Antipho, and Bryso led to numerical approximations for the value of π is doubtful, and their investigations need not detain us. The quadrature of certain lunes by Hippocrates of Chios is ingenious and correct, but a value of π cannot be thence deduced; and it seems likely that the later members of the Athenian School concentrated their efforts on other questions.

* For the methods used in classical times and the results obtained, see the notices of their authors in M. Cantor's *Geschichte der Mathematik*, Leipzig, vol. I, 1880. For medieval and modern approximations, see the article by A. De Morgan on the Quadrature of the Circle in vol. XIX of the *Penny Cyclopaedia*, London, 1841; with the additions given by B. de Haan in the *Verhandelingen* of Amsterdam, 1858, vol. IV, p. 22: the conclusions were tabulated, corrected, and extended by Dr. J. W. L. Glaisher in the *Messenger of Mathematics*, Cambridge, 1873, vol. II, pp. 119—128; and *ibid.*, 1874, vol. III, pp. 27—46.

† *Ein mathematisches Handbuch der alten Aegypter* (*i.e.* the Rhind papyrus), by A. Eisenlohr, Leipzig, 1877, arts. 100—109, 117, 124.

‡ Oppert, *Journal Asiatique*, August, 1872, and October, 1874.

§ 1 Kings, ch. 7, ver. 23; 2 Chronicles, ch. 4, ver. 2.

It is probable that Euclid,* the illustrious founder of the Alexandrian School, was aware that π was greater than 3 and less than 4, but he did not state the result explicitly.

The mathematical treatment of the subject began with Archimedes, who proved that π is less than $3\frac{1}{7}$ and greater than $3\frac{10}{71}$—that is, it lies between $3\cdot1428\ldots$ and $3\cdot1408\ldots$ He established † this by inscribing in a circle and circumscribing about it regular polygons of 96 sides, then determining by geometry the perimeters of these polygons, and finally assuming that the circumference of the circle was intermediate between these perimeters : this leads to a result from which he deduced the limits given above. This method is equivalent to using the proposition $\sin\theta < \theta < \tan\theta$, where $\theta = \pi/96$: the values of $\sin\theta$ and $\tan\theta$ were deduced by Archimedes from those of $\sin\frac{1}{3}\pi$ and $\tan\frac{1}{3}\pi$ by repeated bisections of the angle. With a polygon of n sides this process gives a value of π correct to at least the integral part of $(2\log n - 1\cdot19)$ places of decimals. The result given by Archimedes is correct to two places of decimals. His analysis leads to the conclusion that the perimeters of these polygons for a circle whose diameter is 4970 feet would lie between 15610 feet and 15620 feet—actually it is about 15613 feet 9 inches.

Apollonius discussed these results, but his criticisms have been lost.

Hero of Alexandria gave ‡ the value 3, but he quoted § the result 22/7 : possibly the former number was intended only for rough approximations.

The only other Greek approximation that I need mention is that given by Ptolemy,‖ who asserted that $\pi = 3°\ 8'\ 30''$. This is equivalent to taking $\pi = 3 + \frac{8}{60} + \frac{30}{3600} = 3\frac{17}{120} = 3\cdot141\dot{6}$.

* These results can be deduced from Euc. IV, 15, and IV, 8 : see also book XII, prop. 16.

† *Archimedis Opera*, Κύκλου μέτρησις, prop. III, ed. Torelli, Oxford, 1792, pp. 205—216; ed. Heiberg, Leipzig, 1880, vol. I, pp. 263—271.

‡ *Mensurae*, ed. Hultsch, Berlin, 1864, p. 188.

§ *Geometria*, ed. Hultsch, Berlin, 1864, pp. 115, 136.

‖ *Almagest*, bk. VI, chap. 7; ed. Halma, vol. I, p. 421.

The Roman surveyors seem to have used 3, or sometimes 4, for rough calculations. For closer approximations they often employed $3\frac{1}{8}$ instead of $3\frac{1}{7}$, since the fractions then introduced are more convenient in duodecimal arithmetic. On the other hand, Gerbert * recommended the use of 22/7.

Before coming to the medieval and modern European mathematicians, it may be convenient to note the results arrived at in India and the East.

Baudhayana † took 49/16 as the value of π.

Arya-Bhata,‡ circ. 530, gave 62832/20000, which is equal to 3·1416. He showed that, if a is the side of a regular polygon of n sides inscribed in a circle of unit diameter, and if b is the side of a regular inscribed polygon of $2n$ sides, then $b^2 = \frac{1}{2} - \frac{1}{2}(1 - a^2)^{\frac{1}{2}}$. From the side of an inscribed hexagon, he found successively the sides of polygons of 12, 24, 48, 96, 192, and 384 sides. The perimeter of the last is given as equal to $\sqrt{9\cdot8694}$, from which his result was obtained by approximation.

Brahmagupta,§ circ. 650, gave $\sqrt{10}$, which is equal to 3·1622 .... He is said to have obtained this value by inscribing in a circle of unit diameter regular polygons of 12, 24, 48, and 96 sides, and calculating successively their perimeters, which he found to be $\sqrt{9\cdot65}$, $\sqrt{9\cdot81}$, $\sqrt{9\cdot86}$, $\sqrt{9\cdot87}$ respectively; and to have assumed that as the number of sides is increased indefinitely the perimeter would approximate to $\sqrt{10}$.

Bhaskara, circ. 1150, gave two approximations. One ‖— possibly copied from Arya-Bhata, but said to have been calculated afresh by Archimedes's method from the perimeters of regular polygons of 384 sides—is 3927/1250, which is equal

---

* Œuvres de Gerbert, ed. Olleris, Clermont, 1867, p. 453.

† The Sulvasutras by G. Thibaut, Asiatic Society of Bengal, 1875, arts. 26—28.

‡ Leçons de calcul d'Aryabhata, by L. Rodet in the Journal Asiatique, 1879, series 7, vol. XIII, pp. 10, 21.

§ Algebra . . . from Brahmegupta and Bhascara, trans. by H. T. Colebrooke, London, 1817, chap. XII, art. 40, p. 308.

‖ Ibid., p. 87.

to 3·1416 : the other * is 754/240, which is equal to 3·1416̇, but it is uncertain whether this was not given only as an approximate value.

Among the Arabs the values 22/7, $\sqrt{10}$, and 62832/20000 were given by Alkarism,† *circ.* 830; and no doubt were derived from Indian sources. He described the first as an approximate value, the second as used by geometricians, and the third as used by astronomers.

In Chinese works the values 3, 22/7, 157/50 are said to occur; probably the last two results were copied from the Arabs. The Japanese ‡ approximations were closer.

Returning to European mathematicians, we have the following successive approximations to the value of π : many of those prior to the eighteenth century having been calculated originally with the view of demonstrating the incorrectness of some alleged quadrature.

Leonardo of Pisa,§ in the thirteenth century, gave for π the value $1440/458\frac{1}{3}$, which is equal to 3·1418 . . . . In the fifteenth century, Purbach ‖ gave or quoted the value 62832/20000, which is equal to 3·1416; Cusa believed that the accurate value was $\frac{3}{4}(\sqrt{3} + \sqrt{6})$, which is equal to 3·1423 . . . ; and, in 1464, Regiomontanus ¶ is said to have given a value equal to 3·14243.

Vieta,** in 1579, showed that π was greater than

* *Algebra . . . from Brahmegupta and Bhascara*, trans. by H. T. Colebroke, London, 1817, chap. XII, art. 40, p. 95.

† *The Algebra of Mohammed ben Musa*, ed. by F. Rosen, London, 1831, pp. 71—72.

‡ On Japanese approximations and the methods used, see P. Harzer, *Transactions of the British Association* for 1905, p. 325.

§ Boncompagni's *Scritti di Leonardo*, vol. II (*Practica Geometriae*), Rome, 1862, p. 90. Leonardo was nicknamed Fibonacci (see page 57).

‖ Appendix to the *De Triangulis* of Regiomontanus, Basle, 1541, p. 131.

¶ In his correspondence with Cardinal Nicholas de Cusa, *De Quadratura Circuli*, Nuremberg, 1533, wherein he proved that the cardinal's result was wrong. I cannot quote the exact reference, but the figures are given by competent writers and I have no doubt are correct.

** *Canon Mathematicus seu ad Triangula*, Paris, 1579, pp. 56, 66 : probably this work was printed for private circulation only ; it is very rare.

$31415926535/10^{10}$, and less than $31415926537/10^{10}$. This was deduced from the perimeters of the inscribed and circumscribed polygons of 6×2^{16} sides, obtained by repeated use of the formula $2 \sin^2 \frac{1}{2}\theta = 1 - \cos\theta$. He also gave * a result equivalent to the formula

$$\frac{2}{\pi} = \frac{\sqrt{2}}{2} \frac{\sqrt{(2 + \sqrt{2})}}{2} \frac{\sqrt{\{2 + \sqrt{(2 + \sqrt{2})}\}}}{2} \dots .$$

The father of Adrian Metius,† in 1585, gave $355/113$, which is equal to $3\cdot14159292\ldots$, and is correct to six places of decimals. This was a curious and lucky guess, for all that he proved was that π was intermediate between $377/120$ and $333/106$, whereon he jumped to the conclusion that he would obtain the true fractional value by taking the mean of the numerators and the mean of the denominators of these fractions.

In 1593 Adrian Romanus ‡ calculated the perimeter of the inscribed regular polygon of $1073,741824$ (*i.e.* 2^{30}) sides, from which he determined the value of π correct to 15 places of decimals.

L. van Ceulen devoted no inconsiderable part of his life to the subject. In 1596 § he gave the result to 20 places of decimals : this was calculated by finding the perimeters of the inscribed and circumscribed regular polygons of 60×2^{33} sides, obtained by the repeated use of a theorem of his discovery equivalent to the formula $1 - \cos A = 2 \sin^2 \frac{1}{2}A$. I possess a finely executed engraving of him of this date, with the result printed round a circle which is below his portrait. He died in 1610, and by his directions the result to 35 places of decimals (which was as far as he had calculated it) was engraved

---

* *Vietae Opera*, ed. Schooten, Leyden, 1646, p. 400.

† *Arithmeticae libri duo et Geometriae*, by A. Metius, Leyden, 1626, pp. 88—89. [Probably issued originally in 1611.]

‡ *Ideae Mathematicae*, Antwerp, 1593 : a rare work, which I have never been able to consult.

§ *Van den Circkel*, Delft, 1596, fol. 14, p. 1 ; or *De Circulo*, Leyden, 1619, p. 3.

on his tombstone * in St. Peter's Church, Leyden. His post-humous arithmetic † contains the result to 32 places; this was obtained by calculating the perimeter of a polygon, the number of whose sides is 2^{62}, *i.e.* 4,611686,018427,387904. Van Ceulen also compiled a table of the perimeters of various regular polygons.

Willebrord Snell,‡ in 1621, obtained from a polygon of 2^{30} sides an approximation to 34 places of decimals. This is less than the numbers given by van Ceulen, but Snell's method was so superior that he obtained his 34 places by the use of a polygon from which van Ceulen had obtained only 14 (or perhaps 16) places. Similarly, Snell obtained from a hexagon an approximation as correct as that for which Archimedes had required a polygon of 96 sides, while from a polygon of 96 sides he determined the value of π correct to seven decimal places instead of the two places obtained by Archimedes. The reason is that Archimedes, having calculated the lengths of the sides of inscribed and circumscribed regular polygons of n sides, assumed that the length of $1/n$th of the perimeter of the circle was intermediate between them; whereas Snell constructed from the sides of these polygons two other lines which gave closer limits for the corresponding arc. His method depends on the theorem $3 \sin \theta / (2 + \cos \theta) < \theta <$ $(2 \sin \frac{1}{3}\theta + \tan \frac{1}{3}\theta)$, by the aid of which a polygon of n sides gives a value of π correct to at least the integral part of $(4 \log n - \cdot 2305)$ places of decimals, which is more than twice the number given by the older rule. Snell's proof of his theorem is incorrect, though the result is true.

Snell also added a table § of the perimeters of all regular

* The inscription is quoted by Prof. de Haan in the *Messenger of Mathematics*, 1874, vol. III, p. 25.

† *De Arithmetische en Geometrische Fondamenten*, Leyden, 1615, p. 163; or p. 144 of the Latin translation by W. Snell, published at Leyden in 1615 under the title *Fundamenta Arithmetica et Geometrica*. This was reissued, together with a Latin translation of the *Van den Circkel*, in 1619, under the title *De Circulo*; in which see pp. 3, 29—32, 92.

‡ *Cyclometricus*, Leyden, 1621, p. 55.

§ It is quoted by Montucla, ed. 1831, p. 70.

inscribed and circumscribed polygons, the number of whose sides is 10×2^n where n is not greater than 19 and not less than 3. Most of these were quoted from van Ceulen, but some were recalculated. This list has proved useful in refuting circle-squarers. A similar list was given by James Gregory.[*]

In 1630 Grienberger,[†] by the aid of Snell's theorem, carried the approximation to 39 places of decimals. He was the last mathematician who adopted the classical method of finding the perimeters of inscribed and circumscribed polygons. Closer approximations serve no useful purpose. Proofs of the theorems used by Snell and other calculators in applying this method were given by Huygens in a work [‡] which may be taken as closing the history of this method.

In 1656 Wallis [§] proved that

$$\frac{\pi}{2} = \frac{2}{1} \cdot \frac{2}{3} \cdot \frac{4}{3} \cdot \frac{4}{5} \cdot \frac{6}{5} \cdot \frac{6}{7} \cdot \frac{8}{7} \cdots,$$

and quoted a proposition given a few years earlier by Viscount Brouncker to the effect that

$$\frac{4}{\pi} = 1 + \frac{1^2}{2} + \frac{3^2}{2} + \frac{5^2}{2} + \cdots,$$

but neither of these theorems was used to any large extent for calculation.

Subsequent calculators have relied on converging infinite series, a method that was hardly practicable prior to the invention of the calculus, though Descartes [‖] had indicated a geometrical process which was equivalent to the use of such

[*] *Vera Circuli et Hyperbolae Quadratura*, prop. 29, quoted by Huygens, *Opera Varia*, Leyden, 1724, p. 447.

[†] *Elementa Trigonometrica*, Rome, 1630, end of preface.

[‡] *De Circula Magnitudine Inventa*, 1654; *Opera Varia*, pp. 351—387. The proofs are given in G. Pirie's *Geometrical Methods of Approximating to the Value* of π, London, 1877, pp. 21—23.

[§] *Arithmetica Infinitorum*, Oxford, 1656, prop. 191. An analysis of the investigation by Wallis was given by Cayley, *Quarterly Journal of Mathematics*, 1889, vol. XXIII, pp. 165—169.

[‖] See Euler's paper in the *Novi Commentarii Academiae Scientiarum* Petrograd, 1763, vol. VIII, pp. 157—168.

a series. The employment of infinite series was proposed by James Gregory,* who established the theorem that

$$\theta = \tan \theta - \tfrac{1}{3} \tan^3 \theta + \tfrac{1}{5} \tan^5 \theta - \ldots,$$

the result being true only if θ lies between $-\tfrac{1}{4}\pi$ and $\tfrac{1}{4}\pi$.

The first mathematician to make use of Gregory's series for obtaining an approximation to the value of π was Abraham Sharp,† who, in 1699, on the suggestion of Halley, determined it to 72 places of decimals (71 correct). He obtained this value by putting $\theta = \tfrac{1}{6}\pi$ in Gregory's series.

Machin,‡ earlier than 1706, gave the result to 100 places (all correct). He calculated it by the formula

$$\tfrac{1}{4}\pi = 4 \tan^{-1} \tfrac{1}{5} - \tan^{-1} \tfrac{1}{239}.$$

De Lagny,§ in 1719, gave the result to 127 places of decimals (112 correct), calculating it by putting $\theta = \tfrac{1}{6}\pi$ in Gregory's series.

Hutton,‖ in 1776, and Euler,¶ in 1779, suggested the use of the formula $\tfrac{1}{4}\pi = \tan^{-1}\tfrac{1}{2} + \tan^{-1}\tfrac{1}{3}$ or $\tfrac{1}{4}\pi = 5 \tan^{-1}\tfrac{1}{7} + 2 \tan^{-1}\tfrac{3}{79}$, but neither carried the approximation as far as had been done previously.

Vega, in 1789,** gave the value of π to 143 places of decimals (126 correct); and, in 1794,†† to 140 places (136 correct).

* See the letter to Collins, dated Feb. 15, 1671, printed in the *Commercium Epistolicum*, London, 1712, p. 25, and in the Macclesfield Collection, *Correspondence of Scientific Men of the Seventeenth Century*, Oxford, 1841, vol. II, p. 216.

† See *Life of A. Sharp* by W. Cudworth, London, 1889, p. 170. Sharp's work is given in one of the preliminary discourses (pp. 53 *et seq.*) prefixed to H. Sherwin's *Mathematical Tables*. The tables were issued at London in 1705: probably the discourses were issued at the same time, though the earliest copies I have seen were printed in 1717.

‡ W. Jones's *Synopsis Palmariorum*, London, 1706, p. 243; and Maseres, *Scriptores Logarithmici*, London, 1796, vol. III, pp. vii—ix, 155—164.

§ *Histoire de l'Académie* for 1719, Paris, 1721, p. 144.

‖ *Philosophical Transactions*, 1776, vol. LXVI, pp. 476—492.

¶ *Nova Acta Academiae Scientiarum Petropolitanae* for 1793, Petrograd, 1798, vol. XI, pp. 133—149: the memoir was read in 1779.

** *Nova Acta Academiae Scientiarum Petropolitanae* for 1790, Petrograd, 1795, vol. IX, p. 41.

†† *Thesaurus Logarithmorum* (*logarithmisch-trigonometrischer Tafeln*), Leipzig, 1794, p. 633.

Towards the end of the eighteenth century F. X. von Zach saw in the Radcliffe Library, Oxford, a manuscript by an unknown author which gives the value of π to 154 places of decimals (152 correct).

In 1837, the result of a calculation of π to 154 places of decimals (152 correct) was published.*

In 1841 Rutherford † calculated it to 208 places of decimals (152 correct), using the formula $\frac{1}{4}\pi = 4 \tan^{-1} \frac{1}{5} - \tan^{-1} \frac{1}{70} + \tan^{-1} \frac{1}{99}$.

In 1844 Dase ‡ calculated it to 205 places of decimals (200 correct), using the formula $\frac{1}{4}\pi = \tan^{-1} \frac{1}{2} + \tan^{-1} \frac{1}{5} + \tan^{-1} \frac{1}{8}$.

In 1847 Clausen § carried the approximation to 250 places of decimals (248 correct), calculating it independently by the formulae $\frac{1}{4}\pi = 2 \tan^{-1} \frac{1}{3} + \tan^{-1} \frac{1}{7}$ and $\frac{1}{4}\pi = 4 \tan^{-1} \frac{1}{5} - \tan^{-1} \frac{1}{239}$.

In 1853 Rutherford ‖ carried his former approximation to 440 places of decimals (all correct), and William Shanks prolonged the approximation to 530 places. In the same year Shanks published an approximation to 607 places : ¶ and in 1873 he carried the approximation to 707 places of decimals.** These were calculated from Machin's formula.

In 1853 Richter, presumably in ignorance of what had been done in England, found the value of π to 333 places †† of decimals (330 correct); in 1854 he carried the approximation to 400 places; ‡‡ and in 1855 carried it to 500 places.§§

Of the series and formulae by which these approximations

* J. F. Callet's *Tables, etc., Précis Élémentaire*, Paris, tirage, 1837. Tirage, 1894, p. 96.

† *Philosophical Transactions*, 1841, p. 283.

‡ *Crelle's Journal*, 1844, vol. XXVII, p. 198.

§ Schumacher, *Astronomische Nachrichten*, vol. XXV, col. 207.

‖ *Proceedings of the Royal Society*, Jan. 20, 1853, vol. VI, pp. 273—275.

¶ *Contributions to Mathematics*, W. Shanks, London, 1853, pp. 86—87.

** *Proceedings of the Royal Society*, 1872–3, vol. XXI, p. 318; 1873–4, vol. XXII, p. 45.

†† *Grünert's Archiv*, vol. XXI, p. 119.

‡‡ *Ibid.*, vol. XXIII, p. 476 : the approximation given in vol. XXII, p. 473, is correct only to 330 places.

§§ *Ibid.*, vol. XXV, p. 472; and *Elbinger Anzeigen*, No. 85.

have been calculated, those used by Machin and Dase are perhaps the easiest to employ. Other series which converge rapidly are the following :

$$\frac{\pi}{6} = \frac{1}{2} + \frac{1}{2} \cdot \frac{1}{3 \cdot 2^3} + \frac{1 \cdot 3}{2 \cdot 4} \cdot \frac{1}{5 \cdot 2^5} + \cdots,$$

and

$$\frac{\pi}{4} = 22 \tan^{-1} \frac{1}{28} + 2 \tan^{-1} \frac{1}{443} - 5 \tan^{-1} \frac{1}{1393} - 10 \tan^{-1} \frac{1}{11018};$$

the latter of these is due to Mr. Escott.*

As to those writers who believe that they have squared the circle, their number is legion and, in most cases, their ignorance profound, but their attempts are not worth discussing here. "Only prove to me that it is impossible," said one of them, "and I will set about it immediately"; and doubtless the statement that the problem is insoluble has attracted much attention to it.

Among the geometrical ways of approximating to the truth the following is one of the simplest. Inscribe in the given circle a square, and to three times the diameter of the circle add a fifth of a side of the square; the result will differ from the circumference of the circle by less than one-seventeen-thousandth part of it.

An approximate value of π has been obtained experimentally by the theory of probability. On a plane a number of equi-distant parallel straight lines, distance apart a, are ruled; and a stick of length l, which is less than a, is dropped on the plane. The probability that it will fall so as to lie across one of the lines is $2l/\pi a$. If the experiment is repeated many hundreds of times, the ratio of the number of favourable cases to the whole number of experiments will be very nearly equal to this fraction: hence the value of π can be found. In 1855 Mr. A. Smith † of Aberdeen made 3204 trials, and deduced $\pi = 3 \cdot 1553$. A pupil of Prof. De Morgan,† from 600 trials,

* For a comparison of about thirty such formulae, see D. H. Lehmer, *American Mathematical Monthly*, 1938, vol. XLV, pp. 657–664.

† A. De Morgan, *Budget of Paradoxes*, London, 1872, pp. 171, 172.

deduced $\pi = 3\cdot137$.   In 1864 Captain Fox * made 1120 trails with some additional precautions, and obtained as the mean value $\pi = 3\cdot1419$.

Other similar methods of approximating to the value of π have been indicated.   For instance, it is known that if two numbers are written down at random, the probability that they will be prime to each other is $6/\pi^2$.   Thus, in one case † where each of 50 students wrote down 5 pairs of numbers at random, 154 of the pairs were found to consist of numbers prime to each other.   This gives $6/\pi^2 = 154/250$, from which we get $\pi = 3\cdot12$.

* *Messenger of Mathematics*, Cambridge, 1873, vol. II, pp. 113, 114.

† Note on π by R. Chartres, *Philosophical Magazine*, London, series 6, vol. XXXIX, March, 1904, p. 315.

CHAPTER XIII

CALCULATING PRODIGIES

AT rare intervals there have appeared lads who possess extraordinary powers of mental calculation.* In a few seconds they gave the answers to questions connected with the multiplication of numbers and the extraction of roots of numbers, which an expert mathematician could obtain only in a longer time and with the aid of pen and paper. Nor were their powers always limited to such simple problems. More difficult questions, dealing for instance with factors, compound interest, annuities, the civil and ecclesiastical calendars, and the solution of equations, were solved by some of them with facility as soon as the meaning of what was wanted had been grasped. In most cases these lads were illiterate, and usually their rules of working were of their own invention.

The performances were so remarkable that some observers held that these prodigies possessed powers differing in kind from those of their contemporaries. For such a view there is no foundation. Any lad with an excellent memory and a natural turn for arithmetic can, if he continuously gives his undivided attention to the consideration of numbers, and indulges in constant practice, attain great proficiency in mental arithmetic, and of course the performances of those that are specially gifted are exceptionally astonishing.

In this chapter I propose to describe briefly the doings of

* Most of the facts about calculating prodigies have been collected by E. W. Scripture, *American Journal of Psychology*, 1891, vol. IV, pp. 1—59; by F. D. Mitchell, *ibid.*, 1907, vol. XVIII, pp. 61—143; and G. E. Müller, *Zur Analyse der Gedächtnistätigkeit und des Vorstellungsverlaufes*, Leipzig, 1911. I have used these papers freely, and in some cases where authorities are quoted of which I have no first-hand information have relied exclusively on them. These articles should be consulted for bibliographical notes on the numerous original authorities.

the more famous calculating prodigies. It will be seen that their performances were of much the same general character, though carried to different extents; hence in the later cases it will be enough to indicate briefly peculiarities of the particular calculators.

I confine myself to self-taught calculators, and thus exclude the consideration of a few public performers who by practice, arithmetical devices, and the tricks of the showman have simulated like powers. I also concern myself only with those who showed the power in youth. As far as I know, the only self-taught mathematician of advanced years whom I thus exclude is John Wallis, 1616—1703, the Savilian Professor at Oxford, who in middle-life developed, for his own amusement, his powers in mental arithmetic. As an illustration of his achievements, I note that on 22 December, 1669, he, when in bed, occupied himself in finding (mentally) the integral part of the square root of 3×10^{40}; and several hours afterwards wrote down the result from memory. This fact having attracted notice, two months later he was challenged to extract the square root of a number of fifty-three digits; this he performed mentally, and a month later he dictated the answer, which he had not meantime committed to writing. Such efforts of calculation and memory are typical of calculating prodigies.

One of the earliest of these prodigies of whom we have records was *Jedediah Buxton*, who was born in or about 1707 at Elmton, Derbyshire. Although a son of the village school-master, his education was neglected, and he never learnt to write or cipher. With the exception of his power of dealing with large numbers, his mental faculties were of a low order : he had no ambition, and remained throughout his life a farm labourer, nor did his exceptional skill with figures bring him any material advantage other than that of occasionally receiving small sums of money from those who induced him to exhibit his peculiar gift. He does not seem to have given public exhibitions. He died in 1772.

He had no recollection as to when or how he was first attracted by mental calculations, and of his performances in early life we have no reliable details. Mere numbers, however, seem always to have had a strange fascination for him. If the size of an object was stated, he began at once to compute how many inches or hair-breadths it contained; if a period of time was mentioned, he calculated the number of minutes in it; if he heard a sermon, he thought only of the number of words or syllables in it. No doubt his powers in these matters increased by incessant practice, but his ideas were childish, and do not seem to have gone beyond pride in being able to state accurately the results of such calculations. He was slow-witted, and took far longer to answer arithmetical questions than most of these prodigies. The only practical accomplishment to which his powers led him was the ability to estimate by inspection the acreage of a field of irregular shape.

His fame gradually spread through Derbyshire. Among many questions put to him by local visitors were the following, which fairly indicate his powers when a young man: How many acres are there in a rectangular field 351 yards long and 261 wide? answered in 11 minutes. How many cubic yards of earth must be removed in order to make a pond 426 feet long, 263 feet wide, and $2\frac{1}{2}$ feet deep? answered in 15 minutes. If sound travels 1,142 feet in one second, how long will it take to travel 5 miles? answered in 15 minutes. Such questions involve no difficulties of principle.

Here are a few of the harder problems solved by Buxton when his powers were fully developed. He calculated to what sum a farthing would amount if doubled 140 times: the answer is a number of pounds sterling which requires thirty-nine digits to represent it, with 2s. 8d. over. He was then asked to multiply this number of thirty-nine digits by itself: to this he gave the answer two and a half months later, and he said he had carried on the calculation at intervals during that period. In 1751 he calculated how many cubic inches there are in a right-angled block of stone 23,145,789 yards long, 5,642,732 yards wide, and 54,965 yards thick; how many grains of corn would be required to fill a cube whose volume is 202,680,000,360 cubic miles; and how many hairs one inch long would be required to fill the same space—the dimensions of a grain and a hair being given. These problems involve high numbers, but are not intrinsically difficult, though they could not be solved mentally unless the calculator had a phenomenally good memory. In each case he gave the correct answer, though only after considerable effort. In 1753 he was asked to give the dimensions of a cubical cornbin which holds exactly one quarter of malt. He recognized that to answer this required a process equivalent to the extraction of a cube root, which was a novel idea to him, but in an hour he said that the edge of the cube would be between $25\frac{1}{2}$ and 26 inches, which is correct: it has been suggested that he got this answer by trying various numbers.

Accounts of his performances were published, and his reputation reached London, which he visited in 1754. During his stay there he was examined by various members of the Royal Society, who were satisfied as to the genuineness of his performances. Some of his acquaintances took him to Drury Lane Theatre to see Garrick, being curious to see how a play would impress his imagination. He was entirely unaffected by the scene, but on coming out informed his hosts of the exact number of words uttered by the various actors, and of the number of steps taken by others in their dances.

It was only in rare cases that he was able to explain his methods of work, but enough is known of them to enable us to say that they were clumsy. He described the process by which he arrived at the product of 456 and 378: shortly it was as follows :—If we denote the former of these numbers by a, he proceeded first to find $5a =$ (say) b; then to find $20b =$ (say) c; and then to find $3c =$ (say) d. He next formed $15b =$ (say) e, which he added to d. Lastly he formed $3a$, which, added to the sum last obtained, gave the result. This is

A A

equivalent to saying that he used the multiplier 378 in the form $(5 \times 20 \times 3) + (5 \times 15) + 3$. Mitchell suggests that this may mean that Buxton counted by multiples of 60 and of 15, and thus reduced the multiplication to addition. It may be so, for it is difficult to suppose that he did not realize that successive multiplications by 5 and 20 are equivalent to a multiplication by 100, of which the result can be at once obtained. Of billions, trillions, etc., he had never heard, and in order to represent the high numbers required in some of the questions proposed to him, he invented a notation of his own, calling 10^{18} a tribe and 10^{36} a cramp.

As in the case of all these calculators, his memory was exceptionally good, and in time he got to know a large number of facts (such as the products of certain constantly recurring numbers, the number of minutes in a year, and the number of hair-breadths in a mile), which greatly facilitated his calculations. A curious and perhaps unique feature in his case was that he could stop in the middle of a piece of mental calculation, take up other subjects, and after an interval, sometimes of weeks, could resume the consideration of the problem. He could answer simple questions when two or more were proposed simultaneously.

Another eighteenth-century prodigy was *Thomas Fuller*, a negro, born in 1710 in Africa. He was captured there in 1724, and exported as a slave to Virginia, U.S.A., where he lived till his death in 1790. Like Buxton, Fuller never learnt to read or write, and his abilities were confined to mental arithmetic. He could multiply together two numbers, if each contained not more than nine digits, could state the number of seconds in a given period of time, the number of grains of corn in a given mass, and so on—in short, answer the stock problems commonly proposed to these prodigies, as long as they involved only multiplications and the solutions of problems by rule of three. Although more rapid than Buxton, he was a slow worker as compared with some of those whose doings are described below.

I mention next the case of two mathematicians of note who showed similar aptitude in early years. The first of these was *André Marie Ampère*, 1775—1836, who, when a child some four years old, was accustomed to perform long mental calculations, which he effected by means of rules learnt from playing with arrangements of pebbles. But though always expert at mental arithmetic, and endowed with a phenomenal memory for figures, he did not specially cultivate this arithmetical power. It is more difficult to say whether *Carl Friedrich Gauss*, 1777—1855, should be reckoned among these calculating prodigies. He had, when three years old, taught himself some arithmetical processes, and astonished his father by correcting him in his calculations of certain payments for overtime; perhaps, however, this is only evidence of the early age at which his consummate abilities began to develop. Another remarkable case is that of *Richard Whately*, 1787—1863, afterwards Archbishop of Dublin. When he was about five or six years old he showed considerable skill in mental arithmetic : it disappeared in about three years. " I soon," said he, " got to do the most difficult sums, always in my head, for I knew nothing of figures beyond numeration, nor had I any names for the different processes I employed. But I believe my sums were chiefly in multiplication, division, and the rule of three. . . . I did these sums much quicker than anyone could upon paper, and I never remember committing the smallest error. I was engaged either in calculating or in castle-building . . . morning, noon, and night. . . . When I went to school, at which time the passion was worn off, I was a perfect dunce at ciphering, and so have continued ever since." The archbishop's arithmetical powers were, however, greater in after-life than he here allows.

The performances of *Zerah Colburn* in London, in 1812, were more remarkable. Colburn,* born in 1804, at Cabut, Vermont, U.S.A., was the son of a small farmer. While still

---

* To the authorities mentioned by E. W. Scripture and F. D. Mitchel should be added *The Annual Register*, London, 1812, pp. 507 *et seq.*

less than six years old he showed extraordinary powers of mental calculation, which were displayed in a tour in America. Two years later he was brought to England, where he was repeatedly examined by competent observers. He could instantly give the product of two numbers each of four digits, but hesitated if both numbers exceeded 10,000. Among questions asked him at this time were to raise 8 to the 16th power; in a few seconds he gave the answer 281,474,976,710,656, which is correct. He was next asked to raise the numbers 2, 3, ... 9 to the 10th power : and he gave the answers so rapidly that the gentleman who was taking them down was obliged to ask him to repeat them more slowly; but he worked less quickly when asked to raise numbers of two digits like 37 or 59 to high powers. He gave instantaneously the square roots and cube roots (when they were integers) of high numbers, *e.g.* the square root of 106,929 and the cube root of 268,336,125; such integral roots can, however, be obtained easily by various methods. More remarkable are his answers to questions on the factors of numbers. Asked for the factors of 247,483, he replied 941 and 263; asked for the factors of 171,395, he gave 5, 7, 59, and 83; asked for the factors of 36,083, he said there were none. He, however, found it difficult to answer questions about the factors of numbers higher than 1,000,000. His power of factorizing high numbers was exceptional, and depended largely on the method of two-digit terminals described below. Like all these public performers, he had to face buffoons who tried to make fun of him, but he was generally equal to them. Asked on one such occasion how many black beans were required to make three white ones, he is said to have at once replied, " Three, if you skin them "—this, however, has much the appearance of a pre-arranged show.

It was clear to observers that the child operated by certain rules, and during his calculations his lips moved as if he was expressing the process in words. Of his honesty there seems to have been no doubt. In a few cases he was able to explain the method of operation. Asked for the square of 4,395, he hesitated, but on the question being repeated, he gave the correct answer—namely, 19,316,025. Questioned as to the cause of his hesitation, he said he did not like to multiply four figures by four figures, but said he, " I found out another way; I multiplied 293 by 293 and then multiplied this product twice by the number 15." On another occasion when asked for the product of 21,734 by 543, he immediately replied 11,801,562; and on being questioned explained that he had arrived at this by multiplying 65,202 by 181. These remarks suggest that whenever convenient he factorized the numbers with which he was dealing.

In 1814 he was taken to Paris, but amid the political turmoil of the time his exhibitions fell flat. His English and American friends, however, raised money for his education, and he was sent in succession to the Lycée Napoleon in Paris and Westminster School in London. With education his calculating powers fell off, and he lost the frankness which when a boy had charmed observers. His subsequent career was diversified and not altogether successful. He commenced with the stage, then tried schoolmastering, then became an itinerant preacher in America, and finally a " professor " of languages. He wrote his own biography, which contains an account of the methods he used. He died in 1840.

Contemporary with Colburn we find another instance of a self-taught boy, *George Parker Bidder*, who possessed quite exceptional powers of this kind. He is perhaps the most interesting of these prodigies, because he subsequently received a liberal education, retained his calculating powers, and in later life analysed and explained the methods he had invented and used.

Bidder was born in 1806 at Moreton Hampstead, Devonshire, where his father was a stone-mason. At the age of six he was taught to count up to 100, but though sent to the village school, learnt little there, and at the beginning of his career was ignorant of the meaning of arithmetical terms and of numerical symbols. Equipped solely with this knowledge of counting, he taught himself the results of addition, subtraction, and multiplication of numbers (less than 100) by arranging and rearranging marbles, buttons, and shot in patterns. In after-life he attached great importance to such concrete representations, and believed that his arithmetical powers were strengthened by the fact that at that time he knew nothing about the symbols for numbers. When seven years old he heard a dispute between two of his neighbours about the price of something which was being sold by the pound, and to their astonishment remarked that they were both wrong, mentioning the correct price. After this exhibition the villagers delighted in trying to pose him with arithmetical problems.

His reputation increased and, before he was nine years old, his father found it profitable to take him about the country to exhibit his powers. A couple of distinguished Cambridge graduates (Thomas Jephson, then tutor of St. John's, and John Herschel) saw him in 1817, and were so impressed by his general intelligence that they raised a fund for his education, and induced his father to give up the rôle of showman; but after a few months Bidder senior repented of his abandonment of money so easily earned, insisted on his son's return, and began again to make an exhibition of the boy's powers. In 1818, in the course of a tour, young Bidder was pitted against Colburn, and on the whole proved the abler calculator. Finally the father and son came to Edinburgh, where some members of that University intervened and persuaded his father to leave the lad in their care to be educated. Bidder remained with them, and in due course graduated at Edinburgh, shortly afterwards entering the profession of civil engineering, in which he rose to high distinction. He died in 1878.

With practice Bidder's powers steadily developed. His earlier performances seem to have been of the same type as those of Buxton and Colburn which have been already

described. In addition to answering questions on products of
numbers and the number of specified units in given quantities,
he was, after 1819, ready in finding square roots, cube roots,
etc., of high numbers, it being assumed that the root is an
integer, and later explained his method, which is easy of
application : this method is the same as that used by Colburn.
By this time he was able also to give immediate solutions of
easy problems on compound interest and annuities which
seemed to his contemporaries the most astonishing of all his
feats.   In factorizing numbers he was less successful than
Colburn, and was generally unable to deal at sight with numbers higher than 10,000. As in the case of Colburn, attempts
to be witty at his expense were often made, but he could hold
his own. Asked at one of his performances in London in 1818
how many bulls' tails were wanted to reach to the moon, he
immediately answered one, if it is long enough.

Here are some typical questions put to and answered by
him in his exhibitions during the years 1815—1819 : they are
taken from authenticated lists which comprise some hundreds
of such problems : few, if any, are inherently difficult. His
rapidity of work was remarkable, but the time limits given
were taken by unskilled observers, and can be regarded as only
approximately correct. Of course, all the calculations were
mental without the aid of books, pencil, or paper. In 1815,
being then nine years old, he was asked : If the moon be distant
from the earth 123,256 miles, and sound travels at the rate of
4 miles a minute, how long would it be before the inhabitants
of the moon could hear of the battle of Waterloo ? answer,
21 days 9 hours 34 minutes, given in less than one minute.
In 1816, being then ten years old, just learning to write, but
unable to form figures, he answered questions such as the
following : What is the interest on £11,111 for 11,111 days at
5 per cent. a year ? answer, £16,911 11s., given in one minute.
How many hogsheads of cider can be made from a million of
apples, if 30 apples make one quart ? answer, 132 hogsheads
17 gallons 1 quart and 10 apples over, given in 35 seconds

If a coach-wheel is 5 feet 10 inches in circumference, how many times will it revolve in running 800,000,000 miles? answer, 724,114,285,704 times and 20 inches remaining, given in 50 seconds. What is the square root of 119,550,669,121? answer 345,761, given in 30 seconds. In 1817, being then eleven years old, he was asked: How long would it take to fill a reservoir whose volume is one cubic mile if there flowed into it from a river 120 gallons of water a minute? answered in 2 minutes. Assuming that light travels from the sun to the earth in 8 minutes, and that the sun is 98,000,000 miles off, if light takes 6 years 4 months travelling from the nearest fixed star to the earth, what is the distance of that star, reckoning 365 days 6 hours to each year and 28 days to each month?— asked by Sir William Herschel: answer, 40,633,740,000,000 miles. In 1818, at one of his performances, he was asked: If the pendulum of a clock vibrates the distance of $9\frac{3}{4}$ inches in a second of time, how many inches will it vibrate in 7 years 14 days 2 hours 1 minute 56 seconds, each year containing 365 days 5 hours 48 minutes 55 seconds? answer, $2,165,625,744\frac{3}{4}$ inches, given in less than a minute. If I have 42 watches for sale and I sell the first for a farthing, and double the price for every succeeding watch I sell, what will be the price of the last watch? answer, £2,290,649,224 10s. 8d. If the diameter of a penny piece is $1\frac{3}{8}$ inches, and if the world is girdled with a ring of pence put side by side, what is their value sterling, supposing the distance to be 360 degrees, and a degree to contain 69·5 miles? answer, £4,803,340, given in one minute. Find two numbers whose difference is 12 and whose product, multiplied by their sum, is equal to 14,560? answer, 14 and 26. In 1819, when fourteen years old, he was asked: Find a number whose cube less 19 multiplied by its cube shall be equal to the cube of 6: answer, 3, given instantly. What will it cost to make a road for 21 miles 5 furlongs 37 poles 4 yards, at the rate of £123 14s. 6d. a mile? answer, £2,688 13s. $9\frac{3}{4}d$., given in 2 minutes. If you are now 14 years old and you live 50 years longer and spend half-a-crown a day, how many farthings will you spend in your life? answer, 2,805,120, given in 15 seconds. Mr. Moor contracted to illuminate the city of London with 22,965,321 lamps; the expense of trimming and lighting was 7 farthings a lamp, the oil consumed was ⅔ths of a pint for every three lamps, and the oil cost 3s. 7½d. a gallon; he gained 16½ per cent. on his outlay : how many gallons of oil were consumed, what was the cost to him, and what was the amount of the contract? answer, he used 212,641 gallons of oil, the cost was £205,996 16s. 1¾d., and the amount of the contract was £239,986 13s. 2d.

It should be noted that Bidder did not visualize a number like 984 in symbols, but thought of it in a concrete way as so many units which could be arranged in 24 groups of 41 each. It should also be observed that he, like Inaudi, whom I mention later, relied largely on the auditory sense to enable him to recollect numbers. "For my own part," he wrote, in later life, "though much accustomed to see sums and quantities expressed by the usual symbols, yet if I endeavour to get any number of figures that are represented on paper fixed in my memory, it takes me a much longer time and a very great deal more exertion than when they are expressed or enumerated verbally." For instance, suppose a question put to find the product of two numbers each of nine digits, if they were "read to me, I should not require this to be done more than once; but if they were represented in the usual way, and put into my hands, it would probably take me four times to peruse them before it would be in my power to repeat them, and after all they would not be impressed so vividly on my imagination."

Bidder retained his power of rapid mental calculation to the end of his life, and as a constant parliamentary witness in matters connected with engineering it proved a valuable accomplishment. Just before his death an illustration of his powers was given to a friend who, talking of then recent discoveries, remarked that if 36,918 waves of red light which only occupy one inch are required to give the impression of red, and if light travels at 190,000 miles a second, how immense must be the number of waves which must strike the eye in one second to give the impression of red. " You need not work it out," said Bidder; " the number will be 444,433,651,200,000."

Other members of the Bidder family have also shown exceptional powers of a similar kind as well as extraordinary memories. Of Bidder's elder brothers, one became an actuary, and on his books being burnt in a fire, he rewrote them in six months from memory, but, it is said, died of consequent brain fever; another was a Plymouth Brother, and knew the whole Bible by heart, being able to give chapter and verse for any text quoted. Bidder's eldest son, a lawyer of eminence, was able to multiply together two numbers each of fifteen digits. Neither in accuracy nor rapidity was he equal to his father, but, then, he never steadily and continuously devoted himself to developing his abilities in this direction. He remarked that in his mental arithmetic, he worked with pictures of the figures, and said, " If I perform a sum mentally it always proceeds in a visible form in my mind; indeed I can conceive no other way possible of doing mental arithmetic " : this, it will be noticed, is opposed to his father's method. Two of his children, one son and one daughter, representing a third generation, inherited analogous powers.

I mention next the names of *Henri Mondeux*, and *Vito Mangiamele*. Both were born in 1826 in humble circumstances, were shepherds, and became when children noticeable for feats in calculation which deservedly procured for them local fame. In 1839 and 1840 respectively they were brought to Paris, where their powers were displayed in public, and tested by Arago, Cauchy, and others. Mondeux's performances were the more striking. One question put to him was to solve the equation $x^3 + 84 = 37x$: to this he at once gave the answer 3 and 4, but did not detect the third root, namely, $- 7$. Another question asked was to find solutions of the indeterminate equation $x^2 - y^2 = 133$: to this he replied immediately 66 and 67; asked for a simpler solution he said after an instant 6 and 13. I do not, however, propose to discuss their feats in detail, for there was at least a suspicion that these lads were not frank, and that those who were exploiting them had taught them rules which enabled them to simulate powers they did not really possess. Finally both returned to farm work, and ceased to interest the scientific world. If Mondeux was self-taught, we must credit him with a discovery of some algebraic theorems which would entitle him to rank as a mathematical genius, but in that case it is inconceivable that he never did anything more, and that his powers appeared to be limited to the particular problems solved by him.

Johann Martin Zacharias Dase, whom I next mention, is a far more interesting example of these calculating prodigies. Dase was born in 1824 at Hamburg. He had a fair education, and was afforded every opportunity to develop his powers, but save in matters connected with reckoning and numbers he made little progress, and struck all observers as dull. Of geometry and any language but German he remained ignorant to the end of his days. He was trustworthy, and filled various small official posts in Germany. He gave exhibitions of his calculating powers in Germany, Austria, and England. He died in 1861.

When exhibiting in Vienna in 1840, he made the acquaintance of Strasznicky, who urged him to apply his powers to scientific purposes. This Dase gladly agreed to do, and so became acquainted with Gauss, Schumacher, Petersen, and Encke. To his contributions to science I allude later. In mental arithmetic the only problems to which I find allusions are straightforward examples like the following: Multiply 79,532,853 by 93,758,479: asked by Schumacher, answered in 54 seconds. In answer to a similar request to find the product of two numbers each of twenty digits, he took 6 minutes; to find the product of two numbers each of forty digits, he took

40 minutes; to find the product of two numbers each of a hundred digits, he took 8 hours 45 minutes. Gauss thought that perhaps on paper the last of these problems could be solved in half this time by a skilled computator. Dase once extracted the square root of a number of a hundred digits in 52 minutes. These feats far surpass all other records of the kind, the only calculations comparable to them being Buxton's squaring of a number of thirty-nine digits, and Wallis's extraction of the square root of a number of fifty-three digits. Dase's mental work, however, was not always accurate, and once (in 1845) he gave incorrect answers to every question put to him, but on that occasion he had a headache, and there is nothing astonishing in his failure.

Like all these calculating prodigies, he had a wonderful memory, and an hour or two after a performance could repeat all the numbers mentioned in it. He had also the peculiar gift of being able after a single glance to state the number (up to about 30) of sheep in a flock, of books in a case, and so on; and of visualizing and recollecting a large number of objects. For instance, after a second's look at some dominoes he gave the sum (117) of their points; asked how many letters were in a certain line of print chosen at random in a quarto page, he instantly gave the correct number (63); shown twelve digits, he had in half a second memorized them and their positions so as to be able to name instantly the particular digit occupying any assigned place. It is to be regretted that we do not know more of these performances. Those who are acquainted with the delightful autobiography of Robert-Houdin will recollect how he cultivated a similar power, and how valuable he found it in the exercise of his art.

Dase's calculations, when also allowed the use of paper and pencil, were almost incredibly rapid, and invariably accurate. When he was sixteen years old Strasznicky taught him the use of the familiar formula $\pi/4 = \tan^{-1}\left(\frac{1}{2}\right) + \tan^{-1}\left(\frac{1}{5}\right) + \tan^{-1}\left(\frac{1}{8}\right)$, and asked him thence to calculate π. In two months he carried the approximation to 205 places of decimals, of which 200 are correct.* Dase's next achievement was to calculate the natural logarithms of the first 1,005,000 numbers to 7 places of decimals; he did this in his off-time from 1844 to 1847, when occupied by the Prussian survey. During the next two years he compiled in his spare time a hyperbolic table which was published by the Austrian Government in 1857. Later he offered to makes tables of the factors of all numbers from 7,000,000 to 10,000,000, and, on the recommendation of Gauss, the Hamburg Academy of Sciences agreed to assist him so that he might have leisure for the purpose, but he lived only long enough to finish about half the work.

Truman Henry Safford, born in 1836 at Royalton, Vermont, U.S.A., was another calculating prodigy. He was of a somewhat different type, for he received a good education, graduated in due course at Harvard, and ultimately took up astronomy, in which subject he held a professional post. I gather that though always a rapid calculator, he gradually lost the exceptional powers shown in his youth. He died in 1901.

Safford never exhibited his calculating powers in public, and I know of them only through the accounts quoted by Scripture and Mitchell, but they seem to have been typical of these calculators. In 1842, he amused and astonished his family by mental calculations. In 1846, when ten years old, he was examined, and here are some of the questions then put to him : Extract the cube root of a certain number of seven digits; answered instantly. What number is that which being divided by the product of its digits, the quotient is three, and if 18 be added the digits will be inverted? answer 24, given in about a minute. What is the surface of a regular pyramid whose slant height is 17 feet, and the base a pentagon of which each side is 33·5 feet? answer 3354·5558 square feet, given in two minutes. Asked to square a number of eighteen digits, he gave the answer in a minute or less, but the question was made the more easy as the number consisted of the digits

* The result was published in *Crelle's Journal*, 1844, vol. XXVII, p. 198 : on closer approximations and easier formulae, see Chapter XII.

365 repeated six times. Like Colburn, he factorized high numbers with ease. In such examples his processes were empirical; he selected (he could not tell how) likely factors and tested the matter in a few seconds by actual division.

More recently there have been four calculators of some note : *Ugo Zamebone*, an Italian, born in 1867 ; *Pericles Diamandi*, a Greek, born in 1868 ; *Carl Rückle*, a German ; and *Jacques Inaudi*, born in 1867. The three first mentioned were of the normal type, and I do not propose to describe their performances, but Inaudi's performances merit a fuller treatment.

Jacques Inaudi * was born in 1867 at Onorato in Italy. He was employed in early years as a shepherd, and spent the long idle hours in which he had no active duties in pondering on numbers, but used for them no concrete representations such as pebbles. His calculating powers first attracted notice about 1873. Shortly afterwards his elder brother sought his fortune as an organ-grinder in Provence, and young Inaudi, accompanying him, came into a wider world, and earned a few coppers for himself by street exhibitions of his powers. His ability was exploited by showmen, and thus in 1880 he visited Paris, where he gave exhibitions : in these he impressed all observers as being modest, frank, and straightforward. He was then ignorant of reading and writing : these arts he subsequently acquired.

His earlier performances were not specially remarkable as compared with those of similar calculating prodigies, but with continual practice he improved. Thus at Lyons in 1873 he could multiply together almost instantaneously two numbers of three digits. In 1874 he was able to multiply a number of six digits by another number of six digits. Nine years later he could work rapidly with numbers of nine or ten digits. Still later, in Paris, asked by Darboux to cube 27, he gave the answer in 10 seconds. In 13 seconds he calculated how many

* See Charcot and Darboux, *Mémoires de l'Institut, Comptes Rendus*, 1892, vol. cxiv, pp. 275, 528, 578 ; and Binet, *Révue des deux Mondes*, 1892, vol. cxi, pp. 905—924.

seconds are contained in 18 years 7 months 21 days 3 hours :
and he gave immediately the square root of one-sixth of the
difference between the square of 4,801 and unity. He also
calculated with ease the amount of wheat due according to
the traditional story to Sessa, who, for inventing chess, was
to receive 1 grain on the first cell of a chess-board, 2 on the
second, 4 on the third, and so on in geometrical progression.

He could find the integral roots of equations and integral
solutions of problems, but proceeded only by trial and error.
His most remarkable feat was the expression of numbers less
than 10^5 in the form of a sum of four squares, which he could
usually do in a minute or two; this power was peculiar to him.
Such problems were repeatedly solved at private performances, but the mental strain caused by them was considerable.

A performance before the general public rarely lasted more
than 12 minutes, and was a much simpler affair. A normal
programme included the subtraction of one number of twenty-
one digits from another number of twenty-one digits : the
addition of five numbers each of six digits : the multiplying
of a number of four digits by another number of four digits :
the extraction of the cube root of a number of nine digits, and
of the fifth root of a number of twelve digits : the determination of the number of seconds in a period of time, and the day
of the week on which a given date falls. Of course, the
questions were put by members of the audience. To a professional calculator these problems are not particularly difficult.
As each number was announced, Inaudi repeated it slowly to
his assistant, who wrote it on a blackboard, and then slowly
read it aloud to make sure that it was right. Inaudi then
repeated the number once more. By this time he had generally
solved the problem, but if he wanted longer time he made a few
remarks of a general character, which he was able to do without interfering with his mental calculations. Throughout the
exhibition he faced the audience : the fact that he never even
glanced at the blackboard added to the effect.

It is probable that the majority of calculating prodigies rely on the speech-muscles as well as on the eye and the ear to help them to recollect the figures with which they are dealing. It was formerly believed that they all visualized the numbers proposed to them, and certainly some have done so. Inaudi, however, trusted mainly to the ear and to articulation. Bidder also relied partly on the ear, and when he visualized a number, it was not as a collection of digits, but as a concrete collection of units divisible, if the number was composite, into definite groups. Rückle relied mainly on visualizing the numbers. So it would seem that there are different types of the memories of calculators. Inaudi could reproduce mentally the sound of the repetition of the digits of the number in his own voice, and was confused, rather than helped, if the numbers were shown to him in writing. The articulation of the digits of the number also seemed necessary to enable him fully to exhibit his powers, and he was accustomed to repeat the numbers aloud before beginning to work on them—the sequence of sounds being important. A number of twenty-four digits being read to him, in 59 seconds he memorized the sound of it, so that he could give the sequence of digits forwards or backwards from selected points—a feat which Mondeux had taken 5 minutes to perform. Numbers of about a hundred digits were similarly memorized by Inaudi in 12 minutes, by Diamandi in 25 minutes, and by Rückle in under 5 minutes. This power is confined to numbers, and calculators cannot usually recollect a long sequence of letters. Numbers were ever before Inaudi : he thought of little else, he dreamt of them, and sometimes even solved problems in his sleep. His memory was excellent for numbers, but normal or subnormal for other things. At the end of a séance he could repeat the questions which had been put to him and his answers, involving hundreds of digits in all. Nor was his memory in such matters limited to a few hours. Once, eight days after he had been given a question on a number of twenty-two digits, he was unexpectedly asked about it, and at once repeated the number. He was repeatedly examined, and we know more of his work than of any of his predecessors, with the possible exception of Bidder.

Most of these calculating prodigies find it difficult or impossible to explain their methods. But we have a few analyses by competent observers of the processes used : notably one by Bidder on his own work; another by Colburn on his work; and others by Müller and Darboux on the work of Rückle and Inaudi respectively. That by Bidder is the most complete, and the others are on much the same general lines.

Bidder's account of the processes he had discovered and used is contained in a lecture * given by him in 1856 to the Institution of Civil Engineers. Before describing these processes there are two remarks of a general character which should, I think, be borne in mind when reading his statement. In the first place, he gives his methods in their perfected form, and not necessarily in that which he used in boyhood : moreover, it is probable that in practice he employed devices to shorten the work which he did not set out in his lecture. In the second place, it is certain, in spite of his belief to the contrary, that he, like most of these prodigies, had an exceptionally good memory, which was strengthened by incessant practice. One example will suffice. In 1816, at a performance, a number was read to him backwards : he at once gave it in its normal form. An hour later he was asked if he remembered it : he immediately repeated it correctly. The number was : 2,563,721,987,653,461,598,746,231,905,607,541,128,975,231.

Of the four fundamental processes, addition and subtraction present no difficulty and are of little interest. The only point to which it seems worth calling attention is that Bidder, in adding three or more numbers together, always added them one at a time, as is illustrated in the examples given below. Rapid mental arithmetic depended, in his opinion, on the arrangement of the work, whenever possible, in such a way that only

* *Institution of Civil Engineers, Proceedings,* London, 1856, vol. xv, pp. 251—280. An early draft of the lecture is extant in MS.; the variations made in it are interesting, as showing the history of his mental development, but are not sufficiently important to need detailed notice here.

B B

one fact had to be dealt with at a time. This is also noticeable in Inaudi's work.

The multiplication of one number by another was, naturally enough, the earliest problem Bidder came across, and by the time he was six years old he had taught himself the multiplication table up to 10 times 10. He soon had practice in harder sums, for, being a favourite of the village blacksmith, and constantly in the smithy, it became customary for the men sitting round the forge-fire to ask him multiplication sums. From products of numbers of two digits, which he would give without any appreciable pause for thought, he rose to numbers of three and then of four digits. Halfpence rewarded his efforts, and by the time he was eight years old, he could multiply together two numbers each of six digits. In one case he even multiplied together two numbers each of twelve digits, but, he says, " it required much time," and " was a great and distressing effort."

The method that he used is, in principle, the same as that explained in the usual text-books, except that he added his results as he went on. Thus to multiply 397 by 173 he proceeded as follows :—

We have	$100 \times 397 = 39700,$		
to this must be added	$70 \times 300 = 21000$	making	60,700,
,, ,, ,, ,, ,,	$70 \times 90 = 6300$	,,	67,000,
,, ,, ,, ,, ,,	$70 \times 7 = 490$	,,	67,490,
,, ,, ,, ,, ,,	$3 \times 300 = 900$	,,	68,390,
,, ,, ,, ,, ,,	$3 \times 90 = 270$	,,	68,660,
,, ,, ,, ,, ,,	$3 \times 7 = 21$	,,	68,681.

We shall underrate his rapidity if we allow as much as a second for each of these steps, but even if we take this low standard of his speed of working, he would have given the answer in 7 seconds. By this method he never had at one time more than two numbers to add together, and the factors are arranged so that each of them has only one significant digit : this is the common practice of mental calculators. It will also be observed that here, as always, Bidder worked from left to right : this, though not usually taught in our schools, is the natural and most convenient way. In effect he formed the product of $(100 + 70 + 3)$ and $(300 + 90 + 7)$, or $(a + b + c)$ and $(d + e + f)$ in the form $ad + ae \ldots + cf$.

The result of a multiplication like that given above was attained so rapidly as to seem instantaneous, and practically gave him the use of a multiplication table up to 1000 by 1000. On this basis, when dealing with much larger numbers—for instance, when multiplying 965,446,371 by 843,409,133—he worked by numbers forming groups of 3 digits, proceeding as if 965, 446, etc., were digits in a scale whose radix was 1000 : in middle life he would solve a problem like this in about 6 minutes. Such difficulty as he experienced in these multiplications seems to have been rather in recalling the result of the previous step than in making the actual multiplications.

Inaudi also multiplied in this way, but he was content if one of the factors had only one significant digit : he also sometimes made use of negative quantities : for instance, he thought of 27×729 as $27(730 - 1)$; so, too, he thought of 25×841 in the form $84100/4$; and in squaring numbers he was accustomed to think of the number in the form $a + b$, choosing a and b of convenient forms, and then to calculate the result in the form $a^2 + 2ab + b^2$.

In multiplying concrete data by a number Bidder worked on similar lines to those explained above in the multiplication of two numbers. Thus to multiply £14 15s. $6\frac{3}{4}d$. by 787 he proceeded thus :

We have $\pounds(787)(14) = \pounds11018\ 0s.\ 0d.$
to which we add $(787)(15)$ shillings $= \pounds590\ 5s.\ 0d.$ making $\pounds11608\ 5s.\ 0d.$
to which we add $(787)(27)$ farthings $= \pounds22\ 2s.\ 8\frac{1}{4}d.$ making $\pounds11630\ 7s.\ 8\frac{1}{4}d.$

Division was performed by Bidder much as taught in schoolbooks, except that his power of multiplying large numbers at sight enabled him to guess intelligently and so save unnecessary work. This also was Inaudi's method. A division sum with a remainder presents more difficulty. Bidder was better skilled in dealing with such questions than most of these prodigies, but even in his prime he never solved such problems with the same rapidity as those with no remainder. In public performances difficult questions on division are generally precluded by the rules of the game.

If, in a division sum, Bidder knew that there was no remainder, he often proceeded by a system of two-digit terminals. Thus, for example, in dividing (say) 25,696 by 176, he first argued that the answer must be a number of three digits, and obviously the left-hand digit must be 1. Next he had noticed that there are only 4 numbers of two digits (namely, 21, 46, 71, 96) which when multiplied by 76 give a number which ends in 96. Hence the answer must be 121, or 146, or 171, or 196; and experience enabled him to say without calculation that 121 was too small and 171 too large. Hence the answer must be 146. If he felt any hesitation, he mentally multiplied 146 by 176 (which he said he could do " instantaneously "), and thus checked the result. It is noticeable that when Bidder, Colburn, and some other calculating prodigies knew the last two digits of a product of two numbers, they also knew, perhaps subconsciously, that the last two digits of the separate numbers were necessarily of certain forms. The theory of these two-digit arrangements has been discussed by Mitchell.

Frequently also in division, Bidder used what I will call a digital process, which *a priori* would seem far more laborious than the normal method, though in his hands the method was extraordinarily rapid : this method was, I think, peculiar to him. I define the digital of a number as the digit obtained by finding the sum of the digits of the original number, the sum of the digits of this number, and so on, until the sum is less than 10. The digital of a number is the same as the digital of the product of the digitals of its factors. Let us apply this in Bidder's way to see if 71 is an exact divisor of 23,141. The digital of 23,141 is 2. The digital of 71 is 8. Hence if 71 is a factor, the digital of the other factor must be 7, since 7 times

8 is the only multiple of 8 whose digital is 2. Now the only number which multiplied by 71 will give 41 as terminal digits is 71. And since the other factor must be one of three digits and its digital must be 7, this factor (if any) must be 871. But a cursory glance shows that 871 is too large. Hence 71 is not a factor of 23,141. Bidder found this process far more rapid than testing the matter by dividing by 71. As another example let us see if 73 is a factor of 23,141. The digital of 23,141 is 2; the digital of 73 is 1; hence the digital of the other factor (if any) must be 2. But since the last two digits of the number are 41, the last two digits of this factor (if any) must be 17. And since this factor is a number of three digits and its digital is 2, such a factor, if it exists, must be 317. This on testing (by multiplying it by 73) is found to be a factor.

When he began to exhibit his powers in public, questions concerning weights and measures were, of course, constantly proposed to him. In solving these he knew by heart many facts which frequently entered into such problems, such as the number of seconds in a year, the number of ounces in a ton, the number of square inches in an acre, the number of pence in a hundred pounds, the elementary rules about the civil and ecclesiastical calendars, and so on. A collection of such data is part of the equipment of all calculating prodigies.

In his exhibitions Bidder was often asked questions concerning square roots and cube roots, and at a later period higher roots. That he could at once give the answer excited unqualified astonishment in an uncritical audience; if, however, the answer is integral, this is a mere sleight of art which anyone can acquire. Without setting out the rules at length, a few examples will illustrate his method.

He was asked to find the square root of 337,561. It is obvious that the root is a number of three digits. Since the given number lies between 500^2 or 250,000 and 600^2 or 360,000, the left-hand digit of the root must be a 5. Reflection had shown him that the only numbers of two digits whose squares end in 61 are 19, 31, 69, 81, and he was familiar with this fact. Hence the answer was 519, or 531, or 569, or 581. But he argued that as 581 was nearly in the same ratio to 500 and 600 as 337,561 was to 250,000 and 360,000, the answer must be 581, a result which he verified by direct multiplication in a couple of seconds. Similarly in extracting the square root of 442,225, he saw at once that the left-hand digit of the answer was 6, and since the number ended in 225, the last two digits of the answer were 15 or 35, or 65 or 85. The position of 442,225 between $(600)^2$ and $(700)^2$ indicates that 65 should be taken. Thus the answer is 665, which he verified before announcing it. Other calculators have worked out similar rules for the extraction of roots.

For exact cube roots the process is more rapid. For example, asked to extract the cube root of 188,132,517, Bidder saw at once that the answer was a number of three digits, and since $5^3 = 125$ and $6^3 = 216$, the left-hand digit was 5. The only number of two digits whose cube ends in 17 is 73. Hence the answer is 573. Similarly the cube root of 180,362,125 must be a number of three digits, of which the left-hand digit is a 5, and the two right-hand digits were either 65 or 85. To see which of these was required, he mentally cubed 560, and seeing it was near the given number, assumed that 565 was the required answer, which he verified by cubing it. In general a cube root that ends in a 5 is a trifle more difficult to detect at sight by this method than one that ends in some other digit, but since 5^3 must be a factor of such numbers, we can divide by that and apply the process to the resulting number. Thus the above number 180,362,125 is equal to $5^3 \times 1,442,897$, of which the cube root is at once found to be 5(113)—that is, 565.

For still higher exact roots the process is even simpler, and for fifth roots it is almost absurdly easy, since the last digit of the number is always the same as the last digit of the root. Thus if the number proposed is less than 10^{10}, the answer consists of a number of two digits. Knowing the fifth powers to 10, 20, ... 90, we have, in order to know the first digit of the answer, only to see between which of these powers the number proposed lies, and the last digit being obvious, we can give the answer instantly. If the number is higher, but less than 10^{15}, the answer is a number of three digits, of which the middle digit can be found almost as rapidly as the others. This is rather a trick than a matter of mental calculation.

In his later exhibitions, Bidder was sometimes asked to extract roots, correct to the nearest integer, the exact root involving a fraction. If he suspected this, he tested it by " casting out the nines," and if satisfied that the answer was not an integer, proceeded tentatively as best he could. Such a question, if the answer is a number of three or more digits, is a severe tax on the powers of a mental calculator, and is usually disallowed in public exhibitions.

Colburn's remarkable feats in factorizing numbers led to similar questions being put to Bidder, and gradually he evolved some rules, but in this branch of mental arithmetic I do not think he ever became proficient. Of course, a factor which is a power of 2 or of 5 can be obtained at once and powers of 3 can be obtained almost as rapidly. For factors near the square root of a number he always tried the usual method of express-ing the number in the form $a^2 - b^2$, in which case the factors are obvious. For other factors he tried the digital method already described.

Bidder was successful in giving almost instantaneously the answers to questions about compound interest and annuities : this was peculiar to him, but his method is quite simple, and may be illustrated by his determination of the compound interest on £100 at 5 per cent. for 14 years. He argued that the simple interest amounted to £(14)(5), *i.e.* to £70. At the end of the first year the capital was increased by £5, the annual interest on this was 5*s.* or one crown, and this ran for 13 years, at the end of the second year another £5 was due, and the 5*s.* interest on this ran for 12 years. Continuing this argument, he had to add to the £70 a sum of $(13 + 12 + \ldots + 1)$ crowns, *i.e.* $(13/2)(14)(5)$ shillings, *i.e.* £22 15*s.* 0*d.*, which, added to the £70 before mentioned, made £92 15s. 0d. Next the 5s. due at the end of the second year (as interest on the £5 due at the end of the first year) produced in the same way an annual interest of 3d. All these three-pences amount to (12/3)(13/2)(14)(3) pence, i.e. £4 11s. 0d., which, added to the previous sum of £92 15s. 0d., made £97 6s. 0d. To this we have similarly to add (11/4)(12/3)(13/2)(14)(3/20) pence, i.e. 12s. 6d., which made a total of £97 18s. 6d. To this again we have to add (10/5)(11/4)(12/3)(13/2)(14)(3/400) pence, i.e. 1s. 3d., which made a total of £97 19s. 9d. To this again we have to add (9/6)(10/5)(11/4)(12/3)(13/2)(14)(3/8000) pence, i.e. 1d., which made a total of £97 19s. 10d. The remaining sum to be added cannot amount to a farthing, so he at once gave the answer as £97 19s. 10d. The work in this particular example did in fact occupy him less than one minute—a much shorter time than most mathematicians would take to work it by aid of a table of logarithms. It will be noticed that in the course of his analysis he summed various series.

In the ordinary notation, the sum at compound interest amounts to £$(1 \cdot 05)^{14} \times 100$. If we denote £100 by P and $\cdot 05$ by r, this is equal to $P(1 + r)^{14}$ or $P(1 + 14r + 91r^2 + \ldots)$, which, as r is small, is rapidly convergent. Bidder in effect arrived by reasoning at the successive terms of the series, and rejected the later terms as soon as they were sufficiently small.

In the course of this lecture Bidder remarked that if his ability to recollect results had been equal to his other intellectual powers, he could easily have calculated logarithms. A few weeks later he attacked this problem, and devised a mental method of obtaining the values of logarithms to seven or eight places of decimals. He asked a friend to test his accuracy, and in answer to questions gave successively the logarithms of 71, 97, 659, 877, 1297, 8963, 9973, 115249, 175349, 290011, 350107, 229847, 369353, to eight places of decimals; taking from thirty seconds to four minutes to make the various calculations. All these numbers are primes. The greater part of the answers were correct, but in a few cases there was an error, though generally of only one digit : such mistakes were at once corrected on his being told that his result was wrong. This remarkable performance took place when Bidder was over 50.

His method of calculating logarithms is set out in a paper * by W. Pole. It was, of course, only necessary for him to deal with prime numbers, and Bidder began by memorizing the logarithms of all primes less than 100. For a prime higher than this he took a composite number as near it as he could, and calculated the approximate addition which would have to be added to the logarithm : his rules for effecting this addition are set out by Pole, and, ingenious though they are, need not detain us here. They rest on the theorems that, to the number of places of decimals quoted, if $\log n$ is p, then $\log (n + n/10^2)$ is $p + \log 1.01$, *i.e.* is $p + 0.00432137$, $\log (n + n/10^3)$ is $p + 0.00043408$, $\log (n + n/10^4)$ is $p + 0.00004343$, $\log (n + n/10^5)$ is $p + 0.00000434$, and so on.

The last two methods, dealing with compound interest and logarithms, are peculiar to Bidder, and show real mathematical skill. For the other problems mentioned his methods are much the same in principle as those used by other calculators, though details vary. Bidder, however, has set them out so clearly that I need not discuss further the methods generally used.

A curious question has been raised as to whether a law for the rapidity of the mental work of these prodigies can be found. Personally I do not think we have sufficient data to enable us to draw any conclusion, but I mention briefly the opinions of others. We shall do well to confine ourselves to the simplest case : that of the multiplication of a number of n digits by another number of n digits. Bidder stated that in solving such a problem he believed that the strain on his mind (which he assumed to be proportional to the time taken

* *Institution of Civil Engineers, Proceedings*, London, 1890—1891, vol. CIII, p. 250.

in answering the question) varied as n^4, but in fact it seems in his case according to this time test to have varied approximately as n^5. In 1855 he worked at least half as quickly again as in 1819, but the law of rapidity for different values of n is said to have been about the same. In Dase's case, if the time occupied is proportional to n^x, we must have x less than 3. From this, some have inferred that probably Dase's methods were different in character to those used by Bidder, and it is suggested that the results tend to imply that Dase visualized recorded numerals, working in much the same way as with pencil and paper, while Bidder made no use of symbols, and recorded successive results verbally in a sort of cinematograph way; but it would seem that we shall need more detailed observations before we can frame a theory on this subject.

The cases of calculating prodigies here mentioned, and, as far as I know, the few others of which records exist, do not differ in kind. In most of them the calculators were uneducated and self-taught. Blessed with excellent memories for numbers, self-confident, stimulated by the astonishment their performances excited, the odd coppers thus put in their pockets and the praise of their neighbours, they pondered incessantly on numbers and their properties; discovered (or in a few cases were taught) the fundamental arithmetical processes, applied them to problems of ever increasing difficulty, and soon acquired a stock of information which shortened their work. Probably *constant practice* and *undivided devotion to mental calculation* are essential to the maintenance of the power, and this may explain why a general education has so often proved destructive to it. The performances of these calculators are remarkable, but, in the light of Bidder's analysis, are not more than might be expected occasionally from lads of exceptional abilities.

CHAPTER XIV

CRYPTOGRAPHY AND CRYPTANALYSIS

THE art of writing secret messages—intelligible to those who are in possession of the key and unintelligible to all others—has been studied for centuries. The usefulness of such messages, especially in time of war, is obvious; on the other hand, their solution may be a matter of great importance to those from whom the key is concealed. But the romance connected with the subject, the not uncommon desire to discover a secret, and the implied challenge to the ingenuity of all from whom it is hidden have attracted to the subject the attention of many to whom its utility is a matter of indifference.

Although it is possible to communicate information in many different ways, we shall be concerned here only with secret communications which are in writing or in some other permanent form. Thus, small muscular movements, such as breathing long and short in the Morse dot and dash system, or signalling with a fan or stick, will not concern us. The essential feature is that the information conveyed remain hidden from all those who may have been enabled to obtain copies of the messages transmitted but are not in possession of the key. Thus we would consider secret those messages which are outwardly intelligible, but really convey a different, hidden meaning.* On the other hand, a communication in a foreign language or in any recognized notation like shorthand is *not* a secret message.

The famous diary of Samuel Pepys is commonly said to have been written in cipher, but in reality it was written in

* The reader is referred, for two classic examples of this type, to *Cryptographie Pratique*, A. de Grandpré, Paris, 1905, p. 57.

shorthand according to a system invented by J. Shelton.* It is, however, somewhat difficult to read, for the vowels were usually omitted, and Pepys used some arbitrary signs for terminations, particles, and certain frequent words. Further, in certain places, where the matter was such that it could hardly be expressed with decency, he changed from English to a foreign language, or inserted non-significant symbols. Shelton's system had been forgotten when attention was first attracted to the diary. Accordingly, we may say that, to those who first tried to read it, it was written in cipher; but Pepys' contemporaries would have properly described the diary as being written in shorthand, although it involved a few modifications of his own invention.

The mere fact that a message is concealed or secretly conveyed does not make it a secret message. The majority of stories dealing with secret communication are concerned with the artfulness with which the message is concealed or conveyed, and have nothing to do with cryptography. Many of the ancient instances of secret communication are of this type. Herodotus tells of the practice of shaving a slave's head and inscribing the message on his scalp; then sending the slave to deliver the message after his hair had grown back again. More modern illustrations are to be found in messages conveyed by pigeons or written on the paper wrapping of a cigarette.

Cryptographic Systems. Every method for converting a plain-text message into a secret message consists of two parts: (1) a basic, invariant method, called the *general system*, and (2) a variable, keying element usually consisting of a word, phrase, or sequence of numbers, called the *specific key*. It is ordinarily assumed that the *enemy* (any person who has obtained unauthorized possession of the messages and is

---

* *Tachy-graphy*, by J. Shelton, first edition 1620, sixth edition used by Pepys 1641. A somewhat similar system by W. Cartwright was issued by J. Rich under the title *Semographie*, London, 1644.

attempting to solve them) has full knowledge of the general system. (This assumption is based on the fact that no large communication system can hope to keep its general procedure secret very long, nor can it attempt to vary its procedure at will, in view of the great difficulty of training personnel in new methods.) The relative security of any cryptographic system is then considered to be proportional to the length of time required to determine the specific key. In this connection it must be appreciated that it is ordinarily not practicable to change specific keys more than once a day. Consequently, if all the messages (or most of them, at any rate) are intercepted, the enemy would sometimes have several hundred messages available for the determination of one specific key. This fact is often overlooked, and many systems whose security is quite low are given exaggerated importance, in the minds of their inventors, because they may be very difficult or even impossible to solve when only one message is available.

According to the method of treating the original message, general systems are divided into two main classes. If the characters of the plain-text message are merely rearranged without suffering any change in identity—*i.e.* if some permutation is applied to the original characters—the system is called *transposition*. If, however, the characters themselves are replaced by equivalents in the form of letters, or figures, or arbitrary symbols, without introducing any change in their original sequence, the system is called *substitution*. Both of these systems may be combined in a single cryptogram, by applying one to the result obtained by the other.

In the short treatment of the subject which will be given in this chapter, an attempt will be made to present a brief description of the classic systems of enciphering messages. In each case, a few words will be added with reference to the method of solution. The reader should note in this connection the difference in the use of the words *deciphering* and *solving*. The former refers to the procedure followed by the bona-fide correspondent who is in possession of all the details of the system and who merely reverses the steps followed in enciphering. The latter refers to the method used by an enemy of obtaining an unauthorized translation by applying the principles of the science now called *Cryptanalysis*.

Transposition Systems. Practically every transposition system involves a geometric figure in which the plain-text message is inscribed according to one route and then transscribed according to another route.

The following is an example of encipherment, in a system commonly called *route transposition*. Suppose the message to be transmitted is

I MUST HAVE ANOTHER HUNDRED DOLLARS

The general system, we will say, requires a completely filled rectangle of eight columns, so that it is necessary to add dummy letters if the number of letters in the message is not a multiple of eight. We therefore add two such letters, say XX, at the end of the message, in order to have 32 letters in all. We will assume next that the route for inscription is horizontal, starting at the upper left-hand corner and proceeding alternately to the right and to the left. The following arrangement will then be obtained.

I	M	U	S	T	H	A	V
R	E	H	T	O	N	A	E
H	U	N	D	R	E	D	D
X	X	S	R	A	L	L	O

If the method of transcription is vertical, beginning at the upper right-hand corner and proceeding alternately down and up, the final cipher message, prepared for transmission, would be VEDOL DAAHN ELARO TSTDR SNHUM EUXXH RI. The reversal of the above steps, in deciphering, would involve no particular difficulty.

It is not amiss to observe at this point that, because of international telegraphic regulations governing the cost of transmitting messages. the final text of cryptograms is usually divided up into regular groups of five letters. This consideration is obviously of no consequence from a cryptanalytic standpoint.

A system of the type just described possesses very little security and has the further disadvantage of not being readily adaptable to change. Even if the dimensions of the rectangle and the routes of inscription and transcription were to be changed regularly, an enemy would have little difficulty in reading intercepted messages. The procedure in solution is essentially one of trial, but the number of possibilities is so limited that with a little experience a solution can be obtained in a very short time.

A very widely used variation of route transposition is known as *columnar transposition*. In this system the geometric figure is again a rectangle but with the message inscribed in the *normal* manner of writing. The transcription is vertical, the columns being selected in the order determined by a numerical key, the width of the rectangle being equal to the length of the key. To illustrate, suppose the key is 3–2–7–1–4–6–5 and the message is THE PRISONERS HAVE SEIZED THE RAILWAY STATION.

The first step would be to write the message in a rectangle whose columns are headed by the key numbers.

3	2	7	1	4	6	5
T	H	E	P	R	I	S
O	N	E	R	S	H	A
V	E	S	E	I	Z	E
D	T	H	E	R	A	I
L	W	A	Y	S	T	A
T	I	O	N			

It is inadvisable to complete the last row of the rectangle with dummy letters, as that would give the enemy a clue to the length of the key. Then, transcribing the columns in order according to the numerical key and simultaneously preparing the message for transmission by dividing it up into five-letter groups, we have :

PREEY NHNET WITOV DLTRS IRSSA EIAIH ZATEE SHAO

The first step in deciphering is to determine how many long columns there are—that is, how many letters occur on the last row of the rectangle. This is accomplished by dividing the number of letters in the message by the length of the key; the remainder obtained from this division is the desired number. When it has been calculated, the cipher letters can be put into their proper positions, and the message will reappear.

In cases where the key is fairly long and it is inadvisable to reduce it to writing, it is found convenient to derive the numerical sequence from an easily remembered key word or phrase. This may be done in any one of several ways, the most common being to assign numbers to the letters in accordance with their normal alphabetical order. To illustrate, suppose the key word is CRYPTOGRAPHY. The letter A which appears in it is numbered 1. Then, since there is no B in the word, the letter C is numbered 2. The next letter, alphabetically, is G, and this is numbered 3, etc. This procedure is continued until a number has been assigned to every letter in the word. Whenever a letter appears more than once, the several appearances are numbered consecutively from left to right. The complete numerical key thus obtained is

C	R	Y	P	T	O	G	R	A	P	H	Y
2	8	11	6	10	5	3	9	1	7	4	12

The procedure in solving a columnar transposition is based on the fact that the letters of an entire column have been transcribed as a unit. Let us suppose that we are trying to

solve the cipher message just obtained. The first step is to
fit together two groups of consecutive letters which will form
good plain-text combinations. The most frequent *digraph*
(two-letter combination) in English is TH, and so we might
begin by setting every T next to every H, in turn. In each
such case, several letters just preceding and just following the
T and the H would also be juxtaposed. For example, if we
place the first T in the message against the last H, we have
the following combinations :

```
        Y A
        N T
        H E
        N E
        E S
        T H
        W A
        I O
        T
        O
```

The number of letters to be placed in each column is as yet
unknown, but certain limitations are sometimes imposed by
the positions of the particular letters being used. In the above
instance, the O at the foot of the first column may be discarded,
since the long columns of a transposition rectangle exceed the
short ones by one letter. The T just above the O will be correct
only if it is the last letter of the message, for it would end the
last long column. As another example of how limitations
may be placed upon the length of the columns corresponding
to a given assumption, suppose we had placed the first T
of the message against the first H, which is only three letters
removed. Then only three digraphs would have been obtained.
Consequently with this assumption no column of the rectangle
could contain more than four letters.

There would be one pair of columns such as those given
above for every possible TH combination, and it is next
necessary to choose that pair which is composed of the best
selection of high-frequency combinations. The experienced
cryptanalyst can do this at sight, but the same result can be
obtained by a purely mathematical process. Extended

C C

studies of the relative frequencies of single letters, digraphs, trigraphs, and polygraphs have been made by various authors. These relative frequencies may be considered an invariant property of the corresponding plain-text combinations, since they are derived from studies of a very large amount of text. By assigning to each digraph a weight equal to its relative frequency, it then becomes a very simple matter to select that pair of colums which yields the greatest average weight per digraph.

Such a test will show that the arrangement already set up is an exceptionally good one. The only digraphs which are not high-frequency combinations are YA and WA, and the former may be beyond the limits of the column. If we assume that this arrangement is correct, we then try to add a third column, either on the right or on the left, so as to obtain good plain-text trigraphs.

Now, IO is almost always followed by N. In addition the TH suggests the word THE. This prompts us to seek an E followed at two intervals by an N, and we find just one such place in the cipher message. Note how the addition of the corresponding letters to the combinations already obtained delimits the columns.

```
H E P
N E R
E S E
T H E
W A Y
I O N
T
```

Should there be several possibilities instead of only one, these may again be compared by summing the weights of the trigraphs in each case and choosing the arrangement which gives the greatest average. In the present case, however, it is obvious that we are on the right track, and the solution will follow very readily.

The procedure which has just been carried out is greatly facilitated by a knowledge of particular words which would be likely to appear in the message. Such a knowledge is quite usual in military cryptanalysis, for example. Indeed, many writers on Cryptanalysis refer frequently to the *Probable word* or *Intuitive* method as a means of solution for many different systems.

What has been said thus far about the method of solving columnar transpositions has implied that the cryptanalyst is in possession of only one message. It has already been pointed out that in actual practice there may be many messages in the same key available for study. In such cases several methods can be used to obtain a rapid solution.

Among these the following is of note, since it is applicable to any transposition system whatever. Suppose two or more messages of *identical lengths* are subjected to the same transposition. Then, no matter how complicated the system may be, it is obvious that letters which were in corresponding positions in the plain-text will be in corresponding positions in the cipher text. Suppose the cipher messages are superimposed so that the first letters of all the messages are in one column, the second letters of all the messages are in a second column, etc. Then if it is assumed that two particular letters of one message are sequent in the plain-text, the letters in the corresponding positions of each of the other messages will combine in the same order. They will thus afford a check on the correctness of the first assumption, in the same way that the combinations arising from two columns in columnar transposition served as a check on the juxtaposition of a particular pair of letters in those columns. To each of these digraphs a third letter may be added to form trigraphs, etc. The idea is essentially one of *anagramming* the entire columns of the superimposed messages, and the mathematical method of summing frequencies may be used to advantage.

A good start can often be obtained by choosing an invariant combination, such as QU, or a digraph composed of two letters which have a great affinity for one another, such as TH or RE. If one of the letters of the digraph is infrequent—as, for example, in VE—the number of possibilities is very considerably reduced. Given a minimum of four messages of identical lengths, one can safely be assured of obtaining a solution of those messages. However, it is not always true that this solution will permit the cryptanalyst to translate additional messages of different lengths. In order to accomplish this, he would have to obtain some information about the general system and the specific key from the messages already solved.

A second procedure which is very fruitful in solving columnar transpositions is applicable to two or more messages involving a long repetition. Such repetitions are often found in the messages of large communication systems where there is a tendency to use stereotyped phraseology. In order to appreciate the procedure more fully, let us encipher, with the numerical key 8–6–4–1–5–3–2–7 the following two messages containing the repetition THE FIRST AND SECOND DIVISIONS.

8	6	4	1	5	3	2	7
W	H	A	T	A	R	E	T
H	E	O	R	D	E	R	S
F	O	R	*T*	*H*	*E*	*F*	*I*
R	*S*	*T*	*A*	*N*	*D*	*S*	*E*
C	*O*	*N*	D	D	I	V	I
S	*I*	*O*	N	S			

8	6	4	1	5	3	2	7
T	H	*E*	F	I	R	S	*T*
A	N	D	S	E	*C*	O	N
D	D	I	V	I	S	*I*	O
N	S	W	I	L	L	L	E
A	V	E	A	T	O	N	C
E							

The two cryptograms available for study by the cryptanalyst are

   1   2   3   4   5
1. TR*TAD* NER*FS* VRE*ED* IAOR*T* NOADH NDSHE
   6   7   8
  O*SOIT* S*IEI*W HF*RC*S

   1   2   3   4   5   6   7   8
2. FS*VIA* *SOI*LN R*C*SLO EDI*WE* *I*EILT HNDS*V* TNOEC TAD*NA* E

He would notice and underline the italicised repetitions.

Note how the letters which make up the repetition appear

in the two messages. The number of portions into which
it has been broken up is equal to the number of columns
in the rectangle, and the figure over each repeated portion is
the key number which heads the corresponding column. The
letters *RCS* in cipher message 1 are at the foot of their column.
They indicate that the repeated phrase is at the end of the
corresponding plain-text message. On the other hand, the
letters *FSV*, which are at the head of their column in cipher
message 2, indicate that the repetition is at the beginning of
the corresponding plain-text message. As a result of this
information, the length of each column is at once ascertainable.
In the first message, for example, column 1 contains the
letters TR*TADN*, column 2 contains the letters ER*FSV*, etc.
In the second message column 1 contains the letters *FSV*IA,
column 2 contains the letters *SOI*LN, etc. We thus have
determined which are the long columns and which are the
short columns of each of the two messages.

In addition to the above information, which in itself is of
considerable value, one can almost always get portions of the
key, and sometimes the whole key, from these repetitions.
In order to appreciate how this is done, let us assume for a
moment that the original rectangles are known. Note then
that the letter T, which is the first letter of the repetition,
appears in the fourth column of message 1 and in the first
column of message 2. As a result, any letter of the repetition
will appear, in message 1, three columns to the right of the
position of the corresponding letter in message 2.

The letters *FSV* which begin the second cipher message
must come from the column headed by number 1 of the key.
The letters *FSV* of message 1 come from the column headed
by number 2. But, if these letters in the first message are
three places in advance of the corresponding letters of the
second message, it follows that the numerical key contains
the sequence 1–?–?–2 (where the question marks indicate
undetermined numbers). The portion of the repetition which

appears in the second message in the column headed by the number 2 is *SOI*, and corresponds in message 1 to the column headed by the number 6. Hence, by the same reasoning as before, the key must contain the sequence 1-?-?-2-?-?-6. Column 6 in the second message corresponds to column 5 in the first. Remembering that the key is of length 8, we may now say that it contains the sequence 1-5-?-2-?-?-6-?.

Continuing in this way, we build up the entire key 1-5-3-2-7-8-6-4, which is a cyclic permutation of the correct key. If it is applied to the first cipher message, the result will be :

1	5	3	2	7	8	6	4
T	A	R	E	T	W	H	A
R	D	E	R	S	H	E	O
T	H	E	F	I	F	O	R
A	N	D	S	E	R	S	T
D	D	I	V	I	C	O	N
N	S				S	I	O

and the proper starting-point is at once determined by inspection. Another method of determining the beginning of the cycle is to note how the cipher messages break up into long and short columns. Since the columns which have one extra letter are all at the left in the original rectangle, the cycle begins with the first long column that follows a short column.

The reader will appreciate from what has preceded that we were enabled to derive the entire key because of the fact that the relative displacement of corresponding letters in the two repetitions was prime to the length of the key. If these two numbers had had a common factor, the key would have broken up into as many partial cycles as the greatest common divisor of the two numbers. It would then have become necessary to join the partial cycles into one complete cycle. This would have introduced several possible solutions, but a moment's trial would have determined the correct one.

Now, we assumed, in obtaining the solution just described, that the relative displacement was known. This is sometimes the case. For example, consider two messages whose endings are identical. After the length of the key has been determined by the number of sections into which the repetition breaks up, the number of long columns in each of the rectangles is at once obtained. The difference between these two numbers is the sought displacement. In the two messages just studied it is also possible to determine the relative displacement between the two repetitions, because of the fact that one repetition is at the beginning and the other at the end of their respective messages. Since the repetition is 26 letters long, its last letter must be in the second column of the second message. Moreover, this same letter is in the last long column—*i.e.* the fifth column—of the first message. The displacement is therefore three columns.

If the relative positions of the repetitions are the same, so that there is no displacement, as would happen if they were both at the beginnings of their messages, no information whatever about the actual numerical key would be obtainable by this method.

In those cases where the relative displacement is indeterminate, the assumption of each possibility in turn would still require a relatively small number of tests before the correct answer would be obtained.

The security of columnar transposition is very greatly increased if the resulting cipher is put through a second columnar transposition. This second step may use the same or a different numerical key. In either case, the superimposition of one columnar transposition upon a second yields a result obtainable from the original plain-text by a single transposition, but this latter process is much more complicated than columnar transposition. Such a system is usually called *double transposition*, and a single message so enciphered has a very high degree of security. However, two or more messages of identical lengths can be solved without difficulty in the manner already explained. The numerical keys involved in a double transposition can be obtained if the cryptanalyst is in possession of a single cipher message with its translation.

As a last example of transposition, a few words will be said about a classic system known as the *grille*, an example of which is shown below. It is a perforated card, usually square, which when put over a sheet of paper permits only certain portions of the sheet to be visible. In encipherment, the letters of the message are entered through these perforations. In decipherment, the message is written out in a diagram of the proper dimensions, the grille is superimposed, and only the desired letters of the plain-text will show through.

1	2	3	4	5	1
5	1	2	3	1	2
4	3	1	1	2	3
3	2	1	1	3	4
2	1	3	2	1	5
1	5	4	3	2	1

Grilles may be used in two different ways. With the first of these methods, the final cipher text will involve only the letters of the original plain-text message. One way of accomplishing this is to arrange the grille in such a way that if it is used successively in different positions, every cell of the underlying sheet of paper will be occupied. In the second method, on the other hand, it would be arranged that only certain cells will be filled, and the encipherer then has the further task of surrounding these significant letters with *false text*. This is generally a very difficult procedure, and has the further disadvantage of making the cipher text considerably longer than the plain-text. The inscription and transcription in grille systems may, of course, follow any prearranged routes.

The grille shown above is an example of a *revolving grille* of 36 cells. If it is successively rotated through 90° after the cells exposed by each position have been filled, every cell will be found to have been filled when the grille has returned to its starting position. The numbers which have been entered in the various cells indicate the method of construction. From each concentric band of cells, one cell must be cut to correspond to each number. If the number of cells on a side is odd, the central square of the grille must remain uncut.

Grilles are not very practicable when there is any considerable amount of communication. Besides, their security is quite low. For example, all messages enciphered with a given revolving grille would break up into portions of identical lengths, each of which has been treated identically. The method of anagramming columns is therefore applicable.

In all of the transposition systems which have been described thus far the unit of cryptographic treatment has been a single letter. There is no reason why it could not be changed to a regular group of letters, or to syllabic groupings, or even to whole words. Such systems are by no means uncommon. An outstanding historical instance was the use of a route transposition on words by the Federal Army in the American Civil War, 1861—1865, equivalents being substituted for proper names. Also grilles of a rectangular shape, with rather long perforations, are sometimes used, so that a syllable or even a whole word can be entered at a time.

Substitution Systems. The simplest type of substitution system is that in which the same plain-text letter is always represented by the same equivalent. It is probably the best-known type of cipher, and seems to be the very first idea that comes to the mind of a beginner in Cryptography. Just what form the equivalent takes is obviously of no consequence, and yet it is surprising how many people get the notion that the use of complicated arbitrary symbols yields a more secure system than would be obtained with letters or figures.

The simplest way to employ such a system is to set down the equivalents in the form of a *substitution alphabet*, which consists of a *plain-sequence* and a *cipher sequence*, superimposed one above the other. The plain-text letter is found in the plain sequence, and replaced by the corresponding character in the cipher sequence.

For example, if we employ the substitution alphabet

Plain   A B C D E F G H I J K L M N O P Q R S T U V W X Y Z
Cipher A D G J M P S V Y B E H K N Q T W Z C F I L O R U X

the sentence COME HOME ALL IS FORGIVEN would be enciphered GQKMV QKMAH HYCPQ ZSYLM N.

In the usual method of writing a substitution alphabet, the plain sequence is the *normal* alphabet. In such cases, the assignment of the cipher sequence alone is sufficient to define the entire substitution alphabet. Depending upon the manner in which the cipher sequence is constructed, substitution alphabets are divided into three different classes.

1. *Standard Alphabets.* Here the cipher sequence is a cyclic permutation of either the normal alphabet or the normal alphabet *reversed*. This is the oldest type of substitution alphabet known. Some writers call cipher systems using a standard alphabet *the system of Julius Caesar*. However, Caesar used but one of the possible standard alphabets; his cipher sequence was always the normal alphabet beginning with the letter D.*

2. *Systematically Mixed Alphabets.* The difficulty arising from the use of standard alphabets is obvious. One or two

---

* Of some of Caesar's correspondence, Suetonius says (cap. 56) *si quis investigare et persequi velit, quartam elementorum literam, id est, d pro a, et perinde reliqua commutet.* And of Augustus he says (cap. 88) *quoties autem per notas scribit, b pro a, c pro b, ac deinceps eadem ratione, sequentes literas ponit pro x autem duplex a.* ("If anyone wishes to investigate and follow it up, let him replace the fourth letter of the alphabet, that is, D, by A and in like manner with the others." "Whenever he writes in cipher, he puts B for A, C for B and continues in the same way; for X, however, he puts AA.")

identifications are sufficient to determine the whole alphabet. To circumvent this difficulty and still avoid the necessity of reducing the cipher sequence to writing, some systematic procedure must be employed for disarranging the normal alphabet. Cryptographic literature is full of devices for accomplishing this end, but only one will be described here, merely for the sake of example. Let a key word be chosen which has no repeated letters in it—say FISHER. Write all the remaining letters of the alphabet in order in a rectangular array under the key word.

2	4	6	3	1	5
F	I	S	H	E	R
A	B	C	D	G	J
K	L	M	N	O	P
Q	T	U	V	W	X
Y	Z				

Then transpose the letters of this figure by columns according to the numerical key based on the word FISHER. The resulting cipher sequence is

E G O W F A K Q Y H D N V I B L T Z R J P X S C M U

3. *Random Alphabets.* Here the letters of the cipher sequence are chosen at random, and in such a sequence no aid in determining unknown letters can be obtained from known identifications. The objection to this type of sequence is, of course, that it must be reduced to writing.

The method of solution of a system which uses only one substitution alphabet or, as we shall call it, a *monoalphabetic* system, is fairly well known. It is based on the relative frequencies of the individual letters of the alphabet, together with the relative frequencies of their combinations with one another.

In English, the relative frequencies of occurrence of the individual letters, most frequent digraphs, and trigraphs are as follows : *

E ·131	R ·067	F ·028	G ·014	Q ·001
T ·090	S ·065	U ·028	B ·013	Z ·001
O ·082	H ·059	M ·026	V ·010	
A ·078	D ·044	P ·022	K ·004	
N ·073	L ·036	Y ·015	X ·003	
I ·068	C ·029	W ·015	J ·001	

TH ·034	ER ·019	IN ·014	AT ·013	HA ·012
HE ·026	ON ·019	ED ·014	OF ·013	EN ·011
AN ·019	RE ·017	ND ·014	OR ·012	NT ·011

THE ·015	HAT ·003	FOR ·003	NDE ·003
AND ·005	EDT ·003	ION ·003	HAS ·002
THA ·004	ENT ·003	TIO ·003	MEN ·002

Further aids are : (1) the determination of the vowels as being those high-frequency letters which rarely combine with one another, and hence show definite interval relationships : (2) the selection of unusual combinations of letters which suggest certain definite plain-text words or phrases. Examples : THAT, WHICH, AS SOON AS, BEGINNING, etc. These are detected in the cipher text by the intervals between the repeated letters, their appearance being referred to as *word patterns*; (3) the search for probable words, which are always very helpful to a cryptanalyst.

Once a few identifications have been made by using any one of the above ideas, a complete solution follows very readily.

The relatively low security possessed by a monoalphabetic system is the result of the fact that each plain-text letter has only one equivalent. If we insist that this equivalent may not represent any other letter, and wish at the same time to provide additional equivalents for the individual letters, it becomes necessary to have more than 26 cipher characters. If, for example, we use every two-digit number as a cipher unit, we have 100 possible equivalents : if we use a two-letter combination as a cipher unit, we have 676 possible equivalents.

* P. Valerio, *De la Cryptographie*, Paris, 1893, pp. 202, 204.

It then becomes possible with the introduction of additional cipher equivalents to represent each plain-text letter by any one of several *variant* values. If the number of equivalents assigned to each letter is proportional to its relative frequency of occurrence in plain-text, the resulting system has much more security than an ordinary monoalphabet.

However, it may be solved without too much trouble. The procedure is to reduce the cipher text to monoalphabetic terms by determining which cipher characters are equivalent to one another. This is done in two ways : (1) it will be found by frequency studies that certain characters combine in the same sort of way with all the others. A detailed study of all their appearances will establish the equivalence of those characters which represent the same plain-text letter; (2) a careful study of repetitions will disclose places where the same word has been differently enciphered. Thus, one might find such occurrences as

11	22	27	75	89	16	31
11	22	27	61	89	16	31
11	22	45	75	82	16	31

The obvious conclusion is that 27 and 45, 61 and 75, 82 and 89 are equivalent pairs. An extended study along these lines will yield considerable information, and before many equivalents have been established, the cryptanalyst will be able to take advantage of frequency considerations and word patterns to obtain plain-text identifications.

A cipher system in which one plain-text letter is replaced by two or more cipher characters is called *polyliteral*. Sometimes polyliteral systems are used without taking advantage of variant values. Francis Bacon's cipher, for example, was pentaliteral, each plain-text letter being replaced by a five-letter group consisting of A's and B's only. Since that allowed 32 possibilities (2^5), there were 6 symbols to spare. These were not used by Bacon. The Morse code is an example of a polyliteral system in which the cipher equivalents are not all of the same length.*

A more effective way to suppress frequency than by the use of variants is to make use of more than one substitution alphabet. Such systems are often called *polyalphabetic*, and take two very distinct forms, according as the alphabets are used periodically or aperiodically.

As a simple example of the first type, suppose the correspondents have constructed five different random alphabets.

Plain		A	B	C	D	E	F	G	H	I	J	K	L	M	N	O	P	Q	R	S	T	U	V	W	X	Y	Z
Cipher	1	R	K	S	L	D	P	A	V	E	C	O	G	J	U	B	N	I	F	X	Z	W	H	Y	M	Q	T
	2	J	Y	B	I	W	Q	H	X	D	P	T	F	A	Z	G	O	C	L	S	U	E	K	N	V	M	R
	3	F	K	U	D	N	H	T	A	Z	L	G	Q	Y	R	B	I	J	V	M	O	C	W	E	X	S	P
	4	N	T	Q	I	C	G	S	E	J	O	P	A	W	B	V	U	X	D	L	F	R	H	K	Z	M	Y
	5	K	E	M	A	J	B	T	L	V	D	N	U	F	S	C	Q	G	O	X	I	P	Y	W	Z	R	H

The plain-text message is written out in five columns, and the first alphabet is used to encipher the letters of the first column, the second alphabet is used to encipher the letters of the second column, etc. The effect of this procedure is that the ath alphabet enciphers every letter whose position in the plain-text is a number of the form $5k + a$. With the alphabets given above, the message THREE SHIPS SAILED TODAY would be enciphered ZXVCJ XXZUX XJZAJ LUBIK Q.

Instead of having a fixed number of alphabets, the correspondents may provide arrangements for varying their alphabets by regular changes of a key word. One means of attaining this end will now be explained. It is described by most of the older authors, and is called by some of them the *double key* system. One key word—for example, COPYRIGHT—is used

* The Morse alphabet is listed here for those who are not familiar with it.

A . —	G — — .	M — —	S . . .	Y — . — —
B — . . .	H	N — .	T —	Z — — . .
C — . — .	I . .	O — — —	U . . —	
D — . .	J . — — —	P . — — .	V . . . —	
E .	K — . —	Q — — . —	W . — —	
F . . — .	L . — . .	R . — .	X — . . —	

to construct the following diagram, known as a Vigenère Square (see below). If we consider each row of the square a cipher sequence, and the normal alphabet above the square the plain sequence, the diagram gives us 26 substitution alphabets. Let each of these alphabets be designated by the letter in the first column of the square. Then a second key word—say AUGUST—is employed to select the particular alphabets to be used and the order in which to use them. The first substitution alphabet would be the A alphabet, and

	A	B	C	D	E	F	G	H	I	J	K	L	M	N	O	P	Q	R	S	T	U	V	W	X	Y	Z
C	O	P	Y	R	I	G	H	T	A	B	D	E	F	J	K	L	M	N	Q	S	U	V	W	X	Z	C
Z	C	O	P	Y	R	I	G	H	T	A	B	D	E	F	J	K	L	M	N	Q	S	U	V	W	X	Z
X	Z	C	O	P	Y	R	I	G	H	T	A	B	D	E	F	J	K	L	M	N	Q	S	U	V	W	X
W	X	Z	C	O	P	Y	R	I	G	H	T	A	B	D	E	F	J	K	L	M	N	Q	S	U	V	W
V	W	X	Z	C	O	P	Y	R	I	G	H	T	A	B	D	E	F	J	K	L	M	N	Q	S	U	V
U	V	W	X	Z	C	O	P	Y	R	I	G	H	T	A	B	D	E	F	J	K	L	M	N	Q	S	U
S	U	V	W	X	Z	C	O	P	Y	R	I	G	H	T	A	B	D	E	F	J	K	L	M	N	Q	S
Q	S	U	V	W	X	Z	C	O	P	Y	R	I	G	H	T	A	B	D	E	F	J	K	L	M	N	Q
N	Q	S	U	V	W	X	Z	C	O	P	Y	R	I	G	H	T	A	B	D	E	F	J	K	L	M	N
M	N	Q	S	U	V	W	X	Z	C	O	P	Y	R	I	G	H	T	A	B	D	E	F	J	K	L	M
L	M	N	Q	S	U	V	W	X	Z	C	O	P	Y	R	I	G	H	T	A	B	D	E	F	J	K	L
K	L	M	N	Q	S	U	V	W	X	Z	C	O	P	Y	R	I	G	H	T	A	B	D	E	F	J	K
J	K	L	M	N	Q	S	U	V	W	X	Z	C	O	P	Y	R	I	G	H	T	A	B	D	E	F	J
F	J	K	L	M	N	Q	S	U	V	W	X	Z	C	O	P	Y	R	I	G	H	T	A	B	D	E	F
E	F	J	K	L	M	N	Q	S	U	V	W	X	Z	C	O	P	Y	R	I	G	H	T	A	B	D	E
D	E	F	J	K	L	M	N	Q	S	U	V	W	X	Z	C	O	P	Y	R	I	G	H	T	A	B	D
B	D	E	F	J	K	L	M	N	Q	S	U	V	W	X	Z	C	O	P	Y	R	I	G	H	T	A	B
A	B	D	E	F	J	K	L	M	N	Q	S	U	V	W	X	Z	C	O	P	Y	R	I	G	H	T	A
T	A	B	D	E	F	J	K	L	M	N	Q	S	U	V	W	X	Z	C	O	P	Y	R	I	G	H	T
H	T	A	B	D	E	F	J	K	L	M	N	Q	S	U	V	W	X	Z	C	O	P	Y	R	I	G	H
G	H	T	A	B	D	E	F	J	K	L	M	N	Q	S	U	V	W	X	Z	C	O	P	Y	R	I	G
I	G	H	T	A	B	D	E	F	J	K	L	M	N	Q	S	U	V	W	X	Z	C	O	P	Y	R	I
R	I	G	H	T	A	B	D	E	F	J	K	L	M	N	Q	S	U	V	W	X	Z	C	O	P	Y	R
Y	R	I	G	H	T	A	B	D	E	F	J	K	L	M	N	Q	S	U	V	W	X	Z	C	O	P	Y
P	Y	R	I	G	H	T	A	B	D	E	F	J	K	L	M	N	Q	S	U	V	W	X	Z	C	O	P
O	P	Y	R	I	G	H	T	A	B	D	E	F	J	K	L	M	N	Q	S	U	V	W	X	Z	C	O

would be used to encipher each letter whose position in the plain-text is given by a number of the form $6k + 1$; the second substitution alphabet would be the U alphabet, and would be used to encipher each letter whose position in the plain text is given by a number of the form $6k + 2$; etc. The resulting cipher would be a polyalphabet of six alphabets, of which only five are distinct. With these two keywords the message NEED REINFORCEMENTS AT ONCE would be enciphered VZBXD EMTDA DBFHB TFCAJ STVE.

The first step in solving periodic polyalphabetic systems is to determine the number of alphabets. In order to understand how this is accomplished, suppose a word is repeated several times in a message. Any two appearances for which the relative positions of this word are the same with regard to the key will yield identical cipher text. Two appearances placed differently with respect to the key will not yield cipher repetitions. Hence, the intervals separating cipher repetitions are multiples of the length of the key. The exact length of the key is the greatest common divisor of all the intervals separating such repetitions. Suppose this number has been determined. Then if the message is written out in as many columns as the length of the key, all the letters in any one column will have been enciphered in a single substitution alphabet.

The second step is the analysis of these different mono-alphabets. It involves essentially the same procedure as that described in connection with monoalphabetic systems. If some of the alphabets are the same, this can be determined by statistical methods, and the corresponding frequencies combined. In addition, if the different alphabets are related as in a Vigenère square, certain properties of symmetry can be used to advantage, so that identifications in one alphabet will simultaneously yield identifications in others.

Quite recently there has been considerable research carried on in an attempt to invent cipher machines for the automatic encipherment and decipherment of messages. Most of them employ periodic polyalphabetic systems. The most recent machines are electrical in operation, and in many cases the period is a tremendously large number; in addition, the number of independent alphabets is often of the same order as the period. These machine systems are much more rapid and much more accurate than hand methods. They can even be combined with printing and transmitting apparatus so that, in enciphering, a record of the cipher message is kept and the message transmitted; in deciphering, the secret message is received and translated, all automatically. So far as present cryptanalytic methods are concerned, the cipher systems derived from some of these machines are very close to practical insolvability.

The study of aperiodic polyalphabetic systems would lead us into very involved cryptanalysis, and therefore only two such systems will be mentioned.

1. Suppose a Vigenère square has been constructed, giving 26 different alphabets, each designated by a single letter. Then the letters of the plain-text message itself may serve as the key. For example, suppose the first alphabet is, by prearrangement, known to be the A alphabet. Then the first letter is enciphered in this alphabet. Thereafter, each succeeding letter is enciphered in the alphabet designated by the plain-text letter just preceding. Such a system is called *auto-key*. With the Vigenère square based on the word COPYRIGHT, and A the first substitution alphabet, the message BRIDGE DYNAMITED would be enciphered BOETM BKALN UZXEK.

2. The system known as *running key* is similar to the above except that the key is quite distinct from the message. In this system the key may be the text of a book or periodical beginning on some prearranged page and line. Or, it may be a random collection of letters of which each correspondent has a copy.

Aperiodic systems such as the first of the two just described

D D

have a very serious disadvantage from the standpoint of practicability. If for any reason an error should be introduced into a message, causing a single letter to be incorrectly received, every subsequent letter will be affected. Since the average number of errors involved in just the transmission of a message may be as high as 5%, this makes it difficult, and sometimes impossible, to read a cipher message.

The increased security gained in polyalphabetic systems is basically due to the fact that they suppress monoalphabetic frequencies. But these will reappear if the cryptanalyst can find ways of breaking up the message into its component monoalphabets. This possibility will always exist if the unit of cryptographic treatment is a single letter, as it has been in all the substitution systems described thus far. We are thus led to the idea of *polygraphic substitution*—the replacement of a plain-text polygraph by a cipher group of the same number of letters.

As a first example we give the classic *digraphic* system known as the *Playfair Cipher*. In this system, 25 cells arranged in form of a square are filled in some prearranged manner with the letters of the alphabet (one letter, say Q, is omitted). The square given below contains a systematically mixed sequence based on the word MANCHESTER.

M	A	N	C	H
E	S	T	R	B
D	F	G	I	J
K	L	O	P	U
V	W	X	Y	Z

The plain-text message is divided into pairs of letters, and in order to prevent any pair consisting of the same two letters, a dummy letter like Z is introduced whenever necessary. Thus, if the first word of a message is BATTALION, it would be broken up as follows BA TZ TA LI ON. In encipherment, if both letters of a digraph appear in the same horizontal (or vertical) line of the square, each of them is replaced by the letter in the square immediately to its right (or below it), the letters in each row and column being treated as in cyclical order. If the letters of a pair do not appear in the same row or column, they must necessarily be at opposite angles of some rectangle, and they are then replaced by those at the other angles of the rectangle, each by that which is on the same horizontal line. Thus the message WILL MEET YOU AT NOON would first be written WI LZ LM EZ ET YO UA TN OZ ON. With the square shown above, the message would then be enciphered YFUWK ABVSR XPLHG TUXXT.

The security of this system, or, for that matter, of any digraphic system, is quite low. There exists sufficient variation in the relative frequencies of plain-text digraphs to permit a cryptanalyst to obtain a great deal of information from considerations of frequency alone. The correct identification of only a few digraphs is sufficient to insure solution. In addition, the cryptanalyst can make considerable use of probable words and of word patterns. Of course, he is limited in the latter to patterns based on digraphs. Examples: *RE* FE *RE* NC E, P *RE* PA *RE*, *DE* CI *DE*.

In the Playfair Cipher there are further aids. If it has been determined that TH is replaced by BN, then HT is replaced by NB. In general if $A_1A_2 = B_1B_2$, then $A_2A_1 = B_2B_1$. Moreover, if these four letters A_1, A_2, B_1, B_2 are known to be the vertices of a rectangle, the following additional identifications will result at once: $B_1B_2 = A_1A_2$; $B_2B_1 = A_2A_1$. These facts are quite helpful in special frequency studies— for example, in distinguishing the equivalent of a high-frequency digraph such as TH whose reversal (HT) is infrequent from one such as ER, whose reversal (RE) is frequent. If may be pointed out that in Playfair ciphers the complete square can be reconstructed from just a few identifications.

The security of polygraphic substitution increases very

D D 2

rapidly as the unit of crytographic treatment increases in size. When the unit becomes as large as five or six letters, the security is very high. Unfortunately, a serious practical difficulty enters at this point. An error in one letter of a cipher group will give an incorrect translation for the entire unit of plain-text letters, so that, in effect, it garbles five or six letters at once. Since it is not possible to introduce means for correcting errors in such a system, four or five errors in the transmission of a message may render the entire message unintelligible. Such a difficulty is prohibitive. From a theoretical standpoint, however, such a system is quite interesting, and a very general mathematical treatment of it has been given by Professor Lester S. Hill.*

In every cryptographic system that has been considered thus far, the cipher text has been at least as long as the plain-text. The chief concern was secrecy, and considerations of economy did not enter. But such considerations are often of prime importance, and have led to the development of very highly specialized substitution systems called *code*. In these systems each correspondent is given a copy of a *code book* containing a long list of words, phrases, and sentences, each of which has an arbitrary equivalent set alongside it. These equivalents are most often five-letter groups, although regular groupings of a smaller number of letters and, more rarely, groups of figures are sometimes used. Provision is made for spelling out words which may not appear in the code *vocabulary*, by assigning equivalents to the individual letters of the alphabet and to the most frequent syllables.

Generally, a code book is constructed for a particular industry or for a group of people having special interests, and, as a consequence, long phrases, and even whole sentences, apt to be often repeated, are included in the vocabulary, and can be replaced by one code group. It results quite frequently that a code message is only one-fourth or one-fifth as long as the corresponding plain-text message.

* Concerning certain linear transformation apparatus of cryptography, *American Mathematical Monthly*, 1931, vol. XXXVIII, pp. 135–154.

By way of illustration we reproduce below a portion, under the *caption* ARRIVAL, from the Western Union Traveller's Cable Code.

ADAUX Am awaiting arrival of . . .
ADAVY Arrived all right
ADAXA Arrived all right, address letters to care of . . .
ADBAE Arrived all right, telegraph (cable) me in care of . . .
ADBEI Arrived all right, pleasant passage, advise friends
ADBIM Arrived all right, pleasant passage, am writing
                          etc.

This power of condensation brings with it the difficulty that an error in a single code group may cause the loss of a considerable portion of plain-text.   In order to avoid the necessity of having the message repeated, provision is made for the correction of errors.   What is done is to select the code groups from a special type of code construction table,* which assures that every code group will differ from every other by at least two letters.   It results therefrom that a code group is completely determined by any four of its letters.   If, then, one letter is garbled in transmission, the resulting group will not be found in the book, and the decoder is thus informed of the presence of an error.   By assuming each letter in turn to be the incorrect one, there will be at most five possible translations for the garbled word, and the context will indicate the correct translation.   This procedure is based on the assumption that only one letter of the code group which has been incorrectly received is wrong, and, fortunately, this is almost always true.

A further improvement in code-word construction tables, which assists in the correction of errors, assures that no two code words in the book will differ by only an interchange of two letters.   The necessity for such a feature arises in the

---

* An example of such a table, together with some interesting notes about code, will be found in a paper entitled " Notes on Code Words," W. F. Friedman and C. J. Mendelsohn, *American Mathematical Monthly*, 1932, vol. XXXIX, pp. 394—409.

tendency of some clerks, particularly typists, to introduce such an error, without realizing it, when working rapidly.

Secrecy in code communication is largely dependent upon keeping the code book out of unauthorized hands. But code books are often compromised without passing out of the hands of their rightful owners; for example, they may be copied or photographed. If there is any possibility whatever of such compromise, recourse may be had to *superencipherment*. This means applying some one or more of the possible cipher systems to the code text, treating the code message as though it were plain-text. These systems and the specific keys applying to them may be changed as often as desired.

Determination of Cryptographic System. It has been re-marked that in most cryptanalytic studies it is assumed that the enemy is in possession of the general system. Naturally this is not always true, and the cryptanalyst sometimes has the problem of determining what general system applies to a set of messages under consideration. This is one of the most difficult problems of the entire field, and in order to prevent the present discussion from becoming too involved, a few words will be said about the methods for distinguishing general systems from one another *when only one process is involved*. Given a set of messages for study, the first step is to make a systematic search for repetitions, and to study the external appearance of the messages. If we limit ourselves to repetitions at least five or six letters in length, we can feel assured that we are omitting any repetitions which may be accidental. Suppose it is found that the lengths of all the repetitions which appear and the intervals separating them are all multiples of the same number n. Then the system is either polyliteral, polygraphic, or code.

If we tabulate all the n-letter groups which occur and make a frequency distribution of their appearances, we can then distinguish between these three systems as follows. A poly-literal system which does not use variants will involve at most

26 different groups, whose frequencies will correspond with the normal frequencies of the individual letters of plain-text. If variants are used, this can be determined by establishing equivalents in the manner already described. Code systems differ from polygraphic systems, in that the n-letter groups of code are regular in form and structure, possess a two-letter difference, and may be made to fit a code-word construction table, whose size limits the total number of groups. In a polygraphic system, on the other hand, *every n-letter combination* is a bona-fide cipher group. The number of these groups actually obtained in the set of messages at hand is of the same order as the number of distinct plain-text polygraphs of n letters to be expected in such an amount of text.

If the cipher unit is not a group of two or more letters, the system is monographic, and must be either transposition or substitution. If it is transposition, it is merely a permutation of the original letters of the message, and the relative frequency of each individual letter will be the same as in plain-text. Hence, the proportion of vowels must be the same as in plain-text—*i.e.* about 40%. Very few, if any, long repetitions will be found, as the transposition process has a tendency to break up words and scatter the individual letters throughout the message.

If the system is not transposition, it must be substitution. A monoalphabetic substitution can be distinguished by the fact that the frequencies of the individual letters are of the same relative magnitudes and show the same degree of variation as plain-text frequencies. The noticeable difference in the cipher lies in the fact that the high frequencies may be exhibited by letters which are infrequent in plain-text, and, similarly, letters which are very frequent in a plain-text may be infrequent in the cipher-text. The proportion of vowels generally is much less than in plain-text, since the vowels are all high-frequency letters in plain-text. Then, too, a monoalphabet will contain a considerable number of repetitions, since every plain-text repetition yields a cipher repetition;

and these repetitions will contain recognizable word patterns. The intervals between them will, of course, have no common factor.

If the general system is one of polyalphabetic substitution, the frequency distribution will be quite *flat*—that is, the cipher letters will all have approximately equal frequencies. This is the result of the use of more than one alphabet, causing a particular cipher equivalent sometimes to represent a frequent plain-text letter, and at other times an infrequent one. It remains to determine whether the alphabets are being used periodically or aperiodically. If they are used periodically, the intervals between repetitions will all be multiples of the period. When the messages are broken up into sections equal to the length of the period, and these sections are superimposed, the letters in a single column will constitute a monoalphabet. If, however, the intervals between repetitions show no common factor, then the system is aperiodic.

Further study of any one of these systems with a view towards solution depends upon the particular system encountered, and upon any other elements of pertinent information which may be available to the cryptanalyst as a result of the particular situation.

A Few Final Remarks. In most cases, the information contained in a set of cryptograms is valuable only for a very short period. In fact, a system is generally considered sufficiently secure if the delay caused the enemy in its attempts at solution is long enough to make the information valueless. However, it sometimes happens that the application of the principles of Cryptanalysis will result in obtaining material of definite historic importance. Consider, for example, as a first type of material, the ancient systems of writing. In the real sense of the word, these were not intended to be *secret* writing. Nevertheless they had to be treated as such when attempts were made to read them. On the other hand, historians are sometimes vitally interested in reading secret

messages written many years ago. We might cite, in connection with this type of material, the diplomatic code messages transmitted during the period of the American
Revolution.

Under each of the two heads mentioned above there is
considerable material available for study, even to-day. In
connection with ancient systems of writing there is the outstanding example of the Mayan *glyphs*. To be sure, some
progress in their identification has been made. The numbers,
the calendric symbols, the glyphs representing the various
Mayan gods and a few others have been identified. But a
considerable amount of work still remains to be done.

In conclusion, a word might be said about instances of
attempts to solve ciphers whose very existence has been a
matter of question. We might cite, in particular, all the
work that has been done in connection with the Bacon–
Shakespeare controversy. Very little knowledge of Cryptanalysis is necessary to appreciate that the solutions which have
been obtained are entirely subjective and that no two independent investigators using the methods proposed would arrive
at identical results. It is quite possible for an investigator
to become so obsessed with an idea that he actually forces it
to work out by selecting a system sufficiently flexible to permit
any desired result. A tragic instance of this phenomenon is
provided by the case of Prof. W. R. Newbold,* who imagined
that he had succeeded in reading the Voynich Manuscript.
The latter is a beautifully written and profusely illustrated
medieval treatise of over two hundred pages, discovered in
Italy by Wilfrid M. Voynich, about 1912. It remains an
outstanding challenge to linguists and cryptanalysts.

* *The Cipher of Roger Bacon*, Philadelphia, 1928. There are photostatic
copies of the Voynich Manuscript in the British Museum and the New York
Public Library. (It is no longer attributed to Roger Bacon.)

410

ADDENDUM

References for Further Study

Bazeries, Étienne,
Les chiffres secrets dévoilés, Paris, 1901.

Encyclopædia Britannica :
" Codes and Ciphers."

Figl, A.,
Systeme des chiffrierens, Graz, 1926.

Givierge, Col. M.,
Cours de Cryptographie, Paris, 1925.

Grandpré, A. de,
La cryptographie pratique, Paris, 1905.

Lange, André, and Soudart, E. A.,
Traité de Cryptographie, Paris, 1925.

Langie, André,
De la cryptographie, Paris, 1918.   (English translation by Macbeth, *Cryptography*, New York, 1922.)

Valerio, P.,
De la cryptographie : Part I, Paris, 1893; Part II, Paris, 1896.

Yardley, Herbert O.,
The American Black Chamber, Indianapolis, 1931.

INDEX

THE END

PRINTED IN GREAT BRITAIN BY
RICHARD CLAY AND COMPANY, LTD.,
BUNGAY, SUFFOLK.